Student's Solutions Manual to Accompany

PRECALCULUS

David Cohen
University of California — Los Angeles

Prepared by
Tom Walters
Wilson High School / Los Angeles

WEST PUBLISHING COMPANY
St. Paul   New York   Los Angeles   San Francisco

COPYRIGHT © 1985 by WEST PUBLISHING CO.
50 West Kellogg Boulevard
P.O. Box 43526
St. Paul, MN 55164

Printed in the United States of America

ISBN 0-314-79136-1

Contents

Preface

This manual is intended as a supplemental aid for students and contains detailed solutions for a representative sample of the odd-numbered problems in the text Precalculus by David Cohen.

Much of the significant learning in mathematics takes place as students search out ways to use simple ideas in new applications. For this reason I would remind students to consult this manual only after making a serious attempt at an individual solution. Most good math problems can be solved in a variety of ways, and your work may be an improvement on mine.

We have made every attempt at producing a manual free of errors and have tried to include corrections for all the errata from the first printing of Precalculus. You are encouraged to drop a note to David Cohen at UCLA with any corrections, suggestions or comments. Special thanks go to Laurie Beerman for her help in preparing the manuscript.

Having used the book in teaching both high school and college students, I continue to be impressed by the text's use of interesting and unusual problems. I hope your experience with the book will be as rewarding as mine.

Tom Walters
Wilson High School
Los Angeles

Chapter 1 Topics in Algebra and Coordinate Geometry

Exercise Set 1.1

1. Let $n = 1.77....$ Then $10n = 17.77...$ and we subtract

$$10n = 17.77...$$
$$n = \underline{1.77...}$$
$$9n = 16$$

from which we get $n = 16/9$.

3. $271/33$

5. Since the repeating pattern is 2 digits long we multiply by 100 getting

$$100n = 4.0404...$$
$$n = \underline{.0404...}$$
$$99n = 4$$

or $n = 4/99$

7. Here again the repeating pattern is 2 digits.

$$100n = 571.61616...$$
$$n = \underline{5.71616...}$$
$$99n = 565.9 \qquad\qquad \text{or} \quad n = 565.9/99.$$

Here we need to multiply both the numerator and denominator by 10 to
eliminate the decimal. So n = 5659/990 is our answer, or can we reduce?
(In this case the answer is no.)

9.   (a) $\sqrt{2}$ (b) $\sqrt{2}$ - 1   (c) 4 + $\sqrt{2}$ (d) 4 - $\sqrt{2}$

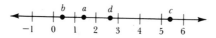

11. (a) -1   (b) 3   (c) 6   (d) 13

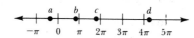

13. (a) False; since $\pi \simeq 3.1$, $2\pi > 6$.

     (b) True; since $\sqrt{2} \simeq 1.4$ and $\frac{\pi}{2} \simeq \frac{3.1}{2}$ or 1.5+.

     (c) True; since $\sqrt{2} \simeq 1.4$, $2\sqrt{2} \simeq 2.8$ which is clearly greater than 2.

     (d) True; since $\pi < 4$, $\pi^2 < 4^2$.

15.   17.   19.

21. 3x - 4 < 11   Remember, we solve inequalities much like equations.
                          Here we first add 4 to both sides then divide by 3.
        3x < 15

         x < 5

23. x < 5/2

25. $4(t - 1) - 2(t + 1) < t$

   $4t - 4 - 2t - 2 < t$ - after clearing parentheses

   $2t - 6 < t$ - combining similar terms

   $t < 6$

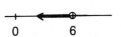

27. $-5 \le \dfrac{-3 - x}{-2} \le 2$ - first multiply by -2 and remember to reverse the inequalities

   $10 \ge -3 - x \ge -4$ - now add 3

   $13 \ge -x \ge -1$ - finally multiply by -1 and reverse again to get x.

   $-13 \le x \le 1$

29. $2/3 < x < 3/2$

31. $2a < \dfrac{1}{3ax} \le \dfrac{1}{a}$ Since a > 0, 2a and 1/a are > 0 and x must be positive also. Therefore we can invert the terms and reverse the inequality getting

   $\dfrac{1}{2a} > 3ax \ge a$ or

   $\dfrac{1}{6a^2} > x \ge \dfrac{1}{3}$ when we divide by 3a.

33. (a) false;   (b) true;   (c) true

35. Simplify $\sqrt{12} + 4\sqrt{27} - \sqrt{3}$. We must look for pervect square factors inside each radical. We find $\sqrt{4 \cdot 3} + 4\sqrt{9 \cdot 3} - \sqrt{3}$ or, since $\sqrt{4 \cdot 3} = \sqrt{4} \cdot \sqrt{3} = 2\sqrt{3}$, $2\sqrt{3} + 12\sqrt{3} - \sqrt{3}$ which equals $13\sqrt{3}$.

37. $4\sqrt{6} - 10\sqrt{24} - \sqrt{18} - \sqrt{96} = 4\sqrt{6} - 10\sqrt{4 \cdot 6} - \sqrt{9 \cdot 2} - \sqrt{16 \cdot 6} =$

$4\sqrt{6} - 20\sqrt{6} - 3\sqrt{2} - 4\sqrt{6} = -20\sqrt{6} - 3\sqrt{2}$

Since the radicands are not similar, these two terms can't be combined, and this is our final answer.

39. Multiply by 1 in the form of $\sqrt{5}/\sqrt{5}$ to obtain:

$$\frac{5}{\sqrt{5}} \cdot \frac{\sqrt{5}}{\sqrt{5}} = \frac{\cancel{5}\sqrt{5}}{\cancel{5}} = \sqrt{5}$$

41.

a	b	$\sqrt{ab}$	$\dfrac{a + b}{2}$	Which is larger?
2	32	8	17	$\dfrac{a + b}{2}$
4	16	8	10	$\dfrac{a + b}{2}$
8	8	8	8	same
2	18	6	10	$\dfrac{a + b}{2}$
4	9	6	$\dfrac{13}{2}$	$\dfrac{a + b}{2}$
6	6	6	6	same

43. We are asked to prove that $\sqrt{20} < 9/2$ using the inequality $\sqrt{ab} \leq \dfrac{a + b}{2}$.
If we let $a = 4$ and $b = 5$, then direct substitution gives

$\sqrt{4 \cdot 5} \leq \dfrac{4 + 5}{2}$ or $\sqrt{20} \leq 9/2$ as required because the equality only holds
if $a = b$.

49. (a) 2 places; (b) 6 places; (c) 9 places

59.

a	b	$\sqrt{ab}$	$\dfrac{2ab}{a + b}$	Which is larger?
1	36	6	72/37	$\sqrt{ab}$
2	18	6	18/5	$\sqrt{ab}$
3	12	6	24/5	$\sqrt{ab}$
4	9	6	72/13	$\sqrt{ab}$
6	6	6	6	same

EXERCISE SET 1.2

1. Since $|x| = -x$ when $x < 0$

$$|-3| = -(-3)$$
$$= 3$$

3. 3   5. 0

7. $||-2| - |-3|| = |2 - 3| = |-1| = 1$

9. $|a - b|^2 = |(-2) - 3|^2 = |-5|^2 = 5^2 = 25$

11. $|c| - |b| - |a| = |-4| - |3| - |-2| = 4 - 3 - 2 = -1$

13. $|a + b|^2 - |b + c|^2 = |-2 + 3|^2 - |3 + (-4)|^2 = |1|^2 - |-1|^2 = 1^2 - 1^2 = 0$

15. We want to write $|\sqrt{2} - 1| - 1$ in a form containing no absolute values.

Since $\sqrt{2} - 1 > 0$ its absolute value is just $\sqrt{2} - 1$ and we have

$$|\sqrt{2} - 1| - 1 = \sqrt{2} - 1 - 1 = \sqrt{2} - 2$$

17. $x - 3$

19. $|t^2 + 1| = t^2 + 1$ since t^2 is always ≥ 0.

21. Since $1 < x < 2$, $|x - 1| = x - 1$ and $|x - 2| = -(x - 2) = 2 - x$ and we
get $|x - 1| + |x - 2| = x - 1 + 2 - x = 1$.

23. (a) $|x| = 8$ if $x = 8$ or $x = -8$.

(b) $|x| = 0$ only if $x = 0$.

(c) $|x|$ can never be negative.

(d) $|x^2 - 5x - 17|$ also is never negative.

25. $x^2 + 5$

27. $|x + 4| = 5$ if $x + 4 = 5$ which gives $x = 1$ or $x + 4 = -5$ which gives
$x = -9$.

29. 2,   14   31. 2.999,   3.001

33. Using the method from Example 6, $|x - 1| < 1/2$ whenever
$-1/2 < x - 1 < 1/2$ which means $1/2 < x < 3/2$.

35. $|4 - 6x| \leq 1$ whenever

$$-1 \leq 4 - 6x \leq 1$$
$$-5 \leq -6x \leq -3$$
$$5/6 \geq x \geq 1/2$$

37. $|x - 4| > 3$ whenever

$$x - 4 > 3 \quad \text{or} \quad x - 4 < -3$$
$$x > 7 \quad \text{or} \quad x < 1$$

39. $19/10 < x < 21/10$

EXERCISE SET 1.3

1.

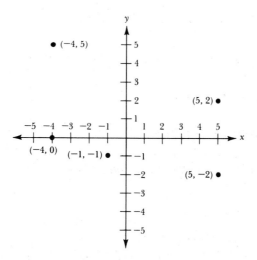

3. (a)

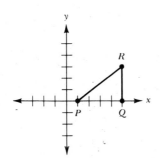

(b) Using A = ½ b·h

A = ½·4·3

A = 6

5. In this problem we apply the mid-point formula letting A be one endpoint and B be the midpoint.

So we have $\dfrac{x_1 + x_2}{2} = x_m$ Similarly $\dfrac{2 + y_2}{2} = 3$

substituting $\dfrac{-1 + x_2}{2} = 5$ $2 + y_2 = -6$

                                                                                 $y_2 = -8$

or $-1 + x_2 = 10$

                  $x_2 = 11$

Therefore the coordinates at C are (11,-8).

7. (a)

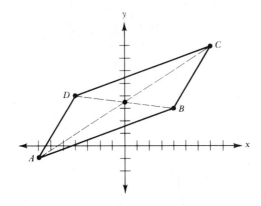

(b) For AC: $x_m = \dfrac{-7 + 7}{2}$ and $y_m = \dfrac{-1 + 8}{2}$

$= 0$ $= 7/2$

   Midpoint of AC is (0,7/2)

   For BD: $x_m = \dfrac{4 + (-4)}{2}$ and $y_m = \dfrac{3 + 4}{2}$

$= 0$ $= 7/2$

   and we see that the midpoint is also (0,7/2)

(c) Since the midpoints coincide we can conclude that the diagonals bisect
     each other. Will this be true for any parallelogram?

9. (a)

x	y = x
0	0
1	1
2	2
-1	-1

(b)

x	y = -x
0	0
1	-1
3	-3
-2	2

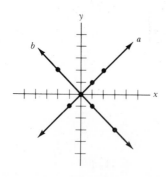

9. (c)

x	$y = x^2$
0	0
1	1
2	4
-1	1
-2	4

(d)

x	$y = -x^2$
0	0
1	-1
2	-4
-1	-1
-2	-4

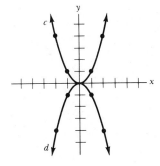

(e)

x	$y = 1/x^2$
±1	1
±2	1/4
±1/2	4
±1/4	16
±4	1/16

(f)

x	$y = -1/x^2$
±1	-1
±2	-1/4
±1/2	-4
±4	-1/16

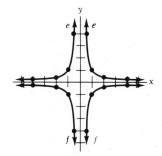

9. (g)

x	y = |x|
0	0
±1	1
±2	2
±3	3

(h)

x	y = $\sqrt{x^2}$
0	0
±1	1
±2	2
±3	3

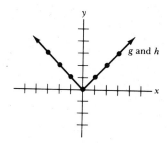

11.

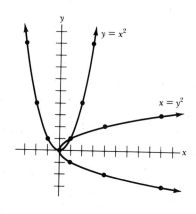

13.

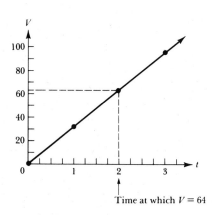

15.

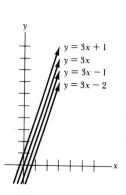

17. (a) (1,-2)

(b) (-5,2)

19.

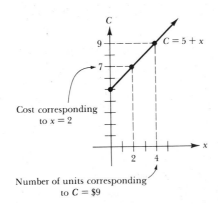

21.

x	y
0	1
1	2
2	4
3	8
-1	1/2
-2	1/4
-3	1/8

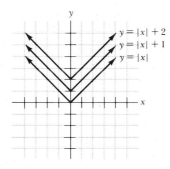

23. (a)

(b) We observe in (a) that adding 1 and 2
to $|x|$ simply shifts the graph up 1
and then 2 units. This leads us to
expect that $|x| + 3$ and $|x| - 1$
will be like $|x|$ shifted up 3 and
down 1 units respectively.

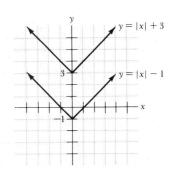

25. (a)

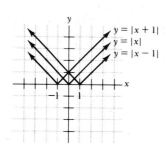

(b)

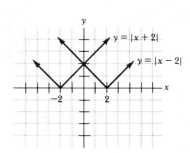

27.

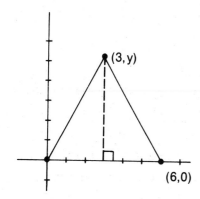

Since we are told that we have an
equilateral triangle, the coordinates of
the third vertex must be of the form
(3,y). We can use the Pythagorean
theorem to find the missing side (height)
of the right triangle. So

$$3^2 + y^2 = 6^2$$

$$y^2 = 27$$

$$y = \sqrt{27}$$

$$y = 3\sqrt{3}$$

A thorough discussion of the Pythagorean relationship follows in the next
section. It is an idea originally developed for you in elementary algebra
and geometry. Review it carefully as it is of the greatest importance.

29. (a)

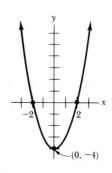

(b)

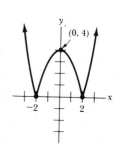

29. (c)

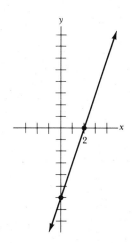

(d)

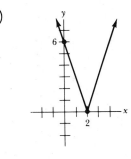

31. (a) We observe that the x-coordinate changes from 3 to 8 between points A
         and B. A similar vertical difference of 4 units between points C and
         A lets us calculate an area of 5 x 4 or 20 sq. units for the
         rectangle. Using A = ½ b·h, we find the areas of the three small
         right triangles to be 2.5, 1.5, and 8 sq. units. So the total for the
         three triangles is 12 and the difference is 8 square units for
         triangle ABC.

    (b)

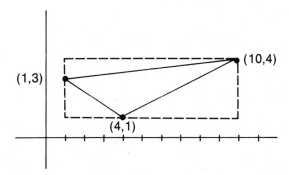

         Follow a similar approach as in part (a). We find the rectangle to be
         9 by 3 or 27 sq. units in area. The 3 right triangles total 16.5, so
         the difference is 10.5 square units.

    (c) Here we are asked to generalize the process we have followed. First,
         observe that the up/down and left/right dimensions of the surrounding
         rectangle are $y_3 - y_1$ and $x_2 - x_1$ respectively. Multiplying gives
         us the area of the rectangle as:

31. (c) Cont.

$$A_R = x_2y_3 - x_1y_3 - x_2y_1 + x_1y_1$$

Now starting with the bottom right triangle and proceeding counter-clockwise we get

$$A_1 = \tfrac{1}{2}(x_2 - x_1)(y_2 - y_1)$$

$$A_2 = \tfrac{1}{2}(x_2 - x_3)(y_3 - y_2) \qquad \text{and}$$

$$A_3 = \tfrac{1}{2}(x_3 - x_1)(y_3 - y_1)$$

where each equation represents $\tfrac{1}{2}bh$. Multiplying each area out gives

$$A_1 = \tfrac{1}{2}(x_2y_2 - x_2y_1 - x_1y_2 + x_1y_1)$$

$$A_2 = \tfrac{1}{2}(x_2y_3 - x_2y_2 - x_3y_3 + x_3y_2) \qquad \text{and}$$

$$A_3 = \tfrac{1}{2}(x_3y_3 - x_3y_1 - x_1y_3 + x_1y_1)$$

In the next step we will carefully combine similar terms getting

$$-\tfrac{1}{2}x_2y_1 - \tfrac{1}{2}x_1y_2 + x_1y_1 - \tfrac{1}{2}x_2y_3 + \tfrac{1}{2}x_3y_2 - \tfrac{1}{2}x_3y_1 - \tfrac{1}{2}x_1y_3$$

for the total of all three triangles. Finally we will find $A_R - (A_1 + A_2 + A_3)$; that is, we will subtract the sum of the three right triangles from the rectangular area.

$$[x_2y_3 - x_1y_3 - x_2y_1 + x_1y_1] -$$

$$[-\tfrac{1}{2}x_2y_1 - \tfrac{1}{2}x_1y_2 + x_1y_1 + \tfrac{1}{2}x_2y_3 + \tfrac{1}{2}x_3y_2 - \tfrac{1}{2}x_3y_1 - \tfrac{1}{2}x_1y_3]$$

or $\qquad \tfrac{1}{2}x_1y_2 - \tfrac{1}{2}x_2y_1 + \tfrac{1}{2}x_2y_3 - \tfrac{1}{2}x_3y_2 + \tfrac{1}{2}x_3y_1 - \tfrac{1}{2}x_1y_3$

Factoring the common factor of $\tfrac{1}{2}$ will give us the desired result, at last. You should realize that the solution to this problem requires careful patient work rather than great insight.

Exercise Set 1.4

1. (a) Using $a^2 + b^2 = c^2$ we have
$$5^2 + 12^2 = c^2$$

   so $c^2 = 169$

   and $c = 13$

   (b) 15   (c) $\sqrt{2}$ (d) $\sqrt{3}$

   (e) $a^2 + 2^2 = (\sqrt{5})^2$ (f) $16^2 + b^2 = 65^2$

   $\qquad\qquad a^2 = 5 - 4$ $\qquad\qquad b^2 = 4225 - 256$

   $\qquad\qquad a^2 = 1$ $\qquad\qquad b^2 = 3969$

   $\qquad\qquad a = 1$ $\qquad\qquad b = 63$

   (g) $\sqrt{13}$ (h) 5

3. Here also we will use the Pythagorean Identity.

   (a) $(\sqrt{2} + 1)^2 + (\sqrt{2} - 1)^2 = x^2$

   $2 + 2\sqrt{2} + 1 + 2 - 2\sqrt{2} + 1 \ = x^2$

   $\qquad\qquad\qquad\qquad 6 = x^2$

   $\qquad\qquad\qquad \sqrt{6} = x$

   (b) $x^2 + 1^2 = (\sqrt{2})^2$ (c) $(1 + \sqrt{2})^2 + 1^2 = x^2$

   $\qquad\quad x^2 = 2 - 1$ $1 + 2\sqrt{2} + 2 + 1 = x^2$

   $\qquad\quad x^2 = 1$ $\qquad 2\sqrt{2} + 4 = x^2$

   $\qquad\quad x = 1$ $\qquad \sqrt{2\sqrt{2} + 4} = x$

3. cont.

(d) $x^2 + (\sqrt{3} - \sqrt{2})^2 = (\sqrt{3} + \sqrt{2})^2$

$x^2 = (3 + 2\sqrt{6} + 2) - (3 - 2\sqrt{6} + 2)$

$x^2 = 4\sqrt{6}$

$x = 2 \sqrt[4]{6}$

(e) $x^2 + (\sqrt{8} - \sqrt{2})^2 = (\sqrt{6})^2$

$x^2 = 6 - (8 - 2\sqrt{16} + 2)$

$x^2 = 6 - 2$

$x^2 = 4$

$x = 2$

5. If the legs are a and a + 1, then

$$a^2 + (a + 1)^2 = (\text{hypotenuse})^2$$

or $\qquad a^2 + a^2 + 2a + 1 = h^2$

$$2a^2 + 2a + 1 = h^2$$

$$\sqrt{2a^2 + 2a + 1} = h$$

7. Since $d = \sqrt{(x_2 - x_1)^2 + (y_2 - y_1)^2}$ we have only to substitute.

(a) $d = \sqrt{(-3 - 0)^2 + (4 - 0)^2}$ (b) 13

$= \sqrt{9 + 16}$

$= \sqrt{25}$

$= 5$

(c) $d = \sqrt{[-5 - (-1)]^2 + [4 - (-3)]^2}$ (d) $\sqrt{58}$

$= \sqrt{(-4)^2 + (7)^2}$ (e) 10

$= \sqrt{16 + 49}$ (f) 9

$= \sqrt{65}$ (g) 5

7. Cont.

   (h) $d = \sqrt{[9/2 - (-2\ 1/2)]^2 + [-1 - 3]^2}$ (i) 4

   $= \sqrt{(7)^2 + (-4)^2}$

   $= \sqrt{49 + 16}$

   $= \sqrt{65}$

   Note that this problem shows that we can reverse the order in which
   we consider the points and not affect the result.

9. To tell if the given vertices form a right triangle we will use the distance
   formula to test whether the sides satisfy the Pythagorean property.

   (a) $d_1 = \sqrt{(7 + 3)^2 + (-1 - 5)^2} = \sqrt{136}$

   $d_2 = \sqrt{(-3 + 12)^2 + (5 + 10)^2} = \sqrt{306}$

   $d_3 = \sqrt{(7 + 12)^2 + (-1 + 10)^2} = \sqrt{442}$

   Since $d_1^2 + d_2^2 = d_3^2$, this must be a right triangle. Similar
   calculations will show that b is also a right triangle but that c
   is not.

11. area = 0;   so the points are collinear

15. (a) Comparing the given equation to the standard form

   $$(x - h)^2 + (y - k)^2 = r^2$$

   we can identify the coordiantes of the center and the radius by
   inspection. Here we find the center is located at (3,1) and the
   radius = 5.

   (b) (0,-1),4   (c) (0,0),1

   (d) (-2,1),½   (e) (0,0),$\sqrt{2}$

15. (f) Remember to get (x + 3/2) we msut let h = -3/2. This equation
          becomes

$$[x - (-3/2)]^2 + [y - (-2/3)]^2 = 20$$

          so the center is at (-3/2,-2/3) and $r = \sqrt{20}$ which becomes $2\sqrt{5}$.

     (g) A circle in this form has its center at the origin. The radius will
          be the square root of the square root of 2 or $\sqrt[4]{2}$.

17. (a)   (b) $x^2 + y^2 = 1$

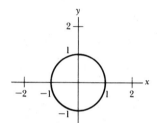

                                                (c) yes

                                                (d) yes

19. (a) $x^2 + y^2 -10x + 2y + 17 = 0$ becomes $x^2 - 10x + y^2 + 2y = -17$
          when we set up to complete the square. Taking one-half of the x and
          y coefficients, squaring each and adding to both sides gives

$$x^2 - 10x + 25 + y^2 + 2y + 1 = -17 + 25 + 1$$

          or $(x - 5)^2 + (y + 1)^2 = 9$

          which we recognize as a circle with a center at (5,-1) and a radius
          at 3.

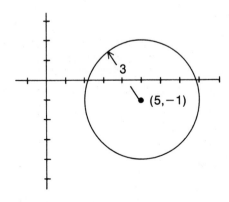

19.   (b) $(x + 4)^2 + (y - 3)^2 = 1$

      (c) $(x + 4)^2 + (y - 3)^2 = 0$ (The graph is a point.)

      (d) $4x^2 - 4x + 4y^2 - 63 = 0$ becomes

$$x^2 - x + y^2 = 63/4 \quad \text{or}$$

$$x^2 - x + 1/4 + y^2 = 63/4 + 1/4 \quad \text{which is}$$

$$(x - \tfrac{1}{2})^2 + (y - 0)^2 = 16$$

clearly a circle of radius 4 centered on $(\tfrac{1}{2},0)$.

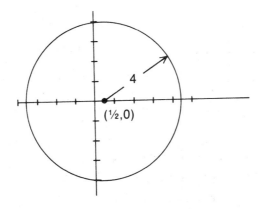

      (e) $x^2 + y^2 - 2x - 2y + 4 = 0$ becomes

$$x^2 - 2x + y^2 - 2y = -4 \quad \text{or}$$

$$x^2 - 2x + 1 + y^2 - 2y + 1 = -4 + 1 + 1. \quad \text{When we factor we get}$$

$$(x - 1)^2 + (y - 1)^2 = -2$$

Since the radius equals $\sqrt{-2}$ we have no graph.

      (f) $(x + 3)^2 + (y - 1/3)^2 = 2$

      (g) $(x + 1)^2 + (y + 1)^2 = 1/2$

      (h) $(x + 3/2)^2 + (y - 5/2)^2 = 9$

21.

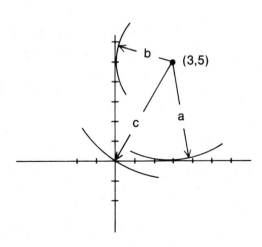

(a) The sketch shows us that for this part the radius must be 5 units so
     we can write the equation as

$$(x - 3)^2 + (y - 5)^2 = 25$$

(b) For tangency at the y axis r = 3 so we have

$$(x - 3)^2 + (y - 5)^2 = 9$$

(c) Here the radius will be the distance from (3,5) to the origin which
     an application of the Pythagorean Thm. shows to be $\sqrt{34}$. So

$$(x - 3)^2 + (y - 5)^2 = 34$$

     is the required answer.

23. (a)

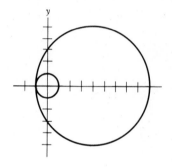

(b) In the large circle r = 5 and
     $A = \pi r^2$, so $A = 25\pi$. The
     small circle, where r = 1, has
     an area equal to π. Therefore
     the required area is $25\pi - \pi$
     or 24π sq. units.

25.

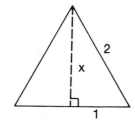

(a) The drawing illustrates the given dimensions and the missing side, x. We see that

$$x^2 + 1^2 = 2^2$$

or

$$x^2 = 3$$

and

$$x = \sqrt{3}$$

which is the required altitude.

(b) Since $A = \frac{1}{2} b \cdot h$

$$A = \frac{1}{2} \cdot 2 \cdot \sqrt{3}$$

$$A = \sqrt{3} \text{ sq. units}$$

27. Applying Pythagoras we have

$$(u^2 - v^2)^2 + (2uv)^2 = x^2$$
$$u^4 - 2u^2v^2 + v^4 + 4u^2v^2 = x^2$$
$$u^4 + 2u^2v^2 + v^4 = x^2$$

or factoring

$$(u^2 + v^2)^2 = x^2$$

so x, our missing hypotenuse is equal to $u^2 + v^2$.

29. (a) Given the diagonal of the square as 10 we can calculate the sides of the square, x, from

$$x^2 + x^2 = 10^2$$

$$2x^2 = 100$$

$$x^2 = 50$$

$$x = 5\sqrt{2}$$

Then this is the length of side BE. Again from

$$\overline{AB}^2 + \overline{AE}^2 = \overline{BE}^2 \quad \text{we get}$$

$$6^2 + \overline{AE}^2 = 50$$

$$\overline{AE}^2 = 14$$

$$\overline{AE} = \sqrt{14}$$

29. (a) Cont.

   Finally $A = \frac{1}{2} \cdot \sqrt{14} \cdot 6$

   $A = 3\sqrt{14}$ sq. units

   (b) Here we must repeat the steps above using d in place of 10. We find $\overline{BE} = d\sqrt{2}/2$ and the area equal to

   $$\sqrt{\frac{d^2 - 8}{2}} \quad \text{sq. units.}$$

31. (b) 3960 miles

33. If PQ is a diameter, the mid-point of PQ will be the center, and $\overline{PQ}/2$ will be the radius. So

   $$x_m = \frac{-3 + 2}{2} \quad \text{and} \quad y_m = \frac{-4 + 8}{2}$$

   $$= -\tfrac{1}{2} \qquad\qquad\qquad = 2$$

   and $(-\tfrac{1}{2}, 2)$ is the center.

   $$\overline{PQ} = \sqrt{(2 + 3)^2 + (8 + 4)^2}$$

   $$= \sqrt{25 + 144}$$

   $$= \sqrt{169}$$

   $$= 13 \qquad \text{and} \qquad r = 13/2$$

   The required equation is therefore

   $$(x + 1/2)^2 + (y - 2)^2 = 169/4$$

EXERCISE SET 1.5

1. (a) In each case we must substitute the given value of x into the equation and simplify to see if the result is a true statement. So

   $$2x^2 - 6x - 36 = 0 \qquad \text{becomes}$$

   $$2(-3)^2 - 6(-3) - 36 = 0$$

   $$18 + 18 - 36 = 0; \qquad 0 = 0; \qquad \text{true}$$

(b) $m^2 + m - 5/16 = 0$; $m = 1/4$

$(1/4)^2 + 1/4 - 5/16 = 0$

$1/16 + 4/16 - 5/16 = 0$

$0 = 0$ again true

(c) no   (d) no

(e) $x^2 - 2x - 6 = 0$; $x = 1 - \sqrt{7}$

$(1 - \sqrt{7})^2 - 2(1 - \sqrt{7}) - 6 = 0$

$1 - 2\sqrt{7} + 7 - 2 + \sqrt{7} - 6 = 0$

$0 = 0$ true

(f) $\dfrac{1}{x - 3} + 4 = \dfrac{x}{2}$; $x = 3$

$\dfrac{1}{3 - 3} = 4 = \dfrac{3}{2}$;   no

Since we have a zero denominator this equation is not defined for $x = 3$.

3. (a) Since factoring is impossible here, at least using rational numbers, let's use the formula.

$$x = \frac{-5 \pm \sqrt{5^2 - 4(1)(-1)}}{2(1)}$$

$$= \frac{-5 \pm \sqrt{25 + 4}}{2}$$

$$= \frac{-5 \pm \sqrt{29}}{2}$$

(b) $12x^2 + 32x + 5 = 0$ in standard form. This will factor. If we try various combinations we find

$12x^2 + 32x + 5 = 0$	$6x + 1 = 0$	$2x + 5 = 0$
$(6x + 1)(2x + 5) = 0$	$6x = -1$	$2x = -5$
	$x = -1/6$	$x = -5/2$

3. (c) $x = \dfrac{1 \pm \sqrt{41}}{10}$ (d) $x = \dfrac{\sqrt{5} \pm 1}{2}$

(e) $x = \pm 1$ (f) $x = 7/2$

(g) $(x + 1)^2 = 5$ taking the square root of both sides gives

$x + 1 = \pm\sqrt{5}$ or

$x = -1 \pm \sqrt{5}$

(h) $\sqrt{2}x^2 + x - \sqrt{2} = 0$

$(\sqrt{2}x - 1)(x + \sqrt{2}) = 0$

$\sqrt{2}x - 1 = 0$	$x + \sqrt{2} = 0$
$\sqrt{2}x = 1$	$x = -\sqrt{2}$
$x = \dfrac{1}{\sqrt{2}}$	
or $x = \dfrac{\sqrt{2}}{2}$	

The same results can be
obtained using the Quadradic
formula.

5. $x = -2,$ $x = -1,$ $x = 1,$ $x = 2$

7. The words tell us that x^2 is bigger than x by 1, or that
$x^2 = x + 1.$ So we solve this equation.

$x^2 - x - 1 = 0$

$x = \dfrac{-(-1) \pm \sqrt{(-1)^2 - 4(1)(-1)}}{2(1)}$

$x = \dfrac{1 \pm \sqrt{5}}{2}$

We reject the negative root because we were asked for a positive number.

9. (a) If we let $x = 0,$ we find $2(0) - 5y = 10;$ $y = -2$ for the
y-intercept. Similarly $2x - 5(0) = 10$ gives $x = 5$ for the
x-intercept.

9. (b) (0,1), (1/7,0)

   (c) $\frac{x}{2} + \frac{y}{3} = 1$. This is sometimes called the intercept form of the
   linear equation because each denominator is the
   intercept for the letter in the numerator. Just substitute x or
   $y = 0$, cross multiply, and see for yourself.

   (d) Letting $x = 0$ gives $y = -1$ directly, but we must use the quadratic
   formula or factor to find $(-\frac{1}{2},0)$ and $(\frac{1}{4},0)$.

   $$8x^2 + 2x - 1 = 0$$

   $$(4x - 1)(2x + 1) = 0$$

   $$x = \frac{1}{4} \qquad x = -\frac{1}{2}$$

   (e) (0,-1), (±1,0)   (f) (0,8), (±2√2,0)

   (g) (0,-4), $\left(\frac{5 \pm \sqrt{73}}{6}, 0\right)$ (h) (0,1)

   (i) $y = |x| - 1$. If $y = 0$, then $|x| - 1 = 0$ or $|x| = 1$ so $x = 1$
   or -1 and we get $(1,0)$ and $(-1,0)$ for the x-intercepts. Letting
   $x = 0$ yields $y = -1$ for $(0,1)$ the y-intercept.

15. (0,24), (1,0), (2,0), (3,0), (4,0)

17. Can this be factored? If it can then we must find two factors of 4187
whose sum is 132. Testing 4187 for divisibility by primes we find 53 x 79
is 4187. We would only need to test up to the square root of 4187 for a
possible prime factor. The alternative here is the quadratic formula which
will give us roots of -53 and -79.

19. The area formula for a triangle is $A = \frac{1}{2} b \cdot h$ so we have
$30 = \frac{1}{2}(m + 5)(m + 4)$ or $m^2 + 9m + 20 = 60$ which is $m^2 + 9m - 40 = 0$ in
standard form. I can't see two factors of 40 with a difference of nine so
I go for the formula.

$$m = \frac{-9 \pm \sqrt{9^2 - 4(1)(-40)}}{2(1)} \qquad \text{or} \qquad m = \frac{-9 \pm \sqrt{241}}{2}$$

19. (cont.)   We select $m = \dfrac{-9 + \sqrt{241}}{2}$ because we were asked for a positive

value.

21. Squaring both sides, as the hint suggests, gives

$$169 = 12^2 + (t - 2)^2 \quad \text{or}$$

$$169 = 144 + t^2 - 4t + 4 \quad \text{which is}$$

$$t^2 - 4t - 21 = 0 \quad \text{in standard form.   By factoring we get roots of}$$

$$t = -3 \quad \text{or} \quad t = 7.$$

25. If the sum of the numbers is 36 then we can let one = x and the other will
will then be 36 - x. So we are told that their product, x(36 - x),
equals 320.

$$x(36 - x) = 320$$

$$36x - x^2 = 320 \quad \text{or}$$

$$x^2 - 36x + 360 = 0$$

By factoring or use of the formula we find roots of 16 and 20, the pair we
were looking for.

27. If the shorter sides are represented by x and x + 1 then the area of
the triangle is $\frac{1}{2}x(x + 1)$ or

$$12 = \tfrac{1}{2}x(x + 1)$$

$$24 = x^2 + x \quad \text{or}$$

$$x^2 + x - 24 = 0$$

Solving by formula gives

$$x = \frac{-1 \pm \sqrt{1^2 - 4(1)(-24)}}{2} \quad \text{or} \quad x = \frac{-1 \pm \sqrt{97}}{2}$$

We reject the negative root; remember it represents the length of a side of
a triangle. The sides are then

$$x = \frac{-1 + \sqrt{97}}{2}$$

27. (cont.)

$$x + 1 = \frac{1 + \sqrt{97}}{2}$$

and using Pythagoras the hypotenuse is

$$\sqrt{\left(\frac{-1 + \sqrt{97}}{2}\right)^2 + \left(\frac{1 + \sqrt{97}}{2}\right)^2} \qquad \text{or } 7.$$

29. (a) Given $P = -t^2 + 26t + 106$ $(1 \le t \le 29)$, we are asked to find P
         when $t = 10$. So,

$$P = -(10)^2 + 26(10) + 106$$

$$= -100 + 260 + 106$$

$$= 266 \text{ people}$$

(b) Here we need to find t for $P = 275$, a more difficult problem
     because we msut solve the equation

$$275 = -t^2 + 26t + 106$$

     Arranging it in standard form gives

$$t^2 - 26t + 169 = 0$$

     which factors nicely into

$$(t - 13)(t - 13) = 0$$

     and we get 13 days for an answer.

31. (a) If $r = 10$ then the area of the circle will be πr^2 or $\pi(10)^2$ or
         100π sq. units. If the increase is to 102π for the area then r^2
         will equal $102\pi/\pi$ or 102 or $r = \sqrt{102}$ which is approximately
         10.0995 (a calculator is useful here). The increase in the radius is
         therefore about .100 cm.

(b) ≈ 0.016 cm

33. If the areas are equal then

$$x \cdot 1 = (1 - x)(1 - x) \quad \text{or}$$

$$x = 1 - 2x + x^2 \quad \text{which is}$$

$$x^2 - 3x + 1 = 0 \quad \text{in standard form.}$$

$$x = \frac{3 \pm \sqrt{9 - 4(1)(1)}}{2}$$

$$x = \frac{3 \pm \sqrt{5}}{2}$$

We must be careful here about the signs in the solution. We have to pick have to pick the negative radical to keep the dimensions of the square, $(1 - x)$, positive. x will be $= \frac{3 - \sqrt{5}}{2}$ only.

39. $\overline{AD}$ is 1 so let $\overline{BC}$ be x. Then,

$$\frac{AC}{AB} = \frac{AB}{BC} \quad \text{or} \quad \frac{1 + x}{1} = \frac{1}{x} .$$

Cross multiplying gives $x(1 + x) = 1$ or $x^2 + x - 1 = 0$, whose roots are $\frac{-1 \pm \sqrt{5}}{2}$. The ratio $\frac{1 + x}{1}$ is then

$$\frac{1 + \dfrac{-1 + \sqrt{5}}{2}}{1} \quad \text{or approximately} \quad \frac{1.62}{1} .$$

41. The roots of $y = x^2 + bx + 15$ are $x = (-b \pm \sqrt{b^2 - 60})/2$ and we require that their difference,

$$\left[\frac{-b + \sqrt{b^2 - 60}}{2} \right] - \left[\frac{-b - \sqrt{b^2 - 60}}{2} \right],$$

be equal to 2. Remember that those roots are the x-intercepts. We have

$$-b + \sqrt{b^2 - 60} + b + \sqrt{b^2 - 60} = 4$$

or

$$2\sqrt{b^2 - 60} = 4$$

$$\sqrt{b^2 - 60} = 2$$

after squaring,

$$b^2 - 60 = 4$$

41. (Cont.)

    so $b^2 = 64$

    and $b = \pm 8$

    as required. The problem also yields to careful reasoning. We are looking
    for 2 factors of 15 which are two apart, so picking 3 and 5, or their
    negatives, we get a sum of ±8 for b.

EXERCISE SET 1.6

1. (a) Since slope is defined to be the ratio of the change in y over the
        change in x, we substitute the coordinates of $P_1(-3,2)$ and
        $P_2(1,-6)$ in the slope formula.

$$m = \frac{y_2 - y_1}{x_2 - x_1}$$

$$= \frac{(-6) - (2)}{(1) - (-3)} \quad \text{or} \quad \frac{(2) - (-6)}{(-3) - (1)}$$

$$= \frac{-8}{4} \qquad \text{which is also}$$

$$= -2 \qquad\qquad -2$$

   m is independent of which point we take as P_1 and which P_2.

   (b) 3   (c) -7/3   (d) 3   (e) 9/7

   (f) $m = \frac{2 - 0}{-1 - 3}$ which is $\frac{-1}{2}$ (g) 27/20

   (h) $m = \dfrac{\frac{17}{3} + \frac{1}{2}}{\frac{-1}{2} - \frac{17}{3}}$ which is -1.

5. Observe in each case the "stepping pattern" of the line. In (a) we are
   clearly going over 1 and up 2, so the slope, Δy over Δx, is 2/1 or 2.
   Sometimes we must examine over a greater distance as in (b). Here we see
   that moving over 4 takes us down 3 for a slope of -3/4. (c) is one,

5. (Cont.) (d) is five and (e) is zero because there is no change in y.

7. In L_1 we find $\Delta y = 1$ and $\Delta x = 3$ for a slope of 1/3. L_2 has an m of
    -2/4 or -1/2, and in L_3 m is 3.

11. (a) Going from (6,0) to (4,3) we get a Δx of -2 and a Δy of +3, so
         m = -3/2.

    (b) Here the signs of Δy and Δx are reversed, but the ratio remains
         the same.

13. (a)

x	y = x
-2	-2
0	0
1	1

m = 1

(b)

x	y = -x
-1	1
0	0
2	-2

m = -1

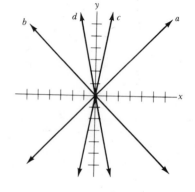

(c)

x	y = 5x
-1	-5
0	0
1	5

m = 5

(d)

x	y = -5x
-1	5
0	0
1	-5

m = -5

15. Here $m = \dfrac{\Delta y}{\Delta x} = \dfrac{(3 + h)^2 - 9}{(3 + h) - 3}$

$$= \frac{9 + 6h + h^2 - 9}{3 + h - 3}$$

$$= \frac{h^2 + 6h}{h}$$

$$= \frac{h(h + 6)}{h}$$

$$= h + 6$$

as required.

17.

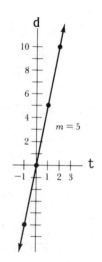

19. (a) We are asked for the velocity and should observe that the units of
of velocity represent a change in position per change in time. For
example, miles/hour or cm/sec are typical units for velocity. Here,
this is the same as the slope of each line. In part (a) we have

$$v = \frac{\Delta d}{\Delta t} \quad \text{or} \quad \frac{8 - 4}{6 - 1}$$

which is 4/5 ft/sec.

(b) 0 cm/sec (Its position remains unchanged.)

(c) 8 mi/hr.

21.

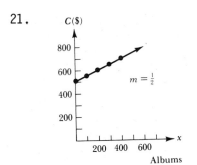

If x = 0 then C = 500, and if x = 200
then C = 600. We could have used any two
values of x but these were convenient. We
see that the slope is $\Delta C/\Delta x$ or 100/200
which is 1/2. The marginal cost is therefore
$.50 per album.

23. (a) Direct substitution into $\dfrac{y_2 - y_1}{x_2 - x_1}$ gives $\dfrac{\sqrt{x + h} - \sqrt{x}}{x + h - x}$ or

$\dfrac{\sqrt{x + h} - \sqrt{x}}{h}$ as required.

(b) The hint suggests we rationalize the numerator of (a)'s result.

$$\frac{\sqrt{x + h} - \sqrt{x}}{h} \cdot \frac{\sqrt{x + h} + \sqrt{x}}{\sqrt{x + h} + \sqrt{x}}$$

Using the rules for multiplying binomials we obtain

$$\frac{(\sqrt{x + h})^2 - (\sqrt{x})^2}{h(\sqrt{x + h} + \sqrt{x})} \quad \text{or} \quad \frac{x + h - x}{h(\sqrt{x + h} + \sqrt{x})}$$

and finally simplifying and canceling we get

$$\frac{1}{\sqrt{x + h} + \sqrt{x}} \quad \text{as required.}$$

23. (b) (Cont.) You might at first think this is a trivial problem designed
       to punish students, but that is hardly the case. It is an important
       step in one of the fundamental problems of Calculus, that of finding
       a "derivative."

27.

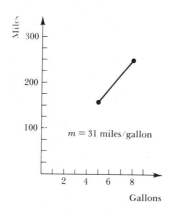

$m = 31$ miles/gallon

29. Let's make a table to organize things.

X	y	m
2.5	6.25	5.5
2.9	8.41	5.9
2.99	8.9401	5.99
2.999	8.994001	5.999

Here is the work for the third point.

$$m = \frac{9 - 8.9401}{3 - 2.99} = \frac{0.0599}{.01} = 5.99$$

The slope of PT seems to be getting closer to 6 as we get closer to the
point (3,9). The process by which we find slopes of tangents to curves
will be studied in great detail in Calculus.

Exercise Set 1.7

1. (a) Using the point-slope equation we have

$$y - y_1 = m(x - x_1)$$

$$y - 1 = -5[x - (-2)]$$

$$y - 1 = -5x - 10$$

or $y = -5x - 9$

   (b) Here we get

$$y + 4 = 4(x - 4)$$

$$y + 4 = 4x - 16$$

or $y = 4x - 20$

   (c) $y = (1/3)x + 4/3$ (d) $y = -x + 1$ (e) $y = 22x$

   (f) $y = -222x$ (g) $y = \sqrt{2}x$

3. (a) Vertical lines have the form $x = a$ if they pass through (a,b) so
        here we get $x = -3$.

   (b) Horizontal lines look like $y = b$, so this means $y = 4$ in this case.

   (c & d) This means that the x-axis must be $y = 0$ and the y-axis, $x = 0$.

5. Recall that the form $y = mx + b$ lets us identify the slope, m, and the
    y-intercept by inspection. In 5a the equation is $y = -7x + 4$. Comparing
    that to $y = mx + b$ we see that the slope is -7 and the y-intercept is 4.

(a)   (b)   (c)

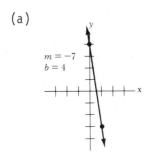
$m = -7$
$b = 4$

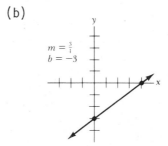
$m = \frac{3}{1}$
$b = -3$

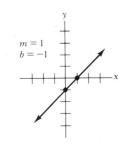
$m = 1$
$b = -1$

5.   (d)

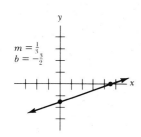

(e)

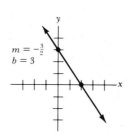

(f)

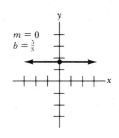

7.   (a)   Given $3x - 2y = 6$ we will let first $x = 0$ then
         $y = 0$ and solve.

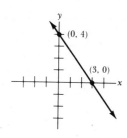

$$3(0) - 2y = 6 \quad \text{and} \quad 3x - 2(0) = 6$$

$$-2y = 6 \qquad\qquad 3x = 6$$

$$y = -3 \qquad\qquad x = 2$$

We conclude that the y-intercept is -3 and the
x-intercept is 2.

(b)

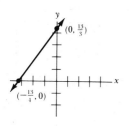

(c)   Let's make a table this
time.   This helps organize
the work.

x	y
0	-1/5
-1/2	0

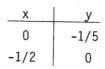

(d)

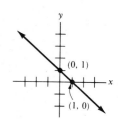

(e)

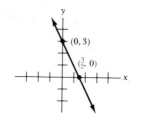

(f)

9.

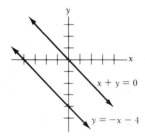

11.   Recall that m in the equation $y = mx + b$ is the slope, so using

$$m = \frac{14 - 3}{8 - (-2)} ,\quad \text{we find}\quad m = \frac{11}{10} .$$

The first printing of the book mistakenly gave the value for b of 26/5.
How would you find that?

13.   (a)   Using the given intercepts we can see that the
         slope is -7/3 and we can substitute directly
         into $y = mx + b$.

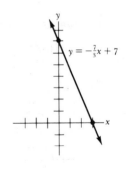

(b)

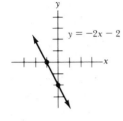

(c)

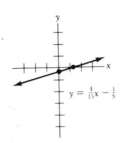

(d)

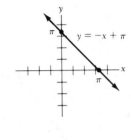

15.   We are given a point and slope so the equation must be

$$y - 6 = -5(x - 3)$$

or $y = -5x + 21$

15. (Cont.) In this equation, if x = 0 then y = 21, and if y = 0 then
    x = 21/5. These intercepts (0,21) and ($\frac{21}{5}$,0) are important because they
    give us the base and height of the triangle. If

$$A = \tfrac{1}{2} \, b \cdot h$$

$$= \frac{1}{2} \left(\frac{21}{5} \right) (21)$$

$$= \frac{441}{10} \text{ sq. units}$$

17. Here again the Area = ½ base x height, so:

$$72 = \tfrac{1}{2} \cdot b \cdot 6$$

or   72 = 3b

and   24 = b

If the base is 24 then the slope must be -6/24 or -1/4. It is negative
because y is decreasing as we move from left to right.

19. (a) Given that C = 450 + 8x then when x = 10, C = 450 + 8·10 or
         C = 530 dollars.

    (b) C = 450 + 8·11 or C = $538.

    (c) The marginal cost, the cost of producing one more fan, is therefore
         $8 per fan.

21. (a) 5 ft/sec   (b) 75 ft.   (c) 80 ft.

25. (a) The problem tells us that the tax T will be $37,667 plus 68% of the
         amount over $81,800 or

$$T = .68(x - 81,800) + 37,667$$

    (b) When x = 90,000, substitution gives a total of $43,243 for T.

 . Following the steps of problem 26 we substitute in the point-slope equation
    and get   y - 1 = m(x - 3)

    or   y = mx - 3m + 1

27. (Cont.)

When $x = 0$, $y = -3m + 1$, the y-intercept.

When $y = 0$, $x = \dfrac{3m - 1}{m}$, the x-intercept.

So, since the area is given as 6

$$6 = \frac{1}{2}\left(\frac{3m - 1}{m}\right)(-3m + 1)$$

$$12m = (3m - 1)(-3m + 1)$$

$$12m = -9m^2 + 6m - 1$$

$$9m^2 + 6m + 1 = 0 \ , \qquad\qquad \text{factoring}$$

$$(3m + 1)(3m + 1) = 0$$

and $\qquad\qquad m = -\dfrac{1}{3}$ from either root.

The required slope is $-\dfrac{1}{3}$. Try it, the intercepts will be at $(6,0)$ and $(0,2)$.

31.

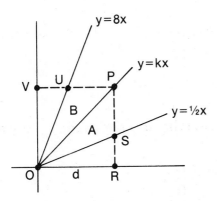

(a) Area A = Area $\triangle$OPR - Area $\triangle$OSR

$$= \tfrac{1}{2}\cdot d(kd) - \tfrac{1}{2}d(\tfrac{1}{2}d)$$

$$= \frac{kd^2}{2} - \frac{d^2}{4}$$

Area B = Area $\triangle$OVP - Area $\triangle$OVU

$$= \tfrac{1}{2}\cdot d(kd) - \tfrac{1}{2}(kd)(kd/8)$$

Remember, if line L has an equation of $y = kx$ and point R is at "d" units on the x-axis, then the height of P is "kd" units. Then in the equation of L_2, $y = 8x$, when $y = kd$ then $x = kd/8$. Equating the areas we get

$$\frac{kd^2}{2} - \frac{d^2}{4} = \frac{kd^2}{2} - \frac{k^2d^2}{16}$$

or $\qquad\qquad\qquad k^2 = 4$

and $\qquad\qquad\qquad k = 2$

31. (a) (Cont.) So line L is y = 2x as required.

     (b) Using the same argument as in 31(a) the line L has the equation

          y = √mn x.

EXERCISE SET 1.8

1. Let's compare slopes to get an answer. Y = x + 1 has an m of 1. If we
    rearrange y = 1 - x into y = -x + 1, we see that here m = -1. The
    slopes are obviously not equal therefore the lines can't be parallel.
    However, since the product, (1)(-1), is -1 they are perpendicular.

3. Given 2x - 5y = 10 we solve for y:

                    -5y = -2x + 10

                    $y = \frac{2}{5} x - 2$

    and identify its slope as 2/5.
    Substituting in point-slope gives

                    $y - 2 = \frac{2}{5} (x + 1)$

                    5y - 10 = 2x + 2

                    5y = 2x + 12

    or $y = \frac{2}{5} x + \frac{12}{5}$, as required.

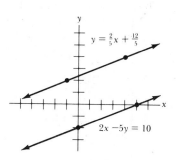

5.

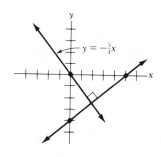

7. Given -5x + 4y = 15 we can find its y-intercept most directly by letting
    x = 0. That gives

$$-5(0) + 4y = 15$$

$$4y = 15$$

$$y = 15/4$$

So we want a line with a zero slope, remember it's parallel to the x-axis,
and a y-intercept of 15/4. The desired equation is y = 15/4. Remember,
all horizontal lines have equations of the form y = a constant while
vertical lines look like x = a constant.

11. (a)

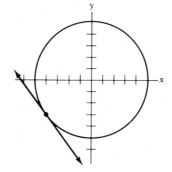

(b) Recall that a tangent to a circle is
     _ to the radius at that point.
     Let's find the slope of the radius
     drawn to (-4,-3). It must be 3/4.
     Why? Then the equation, from point-
     slope, is

$$y + 3 = (-4/3)(x + 4)$$

$$3y + 9 = -4x - 16$$

$$3y = -4x - 25$$

$$y = (-4/3)x - 25/3$$

13. (a)

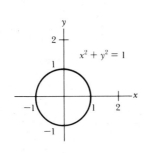

(c) $y = \dfrac{\sqrt{3}}{3} x + \dfrac{2\sqrt{3}}{3}$

15. (a)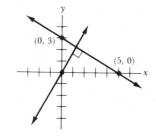

Letting $x = 0$ gives $y = 3$ and letting $y = 0$, x must be 5. Therefore, the intercepts are at $(0,3)$ and $(5,0)$.

(b) The given line has a slope of -3/5 so any line $\perp$ to it must have a slope of 5/3. The $\perp$ line passing through the origin will be

$$y = \frac{5}{3} x.$$

(c) Substituting $y = \frac{5}{3} x$ into $3x + 5y = 15$ gives

$$3x + 5\left(\frac{5x}{3}\right) = 15$$

$$9x + 25x = 45$$

$$34x = 45$$

$$x = 45/34$$

Then, since $y = \frac{5}{3} x$, $y = \frac{5}{3} \cdot \frac{45}{34}$ or $\frac{75}{34}$. They intersect at $\left(\frac{45}{34}, \frac{75}{34}\right)$.

(d) The distance formula tells us that

$$d = \sqrt{\left(\frac{45}{34} - 0\right)^2 + \left(\frac{75}{34} - 0\right)^2} = \sqrt{\frac{45^2}{34^2} + \frac{75^2}{34^2}}$$

Let's pause here. Notice the common factor of 15 in both 45 and 75? Watch,

$$d = \sqrt{\frac{15^2 \cdot 3^2 + 15^2 \cdot 5^2}{34^2}} = \sqrt{\frac{15^2}{34^2}(3^2 + 5^2)} = \frac{15}{34}\sqrt{34}$$

This won't always happen, but it's easier than fighting with $\sqrt{\frac{7650}{1156}}$.

17. (a)

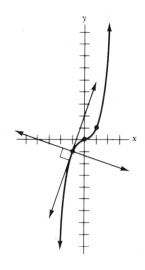

(b) tangent: y = 3x + 2

normal: y = (-1/3)x - 4/3

19. (a)

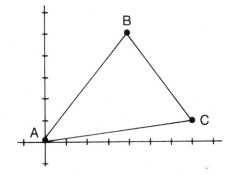

We need to find both slopes and mid-points for the sides of the given triangle. Be careful in organizing the work.

$$\text{Midpoint AB:} \quad x_m = \frac{4 + 0}{2} = 2$$

$$y_m = \frac{5 + 0}{2} = \frac{5}{2}$$

$$\text{Slope AB:} \quad m = \frac{5 - 0}{4 - 0} = \frac{5}{4}$$

For side BC we get a midpoint of (11/2,3) and a slope of -4/3. Similarly for AC, the midpoint is at (7/2,1/2) and m = 1/7. Now, being careful to use negative reciprocal slopes we will find the equations of the perpendicular bisectors. For side AB:

19. (a) (Cont.)

$$y - \frac{5}{2} = -\frac{4}{5}(x - 2) \qquad \text{multiplying through by 10}$$

$$10y - 25 = -8x + 16 \qquad \text{or}$$

$$y = -\frac{4}{5}x + \frac{41}{10}$$

In the same way we find

$$y = \frac{3}{4}x - \frac{9}{8} \quad \text{for } \perp \text{ bisector of BC,}$$

and $\qquad y = -7x + 25 \quad \text{for } \perp \text{ bisector of AC.}$

(b) For side AB we can write the equation of the $\perp$ bisector as

$$8x + 10y = 41$$

and $\qquad 6x - 9y = 9$

is the equation of the $\perp$ bisector of BC. If we multiply the first equation by 4 and the second by 5 we can add and eliminate y. We get

$$32x + 40y = 164$$

$$30x - 40y = \;\; 45 \qquad\qquad \text{adding gives}$$

$$62x \qquad\;\; = 209$$

or $\qquad\qquad x = 209/62$

and substituting in the first equation gives

$$8\left(\frac{209}{62}\right) + 10y = 41$$

or $\qquad 836 + 310y = 1271 \quad \text{after multiplying through by 31.}$

So $\qquad\qquad 310y = 435$

or $\qquad\qquad y = 87/62$

Therefore these lines intersect at $(209/62, 87/62)$

(c) In a similar fashion we find the same point of intersection for these two lines.

23. (c) $(\sqrt{3},-1)$ and $(-\sqrt{3},1)$

29.

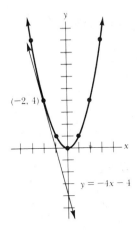

31. (b) P_1: $y = 2ax - a^2$ P_2: $y = -\dfrac{1}{2a} x - \dfrac{1}{16a^2}$

EXERCISE SET 1.9

1.

i^2	i^3	i^4	i^5	i^6	i^7	i^8
-1	$-i$	1	i	-1	$-i$	1

3. (a) We call b the imaginary part of the complex number a + bi, so in
         this case b = -6.

    (b) b = $\sqrt{2}$

    (c) Again, b is the coefficient of i. Here it is 5.

    (d) b = 0

5. To be equal we need for 27 to equal a^3 and 64 to equal b^3. Taking the
    cube root of both sides gives a = 3 and b = 4.

7. -10 + 13i

9. Substituting gives $7 + 8i - 4(2 - 3i)$

    which equals $7 + 8i - 8 + 12i$

    or $-1 + 20i$

11. $(1 - i\sqrt{3})(1 + i\sqrt{3})$ Showing each partial product gives

    $1 \cdot 1 + 1(i\sqrt{3}) - 1(i\sqrt{3}) - (i\sqrt{3})(i\sqrt{3})$. Since the middle two terms are

    additive inverses we get $1 - i^2(\sqrt{3})^2$ or $1 - (-1)(3)$ or $1 + 3$ which

    finally is 4. Notice that the original product has the form of the result

    of factoring the difference of two perfect squares. That observation lets

    us write the result directly as $(1)^2 - (i\sqrt{3})^2$.

13. $z_1 + (z_2 + w) = (2 + 3i) + (2 - 3i + 4 + 9i)$

    $\qquad\qquad = (2 + 3i) + (6 + 6i)$

    $\qquad\qquad = 8 + 9i$

15. $-19 + 30i$

17. $(z_1 z_2)w = [(2 + 3i)(2 - 3i)](4 + 9i)$

    $\qquad\quad = [4 - 9i^2](4 + 9i)$

    $\qquad\quad = 13(4 + 9i)$

    $\qquad\quad = 52 + 117i$

19. $16 + 36i$ 21. $24i$

23. $z_1^2 w^2 = (2 + 3i)^2(4 + 9i)^2$

    $\qquad = (4 + 12i + 9i^2)(16 + 72i + 81i^2)$

    $\qquad = (4 + 12i - 9)(16 + 72i - 81)$

    $\qquad = (-5 + 12i)(-65 + 72i)$ Let's look at all the parts of the next step.

    $\qquad = (-5)(-65) + (-5)(72i) + (-65)(12i) + (12i)(72i)$

    $\qquad = 325 - 360i - 780i - 864 = -539 - 1140i$

25. -119 - 120i

27. $\dfrac{3 - 2i}{4 + 5i} \cdot \dfrac{4 - 5i}{4 - 5i}$

Here we are multiplying by one in the form $(4 + 5i)/(4 + 5i)$, the conjugate of the original denominator. We get.

$$\dfrac{12 - 8i - 15i + 10i^2}{16 + 20i - 20i - 25i^2} \quad \text{or}$$

$$\dfrac{2 - 23i}{4i} \qquad \text{which is}$$

$\dfrac{2}{41} - \dfrac{23}{41} i \quad$ in a + bi form.

29. $\dfrac{1}{i}$ this is $\dfrac{1}{0 + i}$

$\dfrac{1}{0 + i} \cdot \dfrac{0 - i}{0 - i} = \dfrac{0 - i}{-i^2} = \dfrac{0 - i}{1} = 0 - i.$

31. If $z = 3 + 5i$ then $\bar{z} = 3 - 5i$ from the definition and $\bar{\bar{z}} = 3 + 5i$ again, completing the circle.

33. the same;   44 - 52i

35. By definition $|a + bi| = \sqrt{a^2 + b^2}$ so in

(a) $|2 + 4i| = \sqrt{2^2 + 4^2} = \sqrt{20} = 2\sqrt{5}$

(b) $|5 - 3i| = \sqrt{5^2 + (-3)^2} = \sqrt{25 + 9} = \sqrt{34}$

(c) First we find $(2 + 4i)(5 - 3i)$. Multiplying gives $10 + 14i - 12i^2$ or 22 + 14i. Now $|22 + 14i| = \sqrt{22^2 + 14^2} = \sqrt{484 + 196} = \sqrt{680} = \sqrt{4 \cdot 170} = 2\sqrt{170}.$

37. $z^2 = -25$. So $z = \sqrt{-25}$ which is $\pm 5i$, so the roots are $z = 0 + 5i$ and $z = 0 - 5i$.

39. $z^2 + z + 1 = 0.$ We try to factor, but with no success. So let's use the Quadratic Formula.

$$z = \frac{-1 \pm \sqrt{(1)^2 - 4(1)(1)}}{2(1)} = \frac{-1 \pm \sqrt{-3}}{2}$$

and the roots are $-\frac{1}{2} + \frac{\sqrt{3}}{2} i$ and $-\frac{1}{2} - \frac{\sqrt{3}}{2} i.$

41. $z = \frac{3}{4} \pm \frac{\sqrt{7}}{4} i$ 　　　　　　　43. $z = \frac{1}{6} \pm \frac{\sqrt{11}}{6} i$

45. $z^2 + 4z + 6 = 0$ won't factor, at least using real numbers, so we rely on the "formula."

$$z = \frac{-4 \pm \sqrt{4^2 - 4(1)(6)}}{2(1)} = \frac{-4 \pm \sqrt{-8}}{2} = \frac{-4 \pm 2\sqrt{2}\,i}{2}$$

or $-2 \pm \sqrt{2}i$ for roots.

47. We are asked to show that if $\frac{1}{\sqrt{2}} + \frac{1}{\sqrt{2}} i$ is substituted for z in the given equation, the result is true. So we want to show that

$\left(\frac{1}{\sqrt{2}} + \frac{1}{\sqrt{2}} i\right)^2 = i.$ Squaring gives $\frac{1}{2} + 2(\frac{1}{2}i) + \frac{1}{2}i^2$ which is $\frac{1}{2} + i - \frac{1}{2}$ or i, as required.

49. $\frac{a + bi}{a - bi}$ and $\frac{a - bi}{a + bi}$ must have a common denominator to be added because they are fractions. We can use the product $(a + bi)(a - bi)$ as the least common denominator. So we have

$$\frac{(a + bi)}{(a - bi)} \cdot \frac{(a + bi)}{(a + bi)} + \frac{(a - bi)}{(a + bi)} \cdot \frac{(a - bi)}{(a - bi)} \quad \text{which gives}$$

$$\frac{a^2 + 2abi + b^2 i^2 + a^2 - 2abi + b^2 i^2}{a^2 - b^2 i^2} \quad \text{or} \quad \frac{2a^2 + 2b^2 i^2}{a^2 + b^2} \quad \text{or} \quad \frac{2a^2 - 2b^2}{a^2 + b^2}.$$

Factoring we get $\frac{2(a^2 - b^2)}{(a^2 + b^2)}$ for the real part and 0 for the imaginary part.

Chapter 2 Functions

1. In practice, we look for values of the independent variable, here x, which
   produce either zeros in the denominator of fractions or negative radicands.

   (a) Any real number can be used here. The symbol $\mathbb{R}$ is commonly used.

   (b) Any real number except 3. Why?

   (c) Here x must be greater than or equal to zero.

   (d) $\mathbb{R}$ (d) Again, $\mathbb{R}$.

   (f) We must guard against the denominator equaling zero, so we find
        solutions to $x^2 - 3x - 4 = 0$ and exclude them.

   $$x^2 - 3x - 4 = 0 \quad \text{factoring gives}$$

   $$(x - 4)(x + 1) = 0 \quad \text{or}$$

   $$x = 4 \quad \text{or} \quad -1$$

   Therefore the domain is all reals except -1 and 4.

   (g) $\mathbb{R}$

(h) If x is not ≥ 16 we will have a negative radicand.

(i) $\mathbb{R}$

(j) The question here is can $x^2 + x + 1 = 0$? We can't factor so let's try
the Quadratic Formula.

$$x = \frac{-1 \pm \sqrt{1^2 - 4(1)(1)}}{2(1)} \quad \text{or} \quad x = \frac{-1 \pm \sqrt{-3}}{2}$$

So we see that the denominator can not be zero unless x is a complex
number. $x^2 + x + 1$ will be > 0 for any real number x. The domain
is $\mathbb{R}$.

5. If $y = (x - 4)/(x + 5)$, we can see that the domain will be all reals
except x = -5. The range is not obvious. Let's solve for x in terms
of y

$$y(x + 5) = x - 4 \quad \text{from cross-multiplying}$$

$$xy + 4y = x - 4$$

$$xy - x = -5y - 4$$

$$x(y - 1) = -5y - 4$$

$$x = \frac{-5y - 4}{y - 1}$$

Now we can see that y can take any value except 1 and the range will be
all reals except y = 1.

7. In each case if we let y take the given value we can solve for x.
Therefore all of these y values are in the range of the function. Note
that $y = 2x - 5$ represents a line $(y = mx + b)$. For any real number, x,
there is a unique value of y.

9. (a) given a number, square it   (b) $\mathbb{R}$

The definition requires that for any element of D there is only one
element of C. Thus, since f pairs both j and k with b, it is not
a function. The other three meet the standard of the definition.

13. f

17. a, e, f, g, h,
     i, k, l

15.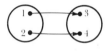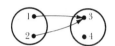

19.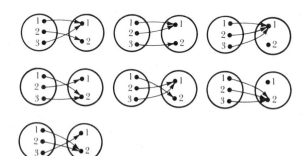

21. If the left hand column is used as inputs the table clearly defines a
     function. For any year there is exactly one national champion. But
     consider why the reverse is not true. UCLA has won the title more than
     once. By the way, can you guess, without looking, where the author of this
     textbook teaches?

23. (a) $y = (x - 3)^2$ (b) $y = x^2 - 3$

     (c) $y = (3x)^2$ (d) $y = 3x^2$

25. (a) By inspection we see that if $x = 1, 2, 3,$ or 4 the denominator will
          contain a zero factor and be equal to zero. Therefore, the domain is
          all reals except 1, 2, 3 or 4.

     (b) Here we want to guard against $x^4 - 4$ equaling zero. $x^4 = 4$ whenever
          $x^2 = \pm 2$ or $x = \pm\sqrt{2}$. So our domain is $\mathbb{R}$ except $\pm\sqrt{2}$. We ignore
          $x = \pm\sqrt{-2}$ because it is not real.

     (c) Let's try some fancy factoring. Notice the x^2 common to the first
          terms? How about the 2 in the last two terms?

$$x^3 + x^2 - 2x - 2 = x^2(x + 1) - 2(x + 1)$$
$$= (x + 1)(x^2 - 2)$$

So we observe that if $x = -1$ or $\pm\sqrt{2}$ we have a zero denominator and the domain is $\mathbb{R}$ except -1 and $\pm\sqrt{2}$.

27. If we work systematically by trial and error we have:

$P(1) = 1^2 + 1 + 11 = 13$ Each of these numbers is prime until

$P(2) = 2^2 + 2 + 11 = 17$ we reach $x = 10$. You will learn more

$P(3) = 3^2 + 3 + 11 = 23$ about the $P(x)$ notation in the next

$P(4) = 4^2 + 4 + 11 = 31$ section.

$P(5) = 5^2 + 5 + 11 = 41$

$P(6) = 6^2 + 6 + 11 = 53$

$P(7) = 7^2 + 7 + 11 = 67$

$P(8) = 8^2 + 8 + 11 = 83$

$P(9) = 9^2 + 9 + 11 = 101$

$P(10) = 10^2 + 10 + 11 = 121$

At last! 121 is the square of eleven. Observe the following interesting thing about $P = x^2 + x + n$. Whenever we choose $x = n - 1$, then

$P = (n - 1)^2 + (n - 1) + n$

$\quad = n^2 - 2n + 1 + n - 1 + n$

$\quad = n^2$

For $n = 11$, $x = 10$ gives us a perfect square 121 for P.

EXERCISE SET 2.2

1. In each case, we must substitute the given value for x and simplity.

(a) $f(x) = x^2 - 3x + 1$ (b) $f(0) = 0^2 - 3 \cdot 0 + 1 = 1$

$\quad f(1) = 1^2 - 3 \cdot 1 + 1 = -1$

(c) $f(-1) = (-1)^2 - 3(-1) + 1 = 5$

(d) $f(3/2) = (3/2)^2 - 3(3/2) + 1$

$$= 9/4 - 9/2 + 1 = -5/4$$

(e) $f(z) = z^2 - 3z + 1$ and no further simplification is necessary.

(f) $f(x + 1) = (x + 1)^2 - 3(x + 1) + 1$

$$= x^2 + 2x + 1 - 3x - 3 + 1$$

$$= x^2 - x - 1$$

(g) $f(a + 1) = a^2 - a - a$ We can write this just by looking at the answer to part f. These letters, x or a, are sometimes referred to as "dummy variables."

(h) $f(-x) = (-x)^2 - 3(-x) + 1$

$$= x^2 + 3x + 1$$

(i) $|f(1)| = 1$ Since $f(1) = -1$ from part a and $|-1| = 1.$

(j) $f(\sqrt{3}) = (\sqrt{3})^2 - 3(\sqrt{3}) + 1 = 3 - 3\sqrt{3} + 1 = 4 - 3\sqrt{3}$

(k) $f(1 + \sqrt{2}) = (1 + \sqrt{2})^2 - 3(1 + \sqrt{2}) + 1 = 1 + 2\sqrt{2} + 2 - 3 - 3\sqrt{2} + 1$

$$= 1 - \sqrt{2}$$

(l) $|1 - f(2)|$ Let's first find $f(2)$.

$f(2) = 2^2 - 3 \cdot 2 + 1 = 4 - 6 + 1 = -1$

So $|1 - f(2)| = |1 - (-1)| = |1 + 1| = |2| = 2$

3. (a) Since $f(x) = 3x^2$

$$f(2x) = 3(2x)^2 = 3(4x^2) = 12x^2$$

(b) $2f(x) = 2(3x^2) = 6x^2$

(c) $f(x^2) = 3(x^2)^2 = 3x^4$

(d) $[f(x)]^2 = [3x^2]^2 = 9x^4$

(e) $f(x/2) = 3(x/2)^2 = 3(x^2/4) = 3x^2/4$

(f) $f(x)/2 = 3x^2/2 = (3/2)x^2$

5. (a) Taking $H(x) = 1 - 2x^2$

$H(0) = 1 - 2 \cdot 0^2 = 1$

(b) $H(2) = 1 - 2(2)^2 = -7$

(c) $H(\sqrt{2}) = 1 - 2(\sqrt{2})^2 = 1 - 2(2) = -3$

(d) $H(5/6) = 1 - 2(5/6)^2 = 1 - 2(25/36) = 1 - 25/18 = -7/18$

(e) $H(1 - \sqrt{3}) = 1 - 2(1 - \sqrt{3})^2 = 1 - 2(1 - 2\sqrt{3} + 3) = 1 - 2 + 4\sqrt{3} - 6$

$= -7 + 4\sqrt{3}$

(f) $H(x^2) = 1 - 2(x^2)^2 = 1 - 2x^4$

(g) $H(x + 1) = 1 - 2(x + 1)^2 = 1 - 2(x^2 + 2x + 1) = 1 - 2x^2 - 4x - 2$

$= -2x^2 - 4x - 1$

(h) $H(x + h) = 1 - 2(x + h)^2 = 1 - 2(x^2 + 2xh + h^2)$

$= 1 - 2x^2 - 4hx - 2h^2$

(i) Using the result of part h we write

$H(x + h) - H(x) = (1 - 2x^2 - 4hx - 2h^2) - (1 - 2x^2) = -4hx - 2h^2$

(j) Now, using i we have

$$\frac{H(x + h) - H(x)}{h} = \frac{-4hx - 2h^2}{h} = \frac{h(-4x - 2h)}{h} = -4x - 2h$$

provided that $h \neq 0$. This sequence of parts h, i and j will be used
frequently in the early stages of a Calculus class. It is a nice
algebra exercise by itself, but it will be very useful later on.

7. (a) The domain of R is $\mathbb{R}$ except 2. Remember, no zero denominators. To
find values which will be excluded from the range, let's solve for x.
Taking $R(x) = y$,

7. (a) (Cont.)

$$y = \frac{2x - 1}{x - 2}$$

$$y(x - 2) = 2x - 1$$

$$xy - 2y = 2x - 1$$

$$xy - 2x = 2y - 1$$

$$x(y - 2) = 2y - 1$$

$$x = \frac{2y - 1}{y - 2}$$

and we see that y can never equal 2, and the range is ℝ except 2 also.

(b) $R(0) = \frac{2(0) - 1}{0 - 2} = \frac{0 - 1}{0 - 2} = \frac{1}{2}$

(c) $r(\frac{1}{2}) = \frac{2(\frac{1}{2}) - 1}{\frac{1}{2} - 2} = \frac{1 - 1}{\frac{1}{2} - 2} = 0$

(d) $R(-1) = \frac{2(-1) - 1}{-1 - 2} = \frac{-2 - 1}{-1 - 2} = \frac{-3}{-3} = 1$

(e) $R(x^2) = \frac{2(x^2) - 1}{x^2 - 2} = \frac{2x^2 - 1}{x^2 - 2}$

(f) $R(1/x) = \frac{2(1/x) - 1}{1/x - 2}$ Multiplying both numerator and denominator by x gives

$\frac{x(2/x - 1)}{x(1/x - 2)}$ or

$\frac{2 - x}{1 - 2x}$

(g) $R(a) = \frac{2a - 1}{a - 2}$

(h) $R(x - 1) = \frac{2(x - 1) - 1}{(x - 1) - 2} = \frac{2x - 2 - 1}{x - 1 - 2} = \frac{2x - 3}{x - 3}$

9. (a) d(1) = 80,   d(3/2) = 108,

         d(2) = 128, $d(t_0) = -16t_0^2 + 96t_0$

11. Given $g(t) = |t - 4|$

then $g(3) = |3 - 4| = |-1| = 1$

and $g(x + 4) = |x + 4 - 4| = |x|$

13. Here again it is worth noting that this form, $\dfrac{f(x + h) - f(x)}{h}$, or the

difference quotient will be very important in Calculus.

(a) -3   (b) $2x + h$ (c) $4x - 3 + 2h$

(d) for $f(x) = x^3$ we have

$$\frac{f(x + h) - f(x)}{h} = \frac{(x + h)^3 - x^3}{h} \ . \ \text{Expanding} \ (x + h)^3 \ \text{gives}$$

$$\frac{(x^3 + 3hx^2 + 3h^2x + h^3) - x^3}{h} \quad \text{or}$$

$$\frac{h(3x^2 + 3hx + h^2)}{h} \quad \text{or} \quad 3x^2 + 3hx + h^2$$

(e) for $f(x) = 7$

$$\frac{f(x + h) - f(x)}{h} = \frac{7 - 7}{h} = 0$$

Remember that if $f(x)$ is constant, in this case 7, then it is the
same no matter what we choose for x.

15. If $H(x) = 1 - x/4$ then

$$\frac{H(x) - H(1)}{x - 1} = \frac{(1 - x/4) - (1 - 1/4)}{x - 1}$$

$$= \frac{\dfrac{4 - x}{4} - \dfrac{4 - 1}{4}}{x - 1}$$

$$= \frac{(1 - x)}{4(x - 1)} \quad \text{or, since} \ (a - b) = -(b - a)$$

$$= \frac{-(x - 1)}{4(x - 1)} = -\frac{1}{4}$$

17. (a) We want $4x_0 - 3$ to equal $8 - x_0$.

$$4x_0 - 3 = 8 - x_0$$

or $\qquad 5x_0 = 11 \qquad$ which means

$$x_0 = 11/5$$

(b) $x_0^2 - 4 = 4 - x_0^2$

$$2x_0^2 = 8$$

$$x_0^2 = 4$$

$$x_0 = \pm 2$$

(c) $x_0^2 = x_0^3$

$$0 = x_0^3 - x_0^2$$

$$= x_0^2(x_0 - 1)$$

Setting each equal to zero gives

$x_0^2 = 0 \qquad$ and $\qquad x_0 - 1 = 0$

$x_0 = 0 \qquad\qquad\qquad x_0 = 1$

19. (a) $5 + h$ $\qquad\qquad$ (b) $t + 3$ $\qquad\qquad$ (c) $t + t_0 + 1$

21. Since $M(x) = \dfrac{x - a}{x + a}$

$$M(1/x) = \frac{(1/x) - a}{(1/x) + a} = \frac{x\,[(1/x) - a)]}{x\,[(1/x) + a)]} = \frac{1 - ax}{1 + ax} \quad \text{as required.}$$

27. Given $F(x) = \dfrac{5x - 7}{2x + 1}$,

$$\frac{F(x + h) - F(x)}{h} = \frac{\dfrac{5(x + h) - 7}{2(x + h) + 1} - \dfrac{5x - 7}{2x + 1}}{h}$$

$$= \frac{(5x + 5h - 7)(2x + 1) - (5x - 7)(2x + 2h + 1)}{h[2(x + h) + 1](2x + 1)}$$

$$= \frac{(10x^2 + 10hx - 14x + 5x + 5h - 7) - (10x^2 + 10hx + 5x - 14x - 14h - 7)}{h[2(x + h) + 1](2x + 1)}$$

27. (Cont.)

$$= \frac{19h}{h[2(x + h) + 1](2x + 1)} \quad \text{finally dividing by } h \text{ gives}$$

$$= \frac{19}{[2(x + h) + 1](2x + 1)}$$

29. $\dfrac{2(u - 2)}{u + 12}$

31. If $F(x) = \dfrac{ax + b}{cx - a}$ then

$$F\left(\frac{ax + b}{cx - a}\right) = \frac{a\left(\dfrac{ax + b}{cx - a}\right) + b}{c\left(\dfrac{ax + b}{cx - a}\right) - a} = \frac{a(ax + b) + b(cx - a)}{c(ax + b) - a(cx - a)} \quad \text{multiplying gives}$$

$$= \frac{a^2x + ab + bcx - ab}{acx + bc - acx + a^2}$$

$$= \frac{a^2x + bcx}{bc + a^2} \qquad \text{If we factor the numerator we have}$$

$$= \frac{x(a^2 + bc)}{(a^2 + bc)} \qquad \text{which is } x.$$

33. We are told that $g(1) = -2$ so substituting gives

$$-2 = (1)^2 - 3(1)(k) - 4$$

$$-2 = 1 - 3k - 4$$

and $\qquad k = -1/3$

37. (a) $\dfrac{f(x + h) - f(x)}{h} = \dfrac{(x + h)^3 - x^3}{h}$

$$= \frac{(x^3 + 3hx^2 + 3h^2x + h^3) - (x^3)}{h}$$

$$= \frac{h(3x^2 + 3hx + h^2)}{h} \qquad \text{or finally}$$

$$= 3x^2 + 3hx + h^2$$

Is it clear why parts b & c have the same answer?

43. By definition, to be a function G must assign a unique output to any
     input. Consider G(6). Since 6 is equidistant from the primes 5 and 7,
     G(6) = 5 and G(6) = 7, a violation of the definition. Therefore G is
     not a function. If G(x) equals the closest prime less than x the
     definition is satisfied.

45. (a) We want $f(x_0) = x_0$ or $6x_0 + 10 = x_0$. Solving we get $x_0 = -2$ for
          the fixed point. Try it, does $-2 = 6(-2) + 10$?

     (b) Here $x_0^2 - 2x_0 - 4 = x_0$

               $x_0^2 - 3x_0 - 4 = 0$

               $(x_0 + 1)(x_0 - 4) = 0$

          $$x_0 = -1 \quad | \quad x_0 = 4$$

     (d) We need $z_0 = \dfrac{z_0 + 1}{z_0 - 1}$

               $z_0(z_0 - 1) = z_0 + 1$

               $z_0^2 - z_0 = z_0 + 1$

          $z_0^2 - 2z_0 - 1 = 0$

          whose solution, using the quadratic formula, is $z_0 = 1 \pm \sqrt{2}$.

49. (a) p(1) = 43

          p(2) = 47

          p(3) = 53

          p(4) = 61

          $p(41) = 41^2 + 41 + 41 = 41(43)$

53. Given $F(x) = 10^x$

     $$\frac{F(x + h) - F(x)}{h} = \frac{10^{(x+h)} - 10^x}{h} = \frac{10^x \cdot 10^h - 10^x}{h} = \frac{10^x(10^h - 1)}{h}$$

Exercise Set 2.3

1. (a) f(0) is the value of the function when x = 0, it is the y-intercept,
       and here it is clearly positive.

   (b) f(-2) = 4, f(1) = 1, f(2) = 2, and f(3) = 0

   (c) f(2) is four larger than f(4).

   (d) f(4) - f(1) = (-2) - (1) = -3

   (e) Its absolute value, |f(4) - f(1)|, is 3.

   (f) Domain [-2,4],   Range [-2,4]

3. By definition [x] is the greatest integer less than or equal to x.

   (a) [3] = 3, [π] = 3, [39/10] = 3, [-3/2] = -2

   (b) Since any output of this function is an integer, the range is simply
       the set of integers.

5. (a) This is false because there is a whole in the graph of the line and
       f(1) = -1.

   (b) True

   (c) False, by looking at the graph, we can see that f(0) > 2.

   (d) False,   f(1) + f(-1) = 3 but not f(0), which equals about 5/2.

   (e) |f(1) - f(-1)| = |(-1) - (4)| = |-5| = 5   True.

7.   y = f(x)   y = g(x)   y = h(x)

     max = 2   max = 3   max = 4

     min = -3   min = -1   min = -2

9.   Since L(0) = 7 the height of the triangle is 7. We are also given that
     A = 40 sq. units. Therefore

$$A = \tfrac{1}{2} \, b \cdot h$$

$$40 = \tfrac{1}{2} \cdot b \cdot 7$$

$$80 = 7b$$

$$\frac{80}{7} = b$$

and the x-intercept must be at (80/7,0).

11.

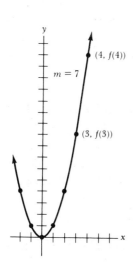

Since $f(3) = 3^2$ or 9

and $f(4) = 4^2$ or 16,

the points given are (3,9) and (4,16).

The slope is

$$\frac{y_2 - y_1}{x_2 - x_1}$$

or $\dfrac{16 - 9}{4 - 3} = 7$

13.   If $T(x) = \sqrt{x}$ then T(1) = 1, T(4) = 2 and T(9) = 3. The slope between
      (1,T(1)) and (4,T(4)) is

$$m = \frac{2 - 1}{4 - 1} = \frac{1}{3}$$

and between the second pair

$$m = \frac{3 - 2}{9 - 4} = \frac{1}{5}$$

Clearly, the slope between the first pair is greater.

15. (a)

     (d)

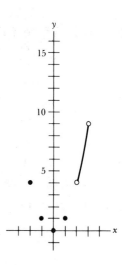

          (c)

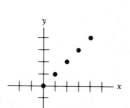

     (b)

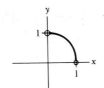

17.   (a)

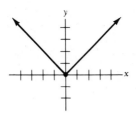

          (b)

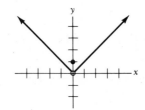

        (c)

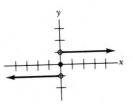

          (d)

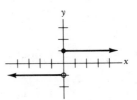

19.

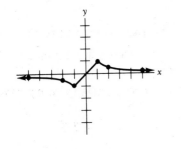

21.

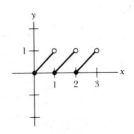

23.

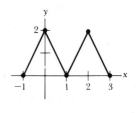

25. (a) If we follow the author's suggestion and let point T have coordinates
        (x, x^2), then the slope from P to T is given by

$$m = \frac{\Delta y}{\Delta x} = \frac{x^2 - 1}{x - 1}$$

$$\text{or} \quad \frac{x^2 - 1}{x - 1} = 5$$

Note that x cannot be one since P & T are different points.
Factor the numerator and get

$$\frac{(x + 1)(x - 1)}{(x - 1)} = 5$$

Now divide by $(x - 1)$ top and bottom to get

$$x + 1 = 5$$

or $x = 4$

and T must be at (4,16).

(b) We use the same argument only here

$$\frac{x^2 - 1}{x - 1} = 1000$$

or $x + 1 = 1000$

and $x = 999$.

So T is at $(999, 999^2)$.

(c) In general, if m = k, then

$$\frac{x^2 - 1}{x - 1} = k$$

and x = k - 1 so the point T has coordinates $[(k - 1), (k - 1)^2]$

27.

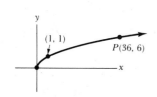

Here $f(x) = \sqrt{x}$ so the coordinates for P
start as $(x, \sqrt{x})$. We have m given as 1/7.

$$\frac{1}{7} = \frac{\sqrt{x} - 1}{x - 1} \quad \text{cross multiplying gives}$$

$$x - 1 = 7\sqrt{x} - 7 \quad \text{or} \quad x + 6 = 7\sqrt{x}$$

27. (Cont.)   Now square both sides to eliminate the radical.

$$x^2 + 12x + 36 = 49x$$

$$x^2 - 37x + 36 = 0$$

$$(x - 36)(x - 1) = 0$$

We take x = 36 (it checks) and reject x = 1 because it gives us a zero
denominator in the original equation. Point P must be at $(36, \sqrt{36})$ or
(36,6).

29. (a)   (b)   31. (a)

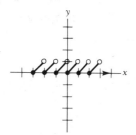   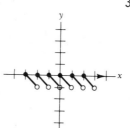   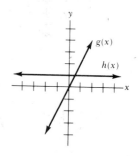

33.

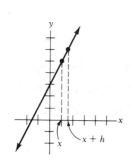

Given x = 1 and h = ½,   F(x + h) = F(3/2).
Using F(x) = 2x + 3

$$\frac{F(x + h) - F(x)}{h}$$

$$= \frac{[2(3/2) + 3] - [2(1) + 3]}{1/2}$$

$$= \frac{(6) - (5)}{1/2} = 2$$

35. (a) 4   (b) -2   (c) 0   (d) 1   (All units are °F/hr)

Exercise Set 2.4

1.

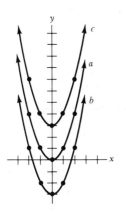

During this, and subsequent calculus courses, you will draw the graphs of common functions, like the ones on page 100, literally hundreds of times. It it well worth your while to memorize the basic shapes involved. Problem one takes the simplest parabola, $y = x^2$, and moves it up and down. Remember the most obvious points on $y = x^2$, $(0,0)$, $(\pm1,1)$, $(\pm2,4)$? The three added or subtracted from x^2 moves the graph vertically.

3.

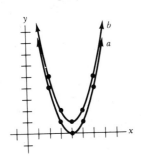

The same idea applies here. $y = x^2$ is moved right 4 units and then up one.

5.

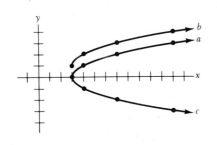

Here, the square root function is shifted right 3 units, then up one and finally inverted or reflected across the x axis.

7.

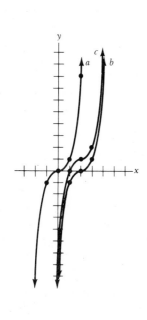

9. (a)

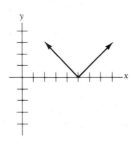

(b)

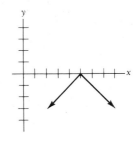

(c)

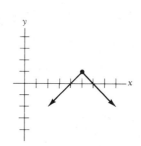

Note the sequence here
- shift |x| right,
then invert, and finally
raise one unit.

11. (a)

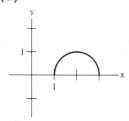

(b)

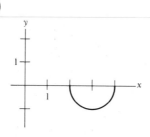

(c)

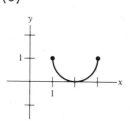

(d)

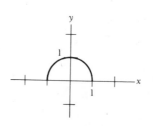

Start with the half circle.
Shift first 2 units to the
right. In part b we take
the negative of that, we
invert it. Part c adds
one unit to part b. It
raises the graph one unit.
Finally, part d looks like
the original function
because reflecting the
original $g(x)$ across the
y-axix gives the same
graph. Since x^2 equals
$(-x)^2$, $g(x)$ and $g(-x)$
are equal here.

13.

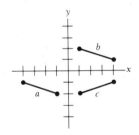

15. (a)   (b)   (c)

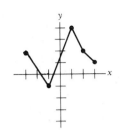   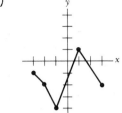   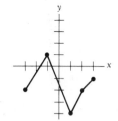

17. We want to show that $\dfrac{x}{x - 1} = \dfrac{1}{x - 1} + 1$. The easiest way will probably

be to add the right hand terms:

$\dfrac{1}{x - 1} + 1 \cdot \dfrac{x - 1}{x - 1}$ to get a common denominator

$\dfrac{1 + x - 1}{x - 1}$ adding numerators

$\dfrac{x}{x - 1}$ as required.

Now observe that $\dfrac{1}{x - 1} + 1$ takes the

graph of $f(x) = 1/x$ from page 100, shifts
it to the right one unit then raises it up
one unit.

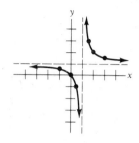

19.

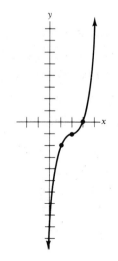

21. (a)

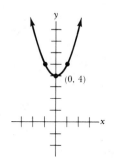

(b)

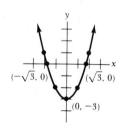

(c)

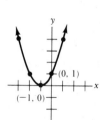

(d)

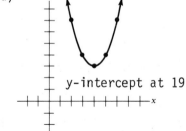

y-intercept at 19

(e)

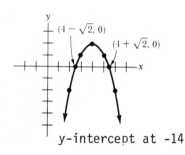

y-intercept at -14

(f)

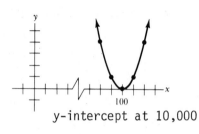

y-intercept at 10,000

The intercepts in part e present something of a problem. Since

$$y = -f(x - 4) + 2$$
$$y = -(x - 4)^2 + 2$$

or

$$y = -(x^2 - 8x + 16) + 2$$

finally $y = -x^2 + 8x - 14.$

Letting x = 0 we find a y-intercept of -14. Solving for x when y = 0, we must use the Quadratic formula. We get $x = 4 \pm \sqrt{2}$ for x-intercepts.

23.

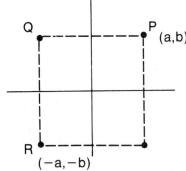

Q •----•----•-- P
            (a,b)

R •----•----•
(−a,−b)

(a) Points P and Q have the same y coordinate but opposite x coordinates. Q and R have the same x's and opposite y's. Therefore, if P is at (a,b), Q is at (-a,b), and R is at (-a,-b).

(b) The slope of line PR is

$$\frac{y_2 - y_1}{x_2 - x_1} \quad \text{or} \quad \frac{b - (-b)}{a - (-a)} = \frac{2b}{2a} = \frac{b}{a}$$

Using point-slope we get

$$y - b = \frac{b}{a}(x - a)$$

$$ay - ab = bx - ab$$

$$ay = bx$$

$$y = \frac{b}{a}x$$

In this form we can see that the y-intercept is 0 and the line must go through the origin.

(c) We could use the distance formula from P to 0 and R to 0, but it will suffice to observe that PO and RO are hypotenuses of right triangles having legs of a and b. They are therefore equal.

25. (a) even   (b) even   (c) neither   (d) neither   (e) odd

EXERCISE SET 2.5

1. (a) $(f + g)(x) = (2x - 1) + (x^2 - 3x - 6) = x^2 - x - 7$

   (b) $(f - g)(x) = (2x - 1) - (x^2 - 3x - 6) = -x^2 + 5x + 5$

   (c) $(f - g)(0) = -(0)^2 + 5(0) + 5 = 5$

3. (a) $(m - f)(x) = (x^2 - 9) - (2x - 1) = x^2 - 2x - 8$

3. (b) $(f - m)(x) = (2x - 1) - (x^2 - 9) = -x^2 + 2x + 8$

What do you notice about these two answers? Could you have predicted it?

5. (a) $(f \cdot k)(x) = (2x - 1)(2) = 4x - 2$

(b) $(k \cdot f)(x) = 4x - 2$ again. Multiplication is commutative, so this is no surprise.

(c) $(fk)(1) - (kf)(2) = [4(1) - 2] - [4(2) - 2] = 2 - 6 = -4$

7. (a) $\dfrac{f}{m}(x) - \dfrac{m}{f}(x) = \dfrac{2x - 1}{x^2 - 9} - \dfrac{x^2 - 9}{2x - 1}$

$$= \frac{(2x - 1)(2x - 1) - (x^2 - 9)(x^2 - 9)}{(x^2 - 9)(2x - 1)}$$

$$= \frac{-x^4 + 22x^2 - 4x - 80}{(x^2 - 9)(2x + 1)}$$

but little is gained by this simplification in the numerator

(b) Much simpler letting $x = 0$:

$$\frac{2(0) - 1}{0^2 - 9} - \frac{0^2 - 9}{2(0) - 1} = \frac{-1}{-9} - \frac{-9}{-1} = \frac{1}{9} - 9 = \frac{-80}{9}$$

9. (a) $[m(k - h)](x) = (x^2 - 9)(2 - x^3)$

(b) $(mk)(x) - (mh)(x) = (x^2 - 9)2 - (x^2 - 9)x^3$

but notice that the $(x^2 - 9)$ common factor can be factored to get the same answer as in part a.

(c) Substituting -1 for x gives

$$[(-1)^2 - 9][2 - (-1)^3] = (-8)(3) = -24$$

1. (a) $(f \circ g)(x) = 3(-2x - 5) + 1$

Notice that the entire function g has been substituted for the x in f. Continuing, we get $= -6x - 14$.

11. (b) Evaluating at 10 gives $-6(10) - 14 = -74$

(c) $(g \circ f)(x) = -2(3x + 1) - 5 = -6x - 7$

(d) when $x = 10$ this is -67

13. (a) $-x$, 2, $2 - x$, 4   (b) $4x^4$, 64, $2x^4$, 32

(c) x^6, 64, x^6, 64   (d) $9x^2 - 3x - 6$, 36, $-3x^2 + 9x + 14$, -16

(e) $(1 - x^4)/3$, -5, $(81 - x^4)/81$, 65/81

(f) $2x^{2}+1$, 32, $2^{2x} + 1$, 17/16

(g) $3x^5 - 4x^2$, -112, $3x^5 - 4x^2$, -112

(h) x, -2, x, -2

15. (a) $\dfrac{-x + 7}{6x}$ (b) $\dfrac{-t + 7}{6t}$ (c) $\dfrac{5}{12}$ (d) $\dfrac{6x - 1}{-7}$ (e) $\dfrac{6y - 1}{-7}$

(f) $-\dfrac{11}{7}$

17. (a) $m(7) = \dfrac{2(7) - 1}{7 - 2} = \dfrac{13}{5}$

so $m[m(7)] = m(13/5) = \dfrac{2\left(\dfrac{13}{5}\right) - 1}{\dfrac{13}{5} - 2} = \dfrac{\dfrac{26}{5} - \dfrac{5}{5}}{\dfrac{13}{5} - \dfrac{10}{5}} = \dfrac{21}{3} = 7$

(b) $(M \circ M)(x) = \dfrac{2\left(\dfrac{2x - 1}{x - 2}\right) - 1}{\left(\dfrac{2x - 1}{x - 2}\right) - 2}$

A little aside here. When you are confronted by this kind of thing, called a complex fraction, it is usually easiest to multiply top and bottom by the common denominator, in this case $x - 2$. Here we get

$$\frac{2(2x - 1) - 1(x - 2)}{(2x - 1) - 2(x - 2)}$$

which is much easier to simplify.

17. (b) (Cont.)

$$\frac{4x - 2 - x + 2}{2x - 1 - 2x + 4} = \frac{3x}{3} = x$$

(c) According to part b $(M \circ M)(7) = 7$ which agrees with our result from part a.

19. (a) To find $f[g(3)]$ we want to first find $g(3)$. The value of $g(x)$ at 3 is zero, so it's zero we substitute for x in $f(x)$. When $x = 0$, $f(x) = 1$, the required result.

(b) Since $f(3) = 4$, $g(4) = -3$

(c) $h(3) = 2$ and $f(2) = -1$

(d) $(h \circ g)(2)$ is another way of saying $h[g(2)]$. Our work is the same: $g(2) = 1$ and $h(1) = 2$.

(e) One more step here, $g(3) = 0$, $f(0) = 1$, and $h(1) = 2$.

(f) Take my word for it, its -3.

21. (a) they are the same, $4x^3 - 3x^2 + 6x - 1$

(b) they are the same, $ax^2 + bx + c$

23.

x	0	1	2	3	4
$(f \circ g)(x)$	1	3	2	–	2

x	−1	0	1	2	3	4
$(g \circ f)(x)$	0	0	3	4	2	–

The results are displayed but let's see how several entries in the table are obtained. Finding $(f \circ g)(x)$ for a particular x requires us to first use the table to find $g(x)$ and then substituting that result as an input in the $f(x)$ table. For example, $g(0) = 3$ and then $f(3) = 1$ as we see under $(f \circ g)(0)$. Why is $(f \circ g)(3)$ missing? Because $g(3) = 4$ but there is no value given for $f(4)$. 4 is not in the domain of f, and therefore $(f \circ g)(3)$ does not exist.

25. (a)

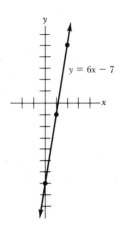

$y = 6x - 7$

(b)

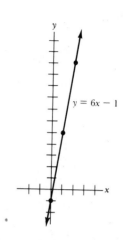

$y = 6x - 1$

27.

(a) domain: $x \geq 0$; range: $y \geq -3$

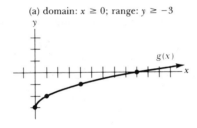

$g(x)$

(b) domain: $\mathbb{R}$; range: $\mathbb{R}$

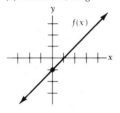

$f(x)$

(c) $\sqrt{x} - 4$, domain: $x \geq 0$; range: $y \geq -4$

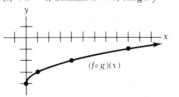

$(f \circ g)(x)$

(d) $g[f(x)] = \sqrt{x - 1} - 3$; domain: $x \geq 1$

(e)

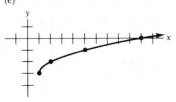

Parts a and b are straight forward, but let's consider part c in some detail. $(f \circ g)(x)$ will equal

$$(\sqrt{x} - 3) - 1 \quad \text{which is} \quad \sqrt{x} - 4$$

The domain will remain $x \geq 0$, and since $\sqrt{x} \geq 0$, the range will be $y \geq -4$. In part d the composition, now $g[f(x)]$, will be $\sqrt{x - 1} - 3$ and here x must be ≥ 1 to avoid a negative radicand. The graph for part e is most easily arrived at by starting with $y = \sqrt{x}$ from page 100 and shifting it right one and down 3. That is so much easier than plotting points.

29. (a) This composite function asks us to find $V[g(t)]$. Since $r = g(t) = \frac{1}{2}t + 2$ and $V = (4/3)\pi r^3$, $(V \circ g)(t) = (4/3)\pi(\frac{1}{2}t + 2)^3$

(b) Setting $V = 36\pi$ we get

$$36\pi = \frac{4}{3}\pi\left(\frac{1}{2}t + 2\right)^3$$

$$\frac{3 \cdot 36\pi}{4\pi} = \left(\frac{1}{2}t + 2\right)^3$$

$$27 = \left(\frac{1}{2}t + 2\right)^3$$

$$3 = \left(\frac{1}{2}t + 2\right)$$

$$6 = t + 4$$

$$2 = t$$

31. (a) $N[T(t)] = -2(10t + 40)^2 + 240(10t + 40) - 5400$

$$= -2(100t^2 + 800t + 1600) + 2400t + 9600 - 5400$$

$$= -200t^2 \cdot\cdot 1600t - 3200 + 2400t + 9600 - 5400$$

$$= -200t^2 + 800t + 1000$$

(b) Substituting $t = 0$ we get 1000 bacteria

$$N[T(2)] = 1800 \text{ and}$$

$$N[T(5)] = -200(5)^2 + 800(5) + 1000 = -5000 + 4000 + 1000 = 0$$

33. Choosing $g(x) = 1 + x^2$ and $f(x) = x^3$ will give $(f \circ g)(x) = (1 + x^2)^3$. Each function is defined for any value of x.

35. (a) $f(x) = \sqrt[3]{x}$, $g(x) = 3x + 4$

(b) $f(x) = |x|$, $g(x) = 2x - 3$

(c) $f(x) = x^5$, $g(x) = ax + b$

(d) $f(x) = 1/x$, $g(x) = \sqrt{x}$

37. (a) $(b \circ c)(x)$ (b) $(a \circ d)(x)$ (c) $(c \circ d)(x)$ (d) $(c \circ b)(x)$

37. (e) $(c \circ a)(x)$ (f) $(a \circ c)(x)$ (g) $(b \circ d)(x)$

39. This seems strange at first. We are used to finding the composition of
two functions, but here we have the result and one of the parts.

$$(g \circ f)(x) = -4x^2 + 4x + 3 \quad \text{and} \quad g(x) = 4 - x^2,$$

so we want an $f(x)$ such that

$$4 - [f(x)]^2 = -4x^2 + 4x + 3$$

$$-[f(x)]^2 = -4x^2 + 4x - 1$$

$$[f(x)]^2 = 4x^2 - 4x + 1 \qquad \text{which conveniently can be factored}$$

$$[f(x)]^2 = (2x - 1)^2$$

so $f(x) = \pm(2x - 1)$

Check by finding $g \circ f$.

41. (a) $(f \circ f) = \dfrac{3\left(\dfrac{3x - 4}{x - 3}\right) - 4}{\left(\dfrac{3x - 4}{x - 3}\right) - 3}$

Multiply numerator and denominator by $x - 3$ to get

$$\frac{3(3x - 4) - 4(x - 3)}{(3x - 4) - 3(x - 3)} \quad \text{or} \quad \frac{9x - 12 - 4x + 12}{3x - 4 - 3x + 9}$$

which is $5x/5$ or x

(b) In part a we concluded that $(f \circ f)(x) = x$. One of the distinguishing
characteristics of great mathematicians is a "constructive laziness."
Observe that $f \circ f$ of a banana should be a banana. Therefore
$(f \circ f)(113/355) = 113/355$. Unfortunately this is not true for all
functions. If $f(x) = x + 2$, $(f \circ f)(x) = x + 4$.

43. (a) $f[g(x)] = (2x - 1)^2$ so the desired quotient is

$$= \frac{(2x - 1)^2 - (2a - 1)^2}{(2x - 1) - (2a - 1)} = \frac{(4x^2 - 4x + 1) - (4a^2 - 4a + 1)}{2x - 1 - 2a + 1}$$

$$= \frac{4x^2 - 4x - 4a^2 + 4a}{2x - 2a} \qquad \text{now reorder and factor}$$

43. (a) (Cont.)

$$= \frac{4(x^2 - a^2) - 4(x - a)}{2(x - a)} = \frac{4(x + a)(x - a) - 4(x - a)}{2(x - a)}$$

$$= \frac{4(x - a)[(x + a) - 1]}{2(x - a)}$$

$$= 2(x + a - 1)$$

(b) This time we have

$$\frac{(2x - 1)^2 - (2a - 1)^2}{x - a}$$

The same simplifications as in part a take us to

$$\frac{4(x - a)(x + a - 1)}{(x - a)}$$

which is $4(x + a - 1)$

45. (a)

0	i	a	b	c
i	i	a	b	c
a	a	i	c	b
b	b	c	i	a
c	c	b	a	i

(b) the operation is commutative (in these cases)

(c) $a^2 = b^2 = c^2 = i$

$c^3 = c$

(d) yes, (ab)c does equal a(bc)

47. (a) $(g \circ h \circ f)(x)$ will be successively

$$g[h(x^2)] = g(x^2/2) = x^2/2 + 1 = (x^2 + 2)/2$$

(b) $(h \circ f \circ g)(x) = (h \circ f)(x + 1) = h(x + 1)^2 = (x + 1)^2/2$

49. (a) $(g \circ f \circ h)(x)$ (b) $(h \circ g \circ f)(x)$ (c) $(f \circ g \circ h)(x)$

(d) $(h \circ f \circ g)(x)$

51. (a) Since $(G - H)(x) = x + 1 - x/2 = (2x + 2 - x)/2 = (x + 2)/2$,

$$[F \circ (G - H)](x) = \left(\frac{x + 2}{2}\right)^2 = \frac{x^2}{4} + x + 1$$

51. (b) $(F - G)(x) = x^2 - x - 1$ so

$$[(F - G) \circ H](x) = \left(\frac{x}{2}\right)^2 - \frac{x}{2} - 1 \text{ or } \frac{x^2}{4} - \frac{x}{2} - 1$$

(c) $(F \circ G)(x)$ is $(x + 1)^2$ so

$$[(F \circ G) - H](x) = (x + 1)^2 - x/2 = x^2 + 2x + 1 - x/2$$
$$= x^2 + 3x/2 + 1$$

(d) First $(G - H)(x) = (x + 1) - x/2 = x/2 + 1$

Then $[F - (G - H)](x) = x^2 - (x/2 + 1) = x^2 - x/2 - 1$

(e) Since $(F - G)(x) = x^2 - x - 1$

$$[(F - G) - H](x) = (x^2 - x - 1) - x/2 = x^2 - 3x/2 - 1$$

53. (a) Start with $F'[G(x)]$. It will be

$$\frac{1}{2\sqrt{x^2 + 2x + 2}}$$

Now that times $G'(x)$ is

$$\frac{1}{2\sqrt{x^2 + 2x + 2}} \cdot (2x + 2)$$

We can divide out twos, but that's about it. We end up with

$$\frac{x + 1}{\sqrt{x^2 + 2x + 2}} \cdot$$

(b) Substitution of 9 for x in both $F'[G(x)]$ and $G'(x)$ gives

$$\frac{9 + 1}{\sqrt{9^2 + 2 \cdot 9 + 2}} = \frac{10}{\sqrt{101}} \text{ or } \frac{10\sqrt{101}}{101} \cdot$$

EXERCISE SET 2.6

1. The definition on page 128 requires that $f[g(x)] = g[f(x)] = x$ for f
    and g to be inverses. Let's see.

    (a) $f[g(x)] = 3(x/3) = x$ and $g[f(x)] = 3x/3 = x$. Yes.

    (b) $f[g(x)] = 4 \dfrac{x + 1}{4} - 1 = (x + 1) - 1 = x$ and

        $g[f(x)] = \dfrac{(4x - 1) + 1}{4} = \dfrac{4x}{4} = x$. Yes again.

    (c) $g[h(x)] = \sqrt{x}^2 = x$ and $h[g(x)] = (\sqrt{x})^2 = x$. Check.

3. (a) 4   (b) -1   (c) $\sqrt{2}$ (d) t + 1   (e) 1,0   (f) -2,-1

5. (a) Given $f(x) = 3x - 1$ we are asked to find $f^{-1}(x)$. Page 130 suggests
        that to accomplish this we interchange x and y and then solve for
        y. So

        $$y = 3x - 1$$
        becomes $$x = 3y - 1$$ and solving for y gives
        $$3y = x + 1$$

        $$y = \frac{x + 1}{3} = f^{-1}(x)$$

    (b) Let's test $f[f^{-1}(x)]$. It will be

        $$3 \frac{x + 1}{3} - 1 \text{ or } x + 1 - 1 \text{ which is } x.$$

        Now we try $f^{-1}[f(x)]$.

        $$\frac{(3x - 1) + 1}{3}$$

        $$= \frac{3x}{3} = x \text{ also.}$$

    (c)

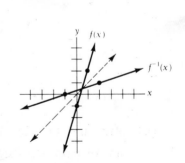

7. (a) $f^{-1}(x) = x^2 + 1$ (c)

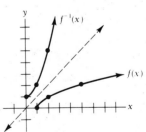

9. (a) $f(x) = \dfrac{x + 2}{x - 3}$

The domain of f will be all reals except 3 because we don't want a zero denominator. To find the range remember that solving the $y = f(x)$ function will help.

$$y = \frac{x + 2}{x - 3}$$

$$xy - 3y = x + 2$$

$$xy - x = 3y + 2$$

$$x(y - 1) = 3y + 2$$

$$x = \frac{3y + 2}{y - 1}$$

and we can see that $y \neq 1$, so the range will be $\mathbb{R}$ except 1.

(b) Interchanging x and y we have

$$x = \frac{y + 2}{y - 3}$$

$$x(y - 3) = y + 2$$

$$xy - 3x = y + 2$$

$$xy - y = 3x + 2$$

$$y(x - 1) = 3x + 2$$

$$y = \frac{3x + 2}{x - 1}$$

This is f^{-1}.

(c) Here we can see that the domain is all $\mathbb{R}$ except 1 and solving for x, as in part a, shows a range of $\mathbb{R}$ except 3. What do you notice about

9. (c) (Cont.)   the answers to parts a and c? Was it expected?

11. Use $y = 2x^3 + 1$, then for the inverse $x = 2y^3 + 1$. Now solve for y

$$x - 1 = 2y^3$$

$$y^3 = \frac{x - 1}{2}$$

$$y = \sqrt[3]{\frac{x - 1}{2}}$$

$$= f^{-1}(x)$$

13.

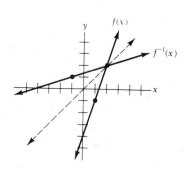

15. (a) Starting from $y = (x - 3)^3 - 1$ we get $x = (y - 3)^3 - 1$ and
successively $x + 1 = (y - 3)^3$, $y - 3 = \sqrt[3]{x + 1}$, $y = \sqrt[3]{x + 1} + 3$.

(b)

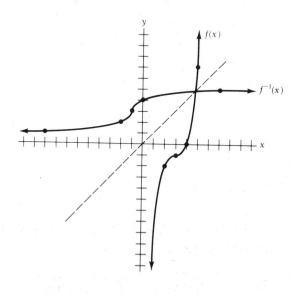

17. (a)    (b)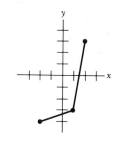

The author wants us to use techniques from section 2.4 to move this graph around. Part (a) is obtained by reflecting g(x) across the line y = x to get $g^{-1}(x)$. In (b) we move it down one unit, in (c) we shift it right one unit. Part (d) reflects it across the y-axis, part (e) the x-axis. Finally (f) reflects in both directions. Study this carefully; it's much easier than plotting points.

(c) 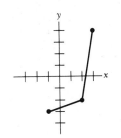   (d)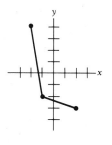

(e) 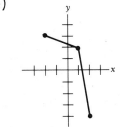   (f)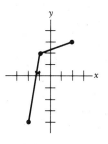

19. f[f(x)] is $\dfrac{3\left(\dfrac{3x-2}{5x-3}\right)-2}{5\left(\dfrac{3x-2}{5x-3}\right)-3}$

(If we wanted (f ∘ f ∘ f)(x) it might start to look like a Morton Salt package.) Multiply top and bottom by 5x - 3 to get

$$\frac{3(3x-2)-2(5x-3)}{5(3x-2)-3(5x-3)} = \frac{9x-6-10x+6}{15x-10-15x+9} = \frac{-x}{-1}$$

which is x as required.

21. (a) f(x) = $\sqrt{x}$ is the given function. Its domain and range are each the real numbers ≥ 0. When we find $f^{-1}(x)$ we let

21. (a) (Cont.)

$$y = \sqrt{x}$$

then switch $x = \sqrt{y}$

$$x^2 = y$$

$$y = f^{-1}(x) = x^2$$

Let's be careful. By itself $y = x^2$ has a domain of <u>all</u> reals, but since y here is the inverse of f, its domain is the range of f, or $x \geq 0$.

(b) The two functions are $f: y = \sqrt{x}$ and $f^{-1}: y = x^2$

(i) Does $2 = \sqrt{4}$ or does $2 = 4^2$? We have substituted (4,2). Clearly the first is correct and (4,2) lies on f.

(ii) f^{-1} (iii) f   (iv) f^{-1}

(v) Let's spend a little time here. $f(a) = \sqrt{a}$, so the point a,f(a) is also $(a,\sqrt{a})$. Substitute. Does $\sqrt{a} = \sqrt{a}$ or $\sqrt{a} = a^2$? No question about that. This point is on f.

(vi) belongs to f^{-1} (vii) f^{-1} (viii) f

23. If $m(x) = y = \dfrac{ax + b}{cx + d}$

(a) Then $m^{-1}(x)$ will be

$$x = \frac{ay + b}{cy + d}$$

$$cxy + dx = ay + b$$

$$cxy - ay = -dx + b$$

$$y(cx - a) = -dx + b$$

$$y = \frac{-dx + b}{cx - a}$$

23. (b) $m[m(x)] = \dfrac{a\left(\dfrac{ax + b}{cx + d}\right) + b}{c\left(\dfrac{ax + b}{cx + d}\right) + d}$

$= \dfrac{a(ax + b) + b(cx + d)}{c(ax + b) + d(cx + d)}$

$= \dfrac{a^2x + ab + bcx + bd}{acx + bc + cdx + d^2}$

$= \dfrac{(a^2 + bc)x + ab + bd}{(ac + cd)x + bc + d^2}$

(c) Letting $x = 0$ gives $\dfrac{ab + bd}{bc + d^2}$

(d) The definition of an inverse requires that $m^{-1}[m(x)] = x$

(e) This must be 0, no matter what m and m^{-1} are.

27. The slope of the line connecting (8,2) and (4,8) is

$$m = \frac{8 - 2}{4 - 8} = -\frac{3}{2}$$

so m for our line is its negative reciprocal, 2/3. We know that the equation is $y = (2/3)x + b$. If we now find the midpoint of the segment connecting the given points, we can use point-slope to find the equation and then b.

$$x_m = \frac{8 + 4}{2} = 6 \qquad\qquad y_m = \frac{2 + 8}{2} = 5$$

so $y - 5 = (2/3)(x - 6)$

$y - 5 = (2/3)x - 4$

$y = (2/3)x + 1$,   the desired equation

m is 2/3 and b is 1.

31. (b) $\left(\dfrac{-am^2 + a + 2bm}{1 + m^2}, \dfrac{bm^2 + 2am - b}{1 + m^2}\right)$

33. The answer is yes, but the question is how can we show that it's true.
Recall that if the coordinates of point P are (x_1,y_1) that its
reflection across $y = x$, its inverse point, will have coordinates (y_1,x_1).
In the same way if Q is at (x_2,y_2) then Q' is at (y_2,x_2). Now use
the distance formula on PQ and P'Q'.

$$\overline{PQ} = \sqrt{(x_2 - x_1)^2 + (y_2 - y_1)^2}$$

$$P'Q' = \sqrt{(y_2 - y_1)^2 + (x_2 - x_1)^2}$$

These two distances are equal, so we can justify our yes answer.

35. (a)

x	f(x)
-2	1/4
-1	1/2
0	1
1	2
2	4
3	8

(b) domain: $x > 0$; range: $\mathbb{R}$

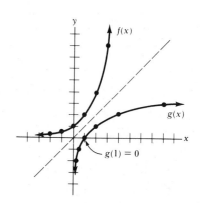

$g(1) = 0$

EXERCISE SET 2.7

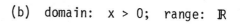

1. (a) $y = kx$ (b) $A = k/B$

3. (a) $x = kuv^2$ (b) $z = kA^2B^3$

5. (a) $F = k/r^2$ (b) $v^2 = k(u^2 + T^2)$

7. (a) $A = k/B$ (b) $A = -2/B$

B	A
2	-1
5/4	?

     $-1 = k/2$

     $k = -2$

7. (c) $A = \dfrac{-2}{\frac{5}{4}} = -\dfrac{8}{5}$

9. $x = kyz$ It is frequently a good idea to make a table to help keep track
    of the given values before proceeding.

y	z	x
2	-3	9
4	4	?

The complete set of data will let us find k next.

$$9 = k \cdot 2 \cdot -3$$

$$-3/2 = k$$

so we have $x = -(3/2)yz$

Then find x when y & z are both 4

$$x = (-3/2) \cdot 4 \cdot 4$$

$$x = -24$$

11. This is a common problem, and the solution will yield to a systematic
     approach. First the equation

$$A = k \, B \cdot C$$

If B is tripled it says that B becomes 3B, and since C is doubled
we have 2C. Now replace B and C in the equation with 3B and 2C
respectively. We get

$$A = k(3B)(2C)$$

$$A = 6k \, B \cdot C$$

Notice that the new A is 6 times the old one. This is true no matter what
value k assumes.

13. it is increased eightfold

15. (a) $A = kr^2$ and the given A and r will let us find k.

$$16\pi = k \cdot 2^2$$

$$4\pi = k$$

So the law of variation here is $A = 4\pi r^2$.

15. (b) $A = 4\pi r^2$

$A = 4\pi (\sqrt{3})^2$

$A = 12\pi$ sq. cm.

17. $F = k \dfrac{M_1 M_2}{d^2}$ is the stated relationship. Make the indicated changes and we
have

$$F = k \frac{(3M_1)(4M_2)}{(\frac{1}{2} d)^2}$$

$$F = k \frac{12M_1 M_2}{d^2/4}$$

$$F = \frac{48k M_1 M_2}{d^2}$$

The force is increased by a factor of 48.

19. $d = kt^2$ Some people prefer to solve these problems using proportions.
Let's do this one by that method. The given equation says that for any d
and t, $k = d/t^2$. So for two sets of condtions

$$\frac{d_1}{t_1^2} = \frac{d_2}{t_2^2} \quad \text{or in this case}$$

$$\frac{490}{10^2} = \frac{d_2}{5^2} \quad \text{and we have}$$

$$d_2 = \frac{490 \cdot 25}{100} = 122.5 \text{ meters}$$

The weakness of this method is that we never find k.

21. (a) $V = k/P$ That makes sense - more pressure, less volume.

$2 = k/1.025$ or

$k = 2.05$ and

$V = 2.05/P$

21. (b) Since $V = 2.05/P$

$$V = 2.05/1$$

$$V = 2.05 \text{ liters}$$

Boyle's Law is famous, but not as well known as Cole's Law.

23. (a) Start with $E = km/r$ then replace with

$$E = k \ 3m/\tfrac{1}{2}r$$

$$E = 6km/r$$

E is increased sixfold.

(b) $V = k/\sqrt{r}$

$V = k/\sqrt{(r/2)}$

$V = k/(\sqrt{r}/\sqrt{2}) = \sqrt{2} \ k/\sqrt{r}$

It is increased by a factor of $\sqrt{2}$.

25. about 111 lb.

33. (a) $R = kS^2$ An increase from 40 to 60 mph multiplies 5 by 1.5. So we have our new $R = k(1.5S)^2$ or $R = 2.25kS^2$ and the increase is by a factor of 2.25.

(b) We want the new R to be twice the first R. Or since $R/S^2 = k$

$$\frac{R_1}{S_1^2} = \frac{2R_1}{S_2^2}$$

$$R_1 \ S_2^2 = 2R_1 \ S_1^2$$

$$S_2^2 = 2R_1 \ S_1^2 /R_1 = 2S_1^2$$

$$S_2 = \sqrt{2} \ S_1$$

The new speed must be $\sqrt{2}$ times the old one to double the resistance. So we use $50\sqrt{2}$ or about 71 mph.

41.   Planet   Earth days for one
                    revolution about the sun

    Mercury -   87.9693
    Venus   -   224.7007
    Earth   -   365.2564
    Mars   -   686.9786
    Jupiter -   4336.6159
    Saturn   -   10826.9994
    Uranus   -   30873.7244
    Neptune -   60300.6863
    Pluto   -   91814.3739

Kepler's 3rd Law says $T^2 = kd^3$. Using a T of 365.2564 and a d of 1 for the earth, we get k = 133412.24. Now let's find the days for a revolution about the sun on Mercury.

$$T^2 = kd^3$$

$$T^2 = 133412.24(0.387099)^3 = 7738.5977$$

$$T = 87.9693 \text{ Earth Days}$$

The other periods can be found in a similar manner.

43. $V = kd$

    $745 = k(78,000,000)$

    $k = 9.55 \times 10^{-6}$

So $V = (9.55 \times 10^{-6})d$

and $37,881 = 9.55 \times 10^{-6} d$

d is about 3.97×10^9 light years.

Chapter 3 Some Applications of Functions

Exercise Set 3.1

1. (a) f(-1) = 0 says that when x = -1, f(x) is 0. Another way of
        expressing this fact is to say that the point (-1,0) is on the line.
        If f(5) = 4, then (5,4) is also on the line. Each part of this
        problem gives two points and tells us to look for a linear function.
        In each problem we will find the slope and then use the point-slope
        equation

$$m = \frac{4 - 0}{5 - (-1)} = \frac{4}{6} = \frac{2}{3}$$

And choosing either point,

$$y - 0 = (2/3)[x - (-1)]$$

$$y = (2/3)x + 2/3$$

Just to reinforce the idea we will also use (5,4).

$$y - 4 = (2/3)(x - 5)$$

$$y = (2/3)x - 10/3 + 4$$

$$y = (2/3)x + 2/3. \qquad \text{Same result.}$$

1. (b) If f(3) = 2 and f(-3) = -4, then out given points are (3,2) and
         (-3,-4).

$$m = \frac{-4 - 2}{-3 - 3} = \frac{-6}{-6} = 1$$

$$y - 2 = 1(x - 3)$$

$$y = x - 1$$

(c) Points are (0,0) and (1,$\sqrt{2}$)

$$m = \frac{\sqrt{2} - 0}{1 - 0} = \sqrt{2}$$

$$y - 0 = \sqrt{2}(x - 0)$$

$$y = \sqrt{2}\, x$$

(d) $m = \dfrac{9 - 4}{3 - 2} = \dfrac{5}{1} = 5$

$$y - 4 = 5(x - 2)$$

$$y = 5x - 6$$

3. Given g(-3) = 0 and g(-2) = 2 we have the points (-3,0) and (-2,2).

$$m = \frac{2 - 0}{-2 - (-3)} = \frac{2}{1} = 2$$

and by point-slope

$$y - 2 = 2(x + 2)$$

$$y = 2x + 6$$

Now we can find g of anything just by substituting for x. g(-1) will be
2(-1) + 6 = 4.

A graphical solution is another possibility. Notice that as we move from
x = -3 to -2 we go up 2 units. Then, since this is a linear function,
moving up to -1 should move us up 2 more units to 4. So, g(-1) = 4. One
more unit to the right, to x = 0, takes us up 2 more, to 6. Notice the
y-intercept of the equation.

7. (f ∘ g)(x) = 3(1 - 2x) - 4 = 3 - 6x - 4 = -6x - 1
    This matches the y = Ax + B pattern for a linear function.

9. y = (9/5)x + 32

11. (a) Here ΔP/Δx = $20/(-4) = -$5

    (b) P - 195 = -5(x - 280)

                P = -5x + 5(280) + 195

                P = -5x + 1595

    (c) Letting P = $250 and solving for x, we get

                250 = -5x + 1595

            -1340 = -5x

                268 = x

13. (a) -25/2   (b) P = (-25/2)x + 1400

    (c) about 71   (d) $275

15. (a)

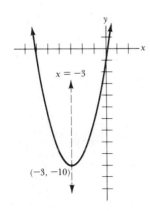

    (b)

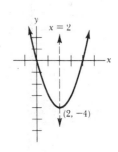

    (c)

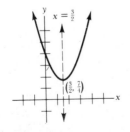

    (d)

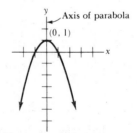

17. When we have a quadratic function in the $f(x) = ax^2 + bx + c$ form, finding
a max or min point requires us to find the coordinates of the vertex. We
have two choices; either completing the square or using the vertex formula
on page 153. The latter is usually easier.

(a) $y = 2x^2 - 6x + 1$ The x coordinate will be $-b/2a$ which is

$-(-6)/2(2)$ or $3/2$. To find the cooresponding value of y we
substitute

$$y = 2(3/2)^2 - 6(3/2) + 1$$

$$= 9/2 - 9 + 1$$

$$= -7/2$$

Finally, since a, the coefficient of x^2, is positive, the parabola
must open up and $(3/2, -7/2)$ is a low point.

(b) $f(x) = -5x^2 - 5x + 3$

$$x = \frac{-b}{2a} = \frac{-(-5)}{2(-5)} = -\frac{1}{2}$$

and $f(-1/2) = -5(-1/2)^2 - 5(-1/2) + 3 = -5/4 + 5/2 + 3$

$$= -5/4 + 10/4 + 12/4 = 17/4$$

Since $a = -5$, $(-1/2, 17/4)$ is a high point.

19. Here we only need to find the x value which produces a max or min.

(a) $x = \frac{-b}{2a} = \frac{4}{2(2)} = 1$

and $x = 1$ produces a minimum output.

(b) $x = \frac{-1}{2(8)} = \frac{-1}{16}$

Again, this is a minimum output.

(c) $x = \frac{-1}{2(-8)} = \frac{1}{16}$, a largest output

21. The largest value for $\sqrt{-x^2 + 8x - 13}$ is the same as for $-x^2 + 8x - 13$. We should point out that it will be a maximum because the -1 coefficient for x^2 means that the parabola will open down.

$$x = \frac{-8}{2(-1)} = 4 \quad \text{tells me that the max happens when } x = 4$$

$$\sqrt{-(4)^2 + 8(4) - 13} = \sqrt{-16 + 32 - 13} = \sqrt{3}$$

shows me that the max is $\sqrt{3}$.

23. Following the lead of example 11 on p. 155 we can let $x^2 = t$ and function f becomes $y = t^2 - 8t$, a quadratic. Again, its min will occur at $-b/2a$ or $-(-8)/2(1) = 4$. Since $t = x^2$, $x^2 = 4$ or $x = \pm 2$. And substituting ± 2 gives a minimum of $f(x) = -16$.

27. Using the result of problem 26 we find the coordinates of the vertex as

$$\frac{-b}{2a} = \frac{-(-6)}{2(1)} = 3 \quad \text{and}$$

$$\frac{4ac - b^2}{4a} = \frac{4(1)(13) - (-6)^2}{4(1)} = 4$$

The distance to the origin will then be

$$d = \sqrt{(3,0)^2 + (4 - 0)^2} = 5 \text{ units}$$

We could have found the coordinates, (3,4), by more conventional means, completing the square, for example.

31. (a) It is clear that $\sqrt{1 + 4x - x^2}$ has a maximum because of the -1 coefficient of x^2. Let's complete the square this time.

$$y = -(x^2 - 4x \quad) + 1$$
$$= -(x^2 - 4x + 4) + 1 + 4$$
$$= -(x - 2)^2 + 5.$$

Since the vertex is at (2,5) the max will be at $\sqrt{5}$.

31. (b) This problem requires that we realize that a fraction is smallest when its denominator is largest. The reciprocal of the maximum value of $F(x)$ is minimum value of $G(x)$. It will be $1/\sqrt{5}$ or $\sqrt{5}/5$.

33. (a) 1   (b) max is 1, min is 0

39. (a)

a	b	$a+b$	a^2+b^2
$\frac{1}{2}$	$\frac{1}{2}$	1	$\frac{1}{2}$
$\frac{1}{3}$	$\frac{2}{3}$	1	$\frac{5}{9}$
$\frac{1}{4}$	$\frac{3}{4}$	1	$\frac{5}{8}$
$\frac{1}{5}$	$\frac{4}{5}$	1	$\frac{17}{25}$
$\frac{2}{5}$	$\frac{3}{5}$	1	$\frac{13}{25}$

(b) Clearly its (1/2,1/2).

(c) $f(a) = a^2 + (1-a)^2$

$= a^2 + 1 - 2a + a^2$

$= 2a^2 - 2a + 1$

The minimum here occurs

when $a = \dfrac{-(-2)}{2(2)} = \dfrac{1}{2}$.

This tells us that 1/2, 1/2 must be "the" smallest value for $a^2 + b^2$.

41. We are told that the width varies directly as the square root of the height. This translates into $w = k\sqrt{h}$, or squaring both sides, $w^2 = k^2 h$. Using the given value (2,12) we can find k.

$$2^2 = k^2 \cdot 12$$

$$k^2 = 4/12 = 1/3$$

and the equation becomes $w^2 = (1/3)h$ or $h = 3w^2$. Since h corresponds to y and w to x we can write this as $y = 3x^2$, a parabola with vertex at the origin, which passes through the point (2,12).

EXERCISE SET 3.2

1. (a)

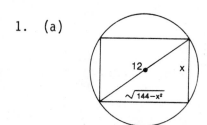

Letting the shorter side of the rectangle be x and following example 1 of this section, we find the length to be $\sqrt{144 - x^2}$ and the perimeter is therefore $2l + 2w$ or $2\sqrt{144 - x^2} + 2x$.

1. (b) The area will simply be the product

$$A = x \sqrt{144 - x^2}$$

3. (a) Any point on the curve has coordinates (x,y) where $y = x^2 + 1$ and the distance formula gives us

$$D = \sqrt{(x - 0)^2 + (x^2 + 1 - 0)^2}$$

$$= \sqrt{x^2 + x^4 + 2x^2 + 1}$$

$$= \sqrt{x^4 + 3x^2 + 1}$$

(b) The slope, $m = \dfrac{y_2 - y_1}{x_2 - x_1}$ or $\dfrac{x^2 + 1 - 0}{x - 0}$.

So $m = \dfrac{x^2 + 1}{x}$.

5. (a) The circumference of the circle is z in. $C = 2\pi r$ becomes $z = 2\pi r$ and $r = z/2\pi$. Substituting this r into $A = \pi r^2$ gives $A = \pi(z/2\pi)^2$ or $A = z^2/4\pi$.

(b) The circumference of the circle is z in.

(c) We would have a square with a side equal to $z/4$ in. Its area would be $z^2/16$ sq. in.

7. (a) $P = -x^2 + 16x$ (b) $S = 2x^2 - 32x + 256$

(c) $d = x^3 - (16 - x)^3$ or $d = (16 - x^3) - x^3$

9. Since Revenue equals units times price per unit, we have $R = x \cdot P$. P is given here as $-\frac{1}{4}x + 8$, so substituting we have,

$$R = x(-\tfrac{1}{4}x + 8)$$
$$R = -\tfrac{1}{4}x^2 + 8x$$

11. $P(1) = 17.87$ $P(2) = 19.49$ $P(3) = 20.83$ $P(4) = 21.86$

$P(5) = 22.49$ $P(6) = 22.58$ $P(7) = 21.75$

13. (a)

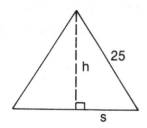

Using the Pythagorean Theorem we have

$$h^2 + s^2 = (2s)^2 \quad \text{or}$$
$$h^2 = 3s^2$$

Therefore $h = \sqrt{3}\ s$

(b) $A = b \cdot h$

$= s \cdot \sqrt{3}\ s$

$= \sqrt{3}\ s^2$

(c) Here we let $2s = 8$ and find h to be $4\sqrt{3}$ cm.

(d) Here $2s = 5$ and $s = 5/2$.

$$A = \sqrt{3}\ (5/2)^2$$
$$A = (25/4)\ \sqrt{3} \text{ sq. in.}$$

17. (a) We know that for such a cylinder $V = \pi r^2 h$, so we substitute 12π for V and solve for h in terms of r

$$12\pi = \pi r^2 h \qquad \text{dividing by } \pi r^2 \text{ we get}$$

$$\frac{12\pi}{\pi r^2} = h$$

or $h = \dfrac{12}{r^2}$

(b) The total surface area from page 162 is $2\pi r^2 + 2\pi rh$. By the way, do you see that the formula is jsut two circles and the side unrolled into a rectangle? When we substitute we have

$$A = 2\pi r^2 + 2\pi r(12/r^2)$$
$$= 2\pi r^2 + 24\pi/r.$$

19. $V = \dfrac{s\sqrt{\pi s}}{6\pi}$

21. If one leg is x then by Pythagoras the other will be $\sqrt{400 - x^2}$. Since the area is one half the product of the two legs (base times height) we get

$$A = \tfrac{1}{2}\, b \cdot h$$

$$= \tfrac{1}{2}\, x \cdot \sqrt{400 - x^2}$$

23. The figure reveals similar triangles and therefore proportional sides, but we must first find an expression for the hypotenuse of the smaller triangle. Again, using our old standby, the Pythagorean Theorem we find it to be $\sqrt{x^2 + 25}$, and we can write the following proportion.

$$\frac{x}{\sqrt{x^2 + 25}} = \frac{x + 4}{AB} \qquad \text{If we cross multiply and divide by } x \text{ we have}$$

$$AB = \frac{(x + 4)\sqrt{x^2 + 25}}{x}$$

25. (a) $m = \dfrac{a^2 + 1}{a}$

27. (a) The drawing tells us that $V = (1/3)\pi r^2 h$ (or 1/3 of the cylinder surrounding it). So, since we are given $h = \sqrt{3}\, r$, $V = (1/3)\pi r^2 h$ becomes $V = (1/3)\pi r^2(\sqrt{3}\, r)$ or $V = (\sqrt{3}/3)\pi r^3$.

   (b) Again we substitute. $S = \pi r\sqrt{r^2 + (\sqrt{3}\, r)^2} = \pi r\sqrt{4r^2} = 2\pi r^2$

29. (a) $r = \dfrac{3h}{\sqrt{h^2 - 9}}$ (b) $h = \dfrac{3r}{\sqrt{r^2 - 9}}$

31. Let's use x inches for the circle and $14 - x$ for the square. Each edge of the square will then be $(14 - x)/4$ in. long and its area will be $\left(\dfrac{14 - x}{4}\right)^2$.

   The circle will have a circumference of x inches. So $x = 2\pi r$, or $r = x/2\pi$.

   The circular area will then be $A = \pi r^2$ or $A = \pi(x/2\pi)^2$ which is $x^2/4\pi$.

31.   (Cont.)

Adding the square and cirlce gives $A_T = \dfrac{x^2}{4\pi} + \left(\dfrac{14 - x}{4}\right)^2$.

33. $A = -\pi r^2 + \tfrac{1}{4}r$ sq. mi.

35.

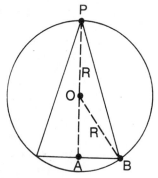

We are given that $\overline{PB} = x$, and since the altitude PA bisects the base, $\overline{AB} = x/2$. Also $\triangle OAB$ is a $30° - 60° - 90°$ triangle so $\overline{OA} = \tfrac{1}{2}\overline{OB}$. Letting OA = y and $\overline{OB} = 2y$ we have

$$y^2 + \left(\frac{x}{2}\right)^2 = (2y)^2 \quad \text{or} \quad y = \frac{x\sqrt{3}}{6}.$$

The radius is therefore 2y or $x\sqrt{3}/3$ and the area = πr^2 which will be

$$\pi\left(\frac{x\sqrt{3}}{3}\right)^2 \quad \text{or} \quad \frac{1}{3}\pi x^2.$$

37.

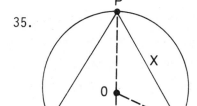

The area of the circle is clearly πR^2 but to answer the question we need to find the area of the triangle and subtract it. If h is $\overline{PA}$ then $\overline{OA} = h - R$ and we can find AB by Pythagoras.

$$R^2 = (h - R)^2 + \overline{AB}^2$$
$$AB^2 = R^2 - (h^2 - 2hR + R)^2$$

and $AB = \sqrt{2hR - h^2}$

Therefore the entire base is $2\sqrt{2hR - h^2}$ and the area of the triangle will be

$$A = \tfrac{1}{2}\, b \cdot h$$

$$= \tfrac{1}{2} \cdot 2\sqrt{2hR - h^2}\ (h)$$

$$= h\sqrt{2hR - h^2}$$

Subtracting the triangle from the circle gives $\pi R^2 - h\sqrt{2hR - h^2}$ as required.

39. $V = 4x^3 - 28x^2 + 48x$

41. If x is the given side, then the length paralleling must be 500 - 2x.
The area will then be $x(500 - 2x)$, or $A = -2x^2 + 500x$.

43. (a) This is a rather difficult task, and will require careful planning.
The area we are seeking consists of half of a circle plus a rectangle.
If r is the radius of the half-circle, its area will be $\frac{1}{2}\pi r^2$. We
can also see that the top of the rectangle will be 2r across, but
how about the height? We must use the total perimeter of 32 ft. here.

P_{total} = half circle + 2 rectangle sides + 1 rectangle base

$32 = \frac{1}{2}(2\pi r) + 2h + 2r$

$2h = 32 - \pi r - 2r$

or $h = 16 - r - \pi r/2$

Now we have h in terms of r so we can find the rectangular area.

A_R = base x height

$= (2r)(16 - r - \pi r/2)$

$= 32r - 2r^2 - \pi r^2$

If we now add the two areas we have

$A_T = A_C + A_R$

$= \frac{1}{2}\pi r^2 + 32r - 2r^2 - \pi r^2$

$= -\frac{1}{2}\pi r^2 - 2r^2 + 32r$

$= -\left(\frac{\pi + 4}{2}\right) r^2 + 32r$

(b) This quadratic opens down because the r^2 coefficient is negative, and
it goes through the origin because when r = 0, A = 0. Let's use the
vertex formula to find r for the maximum A.

$r = \dfrac{-b}{2a} = \dfrac{-32}{2\left[-\left(\frac{\pi + 4}{2}\right)\right]} = \dfrac{32}{\pi + 4}$

43. (b) (Cont.)

and $\quad A = \dfrac{4ac - b^2}{4a} = \dfrac{0 - (32)^2}{4\left[\dfrac{-(\pi + 4)}{2}\right]} = \dfrac{512}{\pi + 4}$

45. (a) $y = \dfrac{3s}{\sqrt{1 - s^2}}$ (b) $s = \dfrac{y}{\sqrt{y^2 + 9}}$ (c) $z = \dfrac{3}{\sqrt{1 - s^2}}$

(d) $s = \dfrac{\sqrt{z^2 - 9}}{z}$

47.

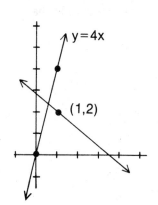

The line passing through m has an equation of the form

$$(y - 2) = m(x - 1)$$

or $\qquad\qquad y = mx - m + 2$

When $y = 0$ we find an x-intercept of

$$0 = mx - m + 2$$

$$m - 2 = mx$$

$$\frac{m - 2}{2} = x$$

which is the base of our triangle. The two lines intersect when

$$4x = mx - m + 2 \qquad \text{or, solving for } x$$

$$4x - mx = -m + 2$$

$$x(4 - m) = 2 - m$$

$$x = \frac{2 - m}{4 - m} \text{ or } \frac{m - 2}{m - 4}$$

and $\qquad\qquad y = 4x = 4\left(\dfrac{2 - m}{4 - m}\right)$

This y is the height of our triangle. Since $A = \frac{1}{2} b \cdot h$

$$A = \frac{1}{2}\left(\frac{m - 2}{m}\right)\left[\frac{4(2 - m)}{4 - m}\right] = \frac{2(m - 2)^2}{m(m - 4)}$$

Exercise Set 3.3

1. Since $x + y = 5$, $y = 5 - x$ and we can write their product as $P = x(5 - x)$ or $P = -x^2 + 5x$. This parabola opens down, which is consistent with our search for a maximum product. The vertex formula says $x = -b/2a$ or $-5/2(-1)$. So our max occurs when $x = 5/2$ and the maximum value will be
$$P = -(5/2)^2 + 5(5/2) = -25/4 + 25/2 = 25/4$$

3. ½

5. If $P = 25$ then $21 + 2w = 25$ or $1 = (25 - 2w)2$. The area will be
$$\left(\frac{25 - 2w}{2} \right) w.$$

Our equation becomes
$$A = -w^2 + (25/2)w$$

and we search for the coordinates of the vertex.
$$w = \frac{-25/2}{2(-1)} = \frac{25}{4}$$

from the vertex formula. Substituting back for 1 gives 25/4 also. Our conclusion, for a given perimeter, the rectangle with the largest area is a square.

7. 1250 sq. in.

9. If their sum is 6, let them be x and $6 - x$.

(a) $T = x^2 + (6 - x)^2$
$$= x^2 + 36 - 12x + x^2$$
$$= 2x^2 - 12x + 36 \qquad \text{which opens up.}$$
$$x_{min} = \frac{-(-12)}{2(2)} = 3$$

Here both numbers are 3, and the minimum T is $3^2 + 3^2$ or 18.

(b) 23/4

9. (c) $u = x + 2(6 - x)^2$

$\quad\quad = x + 2(36 - 12x + x^2)$

$\quad\quad = 2x^2 - 23x + 72$ which has a minimum

$\quad x_{min} = \dfrac{-(-23)}{2(2)} = \dfrac{23}{4}$ and $(6 - x)$ is $1/4$.

$\quad$ So $u = \dfrac{23}{4} + 2\left(\dfrac{1}{4}\right)^2 = \dfrac{23}{4} + \dfrac{1}{8} = \dfrac{47}{8}$

(d) 95/16

11. $h = -16t^2 + 32t$

(a) $h(1) = -16(1)^2 + 32(1) = 16$ ft.

$\quad h(3/2) = -16(3/2)^2 + 32(3/2) = -36 + 48 = 12$ ft.

(b) from the vertex formula

$\quad t_{max} = \dfrac{-32}{2(-16)} = 1$ sec.

$\quad$ and from part (a) we know that $h(1) = 16$ ft.

(c) Letting $h = 7$ we have

$\quad\quad\quad 7 = -16t^2 + 32t$

$\quad$ or $16t^2 - 32t + 7 = 0$

$\quad$ in standard form. Can we factor? It's worth a try.

$\quad\quad\quad (4t - 1)(4t - 7) = 0$ will do it.

$\quad$ So $t = 1/4$ sec. and $t = 7/4$ sec. are both times when $h = 7$.

13. Every point on the given curve has coordinates of the form $(x, \sqrt{x - 2} + 1)$, and using the distance formula gives

$$d = \sqrt{(4 - x)^2 + (1 - \sqrt{x - 2} - 1)^2}$$

$$= \sqrt{16 - 8x + x^2 + x - 2} = \sqrt{x^2 - 7x + 14}$$

and we look for a minimum value of the radicand.

13. (Cont.)

$$x_{min} = \frac{-(-7)}{2(1)} = \frac{7}{2} \quad \text{and} \quad y = \sqrt{(7/2) - 2} + 1 = \frac{2 + \sqrt{6}}{2}$$

The distance is $\sqrt{(7/2)^2 - 7(7/2) + 14} = \sqrt{(49/4) - (49/2) + 14} = \sqrt{7}/2$.

15. (a) ½   (b) ¼

17. If we choose x for the depth of the pasture then 500 - 2x is the length paralleling the river. The area of the pasture will then be given by

$$A = x(500 - 2x)$$
$$= -2x^2 + 500x$$

Let's complete the square this time.

$$A = -2(x^2 - 250x \qquad)$$
$$= -2(x^2 - 250x + 125^2) + 2(125)^2$$
$$= -2(x - 125)^2 + 31{,}250$$

We were not asked for the maximum area, but this form shows it to us as a bonus. The length will be 500 - 2(125) = 250 ft. We find 125 (2 sides) by 250 as required.

19. 40

21. Recall that revenue, R, is x·p. So

$$R = x(-\tfrac{1}{4}x + 30)$$
or $$R = -\tfrac{1}{4}x^2 + 30x$$

From the vertex formula

$$x_{max} = \frac{-30}{2(-\tfrac{1}{4})} = 60$$

and $$R_{max} = -\tfrac{1}{4}(60)^2 + 30(60) = -900 + 1800 = \$900$$

The unit price will be $p = -\tfrac{1}{4}(60) + 30 = \$15$

23.   I'll use x for the triangle and 30 - x for the square. The triangle will
      look like this.

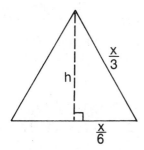

                          To find h we use

                          $h = \sqrt{(x/3)^2 - (x/6)^2}$

                            $= \sqrt{x^2/9 - x^2/36} = (\sqrt{3}/6)x$

An easier observation would be to note that h divides the equilateral
triangle into two 30° - 60° - 90° triangles whose sides are in the ratio
of $1:2:\sqrt{3}$ giving us $(x/6)\sqrt{3}$ directly. In any case the area is

$$\frac{1}{2}\left(\frac{x}{3}\right)\left(\frac{\sqrt{3}}{6}x\right) = \frac{\sqrt{3}}{72}x^2$$

The area of the square is easier. Take the remaining 30 - x, divide by
4 and square. The total area then is

$$A = \frac{\sqrt{3}}{36}x^2 + \left(\frac{30 - x}{4}\right)^2 = \frac{\sqrt{3}}{36}x^2 + \frac{900 - 60x + x^2}{16}$$

We must arrange this in standard quadratic form using 144 for a common
denominator

$$A = \left(\frac{4\sqrt{3} + 9}{144}\right)x^2 - \frac{15}{4}x + \frac{225}{4}$$

and $x_{min} = \dfrac{-\left(-\dfrac{15}{4}\right)}{2\left(\dfrac{4\sqrt{3} + 9}{144}\right)} = \dfrac{15}{4} \cdot \dfrac{72}{4\sqrt{3} + 9} = \dfrac{270}{4\sqrt{3} + 9}$

Rationalizing the denominator we get

$$\frac{270}{4\sqrt{3} + 9} \cdot \frac{4\sqrt{3} - 9}{4\sqrt{3} - 9} = \frac{-90(4\sqrt{3} - 9)}{11}$$

which is about 16.95 inches to be used for the triangle.

25.   Given $L = .059t^2 - .354t + .557.$ This quadratic opens up so let's look
      for the minimum. The minimum L will occur when

$$t = \frac{-(-.354)}{2(.059)} = 3 \text{ pm.}$$

25. (Cont.) At that time L will be

$$L = .059(3)^2 - .354(3) + .557$$

which is .026, not enough to effect performance according to the problem. This is an example of a problem which is simplified by the use of a calculator.

27. (a) To use max/min methods we need to substitute in the quantity $x^2 + y^2$ and write it strictly in terms of x or y. So take $2x + 3y = 6$ and solve for y.

$$3y = 6 - 2x$$

$$y = \frac{6 - 2x}{3}$$

then substitute and the quantity $x^2 + y^2$ becomes

$$Q = x^2 + \left(\frac{6 - 2x}{3}\right)^2 = x^2 + \frac{36 - 24x + 4x^2}{9}$$

$$= \frac{13}{9}x^2 - \frac{8}{3}x + 4$$

which is a minimum when

$$x = \frac{-(-8/3)}{2(13/9)} = \frac{8}{3} \cdot \frac{9}{26} = \frac{12}{13}$$

or

$$Q = \frac{13}{9}\left(\frac{12}{13}\right)^2 - \frac{8}{3}\left(\frac{12}{13}\right) + 4 = \frac{36}{13},$$

the required minimum value.

(b) The equation of a circle with its center at the origin is $x^2 + y^2 = r^2$ where r is the radius. The line $2x + 3y = 6$ will intersect the circle in two points whenever r is sufficiently large. As we reduce r gradually we reach a position where the circle and line are tangent and this is the minimum value of r or $\sqrt{x^2 + y^2}$. In this case it is $(6\sqrt{13})/13$.

29. (a) 225/2

31. ½

33.

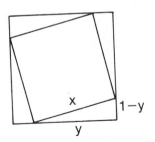

This problem is tricky and requires careful planning. Let the other two sides of each of the four triangles be y and 1 - y. Then the area of the square will be a minimum when the area of these triangles is a maximum. Let's write an expression for the total area of the four triangles.

$$A = 4(\tfrac{1}{2})(y)(1 - y) = 2y - 2y^2$$

or $A = -2y^2 + 2y$

Looking for a max here is approximate. Why? A will be a max when

$$y = \frac{-2}{2(-2)} \quad \text{or} \quad \frac{1}{2}$$

By Pythagoras, when $y = \tfrac{1}{2}$ and $1 - y = \tfrac{1}{2}$, x will be $\sqrt{2}/2$. This will be the x value which will give us a minimum inside square area. Note that if x was any less, the inside square would not touch the outside one. Squaring this gives

$$\frac{\sqrt{2}}{2}^2 \quad \text{or} \quad \frac{1}{2} \text{ sq. unit for the inside area.}$$

37. If the perimeter is a constant, P, then 2L + 2W = P becomes W = (P - 2L)/2 when solved for w. The Pythagorean theorem says that $D^2 = L^2 + W^2$ or

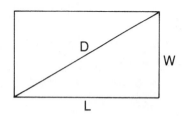

$$D^2 = L^2 + \frac{P - 2L}{2}^2$$

$$= L^2 + \frac{P^2 - 4PL + 4L^2}{4}$$

or finally $= 2L^2 - PL + \tfrac{1}{4}P^2$

when written in standard quadratic form.

Before we go on let's make two points. First, P is a constant here; we are treating it just like a number. Second, we note that D is a minimum when D^2 is a minimum. We are working with D^2 on the left side. Back to work.

$$D^2 = 2L^2 - PL + \tfrac{1}{4}P^2$$

37. (Cont.) $L_{min} = \dfrac{-(-P)}{2(2)} = \tfrac{1}{4}P$

which says that we should use $\tfrac{1}{4}$ of the total perimeter for the length. The minimum diagonal occurs in a square.

45. The rectangular area is x by 2r, so its area is 2rx but we need to write this just in terms of one variable. Let's use the perimeter and find r in terms of x. The total perimeter = 2 straight sides + 2 half circles

$$\tfrac{1}{4} = 2x + 2\pi r$$

$$\tfrac{1}{4} - 2x = 2\pi r$$

$$r = \frac{\tfrac{1}{4} - 2x}{2\pi} = \frac{1 - 8x}{8\pi}$$

Remember we are working in miles here. Substituting in the area formula we have

$$A = 2\left(\frac{1 - 8x}{8\pi}\right)x = \frac{2x}{8\pi} - \frac{16x^2}{8\pi} = -\frac{2}{\pi}x^2 + \frac{1}{4\pi}x$$

This area will be a maximum when

$$x = \frac{-1/4\pi}{2(-2/\pi)} = 1/16 \text{ mile}$$

That happens when

$$r = \frac{1 - 8(1/16)}{8\pi} = \frac{1}{16\pi} \text{ mile.}$$

47. (a) Refer to example 2 on page 148. m here will equal $\Delta P/\Delta x = 10/(-5) =$ -2 so

$$P - P_1 = m(x - x_1)$$
$$P - 200 = -2(x - 150)$$
$$P = -2x + 500$$

(b) We know that Revenue = price times number of units sold. So

$$R = (-2x + 500)x$$
$$= -2x^2 + 500x$$

47. (c) This will max when

$$x = \frac{-500}{2(-2)} = 125 \qquad \text{and} \qquad P = 250,$$

at which time

$$R = -2(125)^2 + 500(125)$$

$$= -31250 + 62500$$

$$= \$31,250$$

We therefore take in a maximum revenue of \$31,250 when the price is \$250 per unit.

EXERCISE SET 3.4

1. $x^2 - 3x + 2 < 0$, so factoring gives

   $(x - 1)(x - 2) < 0$

   The solutions to the equation $x^2 - 3x + 2 = 0$ are therefore 1 and 2, and the rule on page 181 lets us write the solution to this inequality as (1,2).

3. Starting with the equation

   $$8x^2 - 10x + 4 = 0$$

   we look for roots. First divide by 2 getting

   $$4x^2 - 5x + 2 = 0$$

   This won't factor and when we use the quadratic formula we find that

   $$b^2 - 4ac = 25 - 32 = -7.$$

   There are therefore no real roots and we conclude that the inequality is always greater than zero.

5. outside [3,5]

7. $\left(\dfrac{-1 - \sqrt{5}}{2} , \dfrac{-1 + \sqrt{5}}{2} \right)$

9. $3 \leq \dfrac{4}{x - 2}$

Let's follow example 3 and multiply both sides by $(x - 2)^2$, which is certainly positive. We get

$$3(x - 2)^2 \leq 4(x - 2)$$

or $3(x - 2)^2 - 4(x - 2) \leq 0$ factoring gives

$(x - 2)[3(x - 2) - 4] \leq 0$

or $(x - 2)(3x - 6 - 4) \leq 0$

finally $(x - 2)(3x - 10) \leq 0$

The equality is satisfied when $x = 2$ or $x = 10/3$, and the inequality whenever x is in the half open interval $(2, 10/3]$. Why half-open? Remember in our first inequality $x \neq 2$.

11. $(-3, -18/7]$

13. $x^2 + 10x + 25 \geq 0$ factors into

$(x + 5)(x + 5) \geq 0$.

Here we have only one root, $x = -5$. At -5 the quadratic equals zero. Everywhere else it is greater than zero so all real numbers work.

15. This problem is just the opposite of thirteen. We can't factor, but the quadratic formula gives us a negative radicand, indicating no real roots. Since the quadratic opens upward and has no roots it can never be below the x-axis; it is never negative. There is no solution.

17. $\dfrac{1 + x}{1 - x} < 3$;   multiply by $(1 - x)^2$

$$(1 + x)(1 - x) < 3(1 - x)^2$$

$$(1 + x)(1 - x) - 3(1 - x)^2 < 0$$

$$(1 - x)[(1 + x) - 3(1 - x)] < 0$$

$$(1 - x)(1 + x - 3 + 3x) < 0$$

$$(1 - x)(4x - 2) < 0$$

17. (Cont.)   The roots of the equation are 1 and ½. Two things concern us
    here. Note in the last line in the inequality, if we multiply the two
    factors, the x^2 coefficient is -4. That says that this one opens down.
    So between ½ and 1 it is positive. Second, x - 1 is ruled out in the
    original equation. So, our solution will be x < ½ or x > 1.

19. 0 < x < 1/19   21. no solution

23. If we transpose we have

    $$5x^2 - \sqrt{5}x > 0 \qquad \text{factoring gives}$$

    $$x(5x - \sqrt{5}) > 0$$

    The zeros of the equation are x = 0 and x = $\sqrt{5}/5$ and the inequality
    will be satisfied if x < 0 or x > $\sqrt{5}/5$.

25. -13/4 ≤ x < -2

27. Rather than expanding the left side let's just take the equation
    $(x - 7)^2 = 16$ and take the square root of both sides getting x - 7 = ±4
    from which the roots are x = 11 and x = 3. So $(x - 7)^2$ will be greater
    than 16 whenever x ≥ 11 or x ≤ 3.

29. ℝ

31. Multiply both sides by $(x + b)^2$ remembering that x = -b is excluded
    from the domain. We have

    $$(x - b)(x + b) \geq 2(x + b)^2$$

    or $(x - b)(x + b) - 2(x + b)^2 \geq 0$ now factor

    $$(x + b)[(x - b) - 2(x + b)] \geq 0$$

    $$(x + b)(x - b - 2x - 2b) \geq 0$$

    $$(x + b)(-x - 3b) \geq 0$$

    The zeros are x = -b and x = -3b. But be careful, this opens down
    because the x^2 coefficient is negative. The solution will be
    -3b ≤ x < -b. Why the < on the right side here?

33. $(mx + b)^2 - (bx + m)^2 \leq 0$ Expand,

$m^2x^2 + 2bmx + b^2 - b^2x^2 - 2bmx - m^2 \leq 0$

$\cdot(m^2 - b^2)x^2 - m^2 + b^2 \leq 0$

Note that since $0 < b < m$, $m^2 - b^2$ is positive and this quadratic opens up. Solving as an equation we get

$$(m^2 - b^2)x^2 = m^2 - b^2$$

$$x^2 = \frac{m^2 - b^2}{m^2 - b^2} = 1$$

so $x = \pm 1$ and our solution is

$$-1 \leq x \leq 1$$

The same result is obtained if we set

$$(mx + b)^2 = (bx + m)^2$$

and take the square root on both sides, perhaps saving some work.

35. Remember, the points on the parabola have coordinates of the form (x, x^2).
Using the distance formula we have

$$d \text{ to origin} = \sqrt{(x - 0)^2 - (x^2 - 0)^2}$$

and we want this d to be less than 1. Squaring both sides we have

$$x^2 + x^4 < 1$$

or $x^4 + x^2 - 1 < 0$

This is not quadratic but it has a quadratic form if we let $a = x^2$

$$a^2 + a - 1 < 0$$

The quadratic formula gives roots of

$$a = \frac{-1 \pm \sqrt{1^2 - 4(1)(-1)}}{2(1)} = \frac{-1 \pm \sqrt{5}}{2}$$ since a is x^2

$$x = \pm\sqrt{\frac{-1 + \sqrt{5}}{2}} \text{ and our solution is } -\sqrt{\frac{-1 + \sqrt{5}}{2}} < x < \sqrt{\frac{-1 + \sqrt{5}}{2}}$$

Note that we ignored the $-\sqrt{5}$ case which gives us a negative radicand.

Chapter 4   Polynomial and Rational Functions

1. (a)   yes, degree 6

    (b)   no, this is really $2/x^3 + x$.   The exponents in polynomials must be non-negative

    (c)   yes, degree 1   (d)   yes, 0

    (e)   no   (f)   no

3. $g(x) = 1 + x^2$

    $g(-1) = 1 + (-1)^2 = 2$,   not a zero

5. yes

7. $f(t) = 1 + 2t + t^3 - t^5$

    $f(\sqrt{2}) = 1 + 2\sqrt{2} + (\sqrt{3})^3 - (\sqrt{2})^5$

    $= 1 + 2\sqrt{2} + 2\sqrt{2} - 4\sqrt{2} = 1$,   not a zero

9. Given $1 - x + x^2 - x^3 = 0$ and checking $x = -1$, we get

$$1 - (-1) + (-1)^2 - (-1)^3 \overset{?}{=} 0$$

$$1 + 1 + 1 + 1 \overset{?}{=} 0$$

$$4 \overset{?}{=} 0$$

No, -1 is not a root.

11. (a) $(x - 1)(x - 2)^3(x - 3) = 0$

   Setting each of the factors equal to zero and solving we find these roots,

$$x = 1$$
$$x = 2 \quad \text{the multiplicity here is 3}$$
   and $\quad\quad\quad x = 3$

   (b) Here $x = 1$ occurs 3 times, it is of multiplicity 3.

   (c) $x = 5$, multiplicity 6 and

   $x = -1$, multiplicity 4, are the roots

   (d) $x = 0$, multiplicity 5 and $x = 1$ are the roots

13. (a) $3x^4 - 48x^2$ is to be factored. Remember, always look for a common factor. Here we get first

$$3x^2(x^2 - 16) \quad \text{which becomes}$$
$$3x^2(x + 4)(x - 4)$$

   (b) Using these factors we get

$$3x^2 = 0 \quad \text{or} \quad x = 0$$
$$x + 4 = 0 \quad \text{or} \quad x = -4$$
$$x - 4 = 0 \quad \text{or} \quad x = 4$$

   So -4, 0, and 4 are the roots.

15. (a) $x^3(10 + x)(10 - x)$ $\quad\quad\quad\quad\quad$ (b) 0, -10, 10

17. (a) $(2x - 3)(x + 4)$ (b) $3/2, -4$

19. (a) $4x^3 - 20x^2 + 25x = x(4x^2 - 20x + 25) = x(2x - 5)(2x - 5)$

(b) Setting the product = to zero we get

$$x = 0 \quad \text{or} \quad 2x - 5 = 0 \quad \text{or} \quad 2x - 5 = 0$$

$$x = 5/2 \qquad\qquad x = 5/2$$

The zeros of the function are 0 and 5/2 which occurs twice.

21. (a) $x^3 + 64$ is the sum of cubes. It becomes $(x + 4)(x^2 - 4x + 16)$

(b) one root is $x = -4$, but can $x^2 - 4x + 16 = 0$? It won't factor and $b^2 - 4ac$ is negative so there are no other roots.

23. (a) $x(10 - 3x)(100 + 30x + 9x^2)$ (b) 0, 10/3

25. $x^2z^2 + xzt + xyz + yt$. In general, if an expression has four terms, we look for common factors in groups of two terms. In this case we see xz in the first two terms and y in the other pair.

$$xz(xz + t) + y(xz + t)$$

Now we have the common factor $(xz + t)$ in each term, and we factor it out leaving

$$(xz + t)(xz + y)$$

which is the complete factorization.

27. $a^2t^2 + b^2t^2 - cb^2 - ca^2$ Same idea here, but be careful of signs.
$t^2(a^2 + b^2) - c(b^2 + a^2)$
$(a^2 + b^2)(t^2 - c)$

29. $(x^2 - 3)^2$ 31. $(a^2 - 2b^2c^2)^2$ 33. irreducible

5. $1 - (x + y)^2$ Despite the form, this is a difference of

$[1 + (x + y)][1 - (x + y)]$ perfect squares.

$(1 + x + y)(1 - x - y)$

37. $x^8 - 1$

$(x^4 + 1)(x^4 - 1)$

$(x^4 + 1)(x^2 + 1)(x^2 - 1)$

$(x^4 + 1)(x^2 + 1)(x + 1)(x - 1)$ Aren't you glad it wasn't $x^{1024} - 1$?

39. $x^3 + 3x^2 + 3x + 1$ is tricky. If you start with $x^2(x + 3) + (3x + 1)$ you find a dead end. Experiment!

$x^3 + 1 + 3x^2 + 3x$ First two are a sum of cubes.

$(x + 1)(x^2 - x + 1) + 3x(x + 1)$

$(x + 1)[(x^2 - x + 1) + 3x]$

$(x + 1)(x^2 + 2x + 1)$ This is similar to example 8 on page 192.

$(x + 1)(x + 1)(x + 1)$

$(x + 1)^3$

41. $(3x + 4)^3$

43. $(2a + b)(2a - b)(4a^2 - 2ab + b^2)(4a^2 + 2ab + b^2)$

45. $(a + b - 1)[(a + b)^2 + (a + b) + 1]$ or $(a + b - 1)(a^2 + 2ab + b^2 + a + b + 1)$

47. $(x^2 + 3z)(x^4 - 3x^2z + 9z^2)$ 49. irreducible

51. The trick, according to the hint, is to add and subtract the same quantity so as to make $x^4 + 64$ a perfect square trinomial.

$x^4 + 16x^2 + 64 - 16x^2$

$(x^2 + 8)^2 - 16x^2$ which is the difference of perfect squares

$[(x^2 + 8) + 4x][(x^2 + 8) - 4x]$

or $(x^2 + 4x + 8)(x^2 - 4x + 8)$ Try multiplying.

55. (a) $x^2 + 2xy + y^2 - z^2 = (x + y)^2 - z^2$

$= [(x + y) + z][(x + y) - z]$

$= (x + y + z)(x + y - z)$

55. (b) $4x^2y^2 - (x^2 + y^2 - z^2)^2$ is first a difference of perfect squares,

$[2xy + (x^2 + y^2 - z^2)][2xy - (x^2 + y^2 - z^2)]$ or regrouping

$[(x^2 + 2xy + y^2) - z^2][z^2 - (x^2 - 2xy + y^2)]$

$[(x + y)^2 - z^2][z^2 - (x - y)^2]$

$[(x + y + z)(x + y - z)][z + (x + y)][z - (x - y)]$ finally

$(x + y + z)(x + y - z)(z + x - y)(z - x + y)$ child's play!

61. $(a + b + c)^3 - a^3 - b^3 - c^3 =$

$[(a + b + c)^3 - a^3] - (b^3 + c^3) =$

$(a + b + c - a)[(a + b + c)^2 + a(a + b + c) + a^2] - (b + c)(b^2 - bc + c^2) =$

$(b + c)[(a + b + c)^2 + a^2 + ab + ac + a^2] - (b + c)(b^2 - bc + c^2) =$

$(b + c)[(a + b + c)^2 + 2a^2 + ab + ac - b^2 + bc - c^2] =$

$(b + c)(3a^2 + 3ab + 3ac + 3bc) =$

$(b + c)[3a(a + b) + 3c(a + b)] =$

$(b + c)(a + b)(3a + 3c) =$

$3(b + c)(a + b)(a + c)$

63. $x^2(z - y) + y^2(x - z) + z^2(y - x) =$

$x^2z - x^2y + xy^2 - y^2z + yz^2 - xz^2 =$

$(x^2z - xz^2) + (xy^2 - y^2z) + (yz^2 - x^2y) =$

$xz(x - z) + y^2(x - z) + y(z - x)(z + x) =$

$(x - z)[xz + y^2 - y(z + x)] =$

$(x - z)(xz + y^2 - yz - xy) =$

$(x - z)[(y^2 - yz) + (xz - xy)] =$

$(x - z)[y(y - z) + x(z - y)] =$

$(x - z)(y - z)(y - x)$

Now go back and try these last two on your favorite high school algebra teacher.

Exercise Set 4.2

1.
$$
\begin{array}{r}
x - 11 \\
x + 5 \overline{\smash{\big)}\ x^2 - 6x - 2} \\
\underline{x^2 + 5x} \\
-11x - 2 \\
\underline{-11x - 55} \\
53
\end{array}
$$

Subtract and bring down

subtract

Quotient: $x - 11$, remainder: 53

3.
$$
\begin{array}{r}
3x^2 - \frac{3}{2}x - \frac{1}{4} \\
2x + 1 \overline{\smash{\big)}\ 6x^3 + 0x^2 - 2x + 3} \\
\underline{6x^3 + 3x^2} \\
-3x^2 - 2x \\
\underline{-3x^2 - \frac{3}{2}x} \\
-\frac{1}{2}x + 3 \\
\underline{-\frac{1}{2}x - \frac{1}{4}} \\
\frac{13}{4}
\end{array}
$$

Quotient: $3x^2 - (3/2)x - 1/4$,   remainder: 13/4

5. $q(x) = x^4 - 3x^3 + 9x^2 - 27x + 81$; $R(x) = -241$

7. $q(x) = x^5 + 2x^4 + 4x^3 + 8x^2 + 16x + 32$; $R(x) = 0$

$$\begin{array}{r} 5x^2 + 15x + 17 \\ x^2 - 3x + 5 \overline{\smash{\big)}\ 5x^4 + 0x^3 - 3x^2 + 0x + 2} \\ \underline{5x^4 - 15x^3 + 25x^2} \\ 15x^3 - 28x^2 + 0x \\ \underline{15x^3 - 45x^2 + 75x} \\ 17x^2 - 75x + 2 \\ \underline{17x^2 - 51x + 85} \\ -24x - 83 \end{array}$$

9.

Quotient: $5x^2 + 15x + 17$,   remainder: $-24x - 83$

11. Looking at the rule on the bottom of page 197 shows us that

$$x^5 - 32 = (x - 2)(x^4 + 2x^3 + 4x^2 + 8x + 16).$$

13. $(x - 1)(x^5 + x^4 + x^3 + x^2 + x + 1)$ or

$(x + 1)(x - 1)(x^2 + x + 1)(x^2 - x + 1)$

15. Dividing, we get

$$\begin{array}{r} x \\ x^2 + 1 \overline{\smash{\big)}\ x^3 + 0x^2 + 2x - 1} \\ \underline{x^3 \qquad\quad + x} \\ x - 1 \end{array}$$

So $x^3 + 2x - 1 = (x^2 + 1)(x) + (x - 1)$

17. $q(x) = 3x^3 + 12x^2 + 60x + 288$, $R(x) = 1392x + 1153$

19. $\dfrac{4x^2 - x - 5}{x - 1}$ becomes

$$\begin{array}{r} \underline{1}|\ \ 4 \ \ -1 \ \ -5 \\ 4 \quad 3 \\ \hline 4 \quad 3 \ \ -2 \end{array}$$ Quotient: $4x + 3$,   remainder: -2

21. $\underline{2|}$ 1   0   0   0   0   -1

                    2   4   8 16   32

             1   2   4   8 16   31

Quotient: $x^4 - 2x^3 + 4x^2 - 8x + 16,$ Remainder: 31

23. $q(x) = x^2 - 11x + 33;$ $R(x) = -100$

25. $q(x) = x^5 + x^4 + x^3 + x^2 + x + 1;$ $R(x) = 0$

27. $\underline{-1/2|}$ 5   -4   3   -2   1

                    -2 1/2   3 1/4   -3 1/8   2 9/16

            5   -6 1/2   6 1/4   -5 1/8   3 9/16

Quotient: $5x^3 - (13/2)x^2 + (25/4)x - 41/8;$ Remainder: 57/16

29. $q(x) = 54x^2 - 63x + 15;$ $R(x) = 4$

31. We must first put this divisor into proper x - a form. Look at example 3
on page 201.

$$\frac{2x^2 - 8x + 1}{3x + 4} \quad \text{becomes} \quad \frac{2x^2 - 8x + 1}{3(x + 4/3)}$$

Now divide numerator and denominator by 3 getting

$$\frac{(2/3)x^2 - (8/3)x + 1/3}{x + 4/3}$$

So we have

$\underline{-4/3|}$ 2/3   -8/3   1/3

                   -8/9   128/27

        2/3   -32/9   137/27

So $q(x) = (2/3)x - (32/9)$ and $R(x) = 137/27$

33. $q(x) = (1/2)x^4 - (3/4)x^3 + (7/8)x^2 - (7/16)x - 9/32;$ $R(x) = 41/64$

35. To be a factor (x - 1) must divide both quantities evenly. There must be
no remainder. Let's divide.

First <u>1|</u>   1   1   a   b

                  1   2   a+2

            1   2   a+2   a+b+2

So a + b + 2 must equal zero. Next

<u>1|</u>   1   -1   -a   b

            1   0   -a

      1   0   -a   a-b

and also a - b must equal zero. That means

               a - b = 0

or   a = b

and   a + b + 2 = 0   or substituting

           a + a + 2 = 0

              2a = -2

              a = -1

therefore a and b are both -1.

41. The given condition can be written as f(x) = (x - a)(x - b)q(x) + Ax + B,
where q(x) is some polynomial (which need not be determined.) If we let
x = a in this equation, we have f(a) = aA + B. Similarly, if we let
x = b, we obtain f(b) = Ab + B. From this last equation we have
B = f(b) - Ab. Using this B-value in the equation f(a) = Aa + B yields
f(a) = Aa + f(b) - Ab. Therefore f(a) - f(b) = A(a - b), and consequently
$A = \frac{f(a) - f(b)}{a - b}$, as required. The corresponding B-value can now be
obtained using this A-value in the equation B = f(b) - Ab.

EXERCISE SET 4.3

1. f(-3) will be the remainder when f(x) is divided by x + 3. Let's use synthetic division.

    $$\begin{array}{r|rrrr} -3 & 4 & -6 & 1 & -5 \\ & & -12 & 54 & -165 \\ \hline & 4 & -18 & 55 & -170 \end{array}$$

    The remainder is -170, so f(-3) = -170. In practice it is easier to substitute directly to find f(-3), but here we want to make a point about the Remainder Theorem.

3. -9

5. $$\begin{array}{r|rrr} -\sqrt{2} & 1 & 3 & -4 \\ & & -\sqrt{2} & 2 - 3\sqrt{2} \\ \hline & 1 & 3 - \sqrt{2} & -2 - 3\sqrt{2} \end{array}$$

    We conclude that $f(-\sqrt{2}) = -2 - 3\sqrt{2}$.

7. -22

9. We are told that -3 is a root so we will use synthetic division to help factor.

    $$\begin{array}{r|rrrr} -3 & 1 & -4 & -9 & 36 \\ & & -3 & 21 & -36 \\ \hline & 1 & -7 & 12 & 0 \end{array}$$

    So we can write $x^3 - 4x^2 - 9x + 36 = 0$ as $(x + 3)(x^2 - 7x + 12) = 0$ and since the quadratic will factor again we have $(x + 3)(x - 4)(x - 3) = 0$ and we get roots of x = -3, 4, 3.

11. 1, $-1 + \sqrt{6}$, $-1 - \sqrt{6}$

13. -2,   2/3,   3

15. $\underline{-3/2|}$ 2   1   -5   -3

 -3   3   3

 2   -2   -2   0

and we have

$$(x + 3/2)(2x^2 - 2x - 2) = 0$$

We can take a common factor of 2 out of the trinomial, but it still won't factor. We will use the quadratic formula. The required roots are

$$x = -\frac{3}{2}, \quad \frac{1 + \sqrt{5}}{2}, \quad \text{and} \quad \frac{1 - \sqrt{5}}{2}.$$

17. 0, 5 (multiplicity 3)

19. -4, 3 (each of multiplicity 2)

21. -9, $1 - \sqrt{2},$ $1 + \sqrt{2}$

23. The first step is easy, divide by x - 2.

$\underline{2|}$ 2   -3   -10   12   13   -10

 4   2   -16   -8   10

 2   1   -8   -4   5   0

It will be awkward to try dividing by the individual factors of

$$x - \frac{-1 \pm \sqrt{5}}{2}$$

Instead think where those roots come from. $(x + 1/2 - \sqrt{5}/2)$ and $(x + 1/2 + \sqrt{5}/2)$ must be factors and their product will be a factor. Let's multiply them.

23. (Cont.)

$$x + 1/2 - \sqrt{5}/2$$

$$\underline{x + 1/2 + \sqrt{5}/2}$$

$$x^2 + (1/2)x - (\sqrt{5}/2)x$$

$$+ (1/2)x \qquad\qquad + 1/4 - \sqrt{5}/4$$

$$\underline{\qquad\qquad + (\sqrt{5}/2)x \qquad\qquad + \sqrt{5}/4 - 5/4}$$

So $x^2 + x \qquad\qquad\qquad + 1/4 \qquad\qquad -5/4$

or $x^2 + x - 1$ is a factor.

Now divide the result of the first step by this factor.

$$
\require{enclose}
\begin{array}{r}
2x^2 - x - 5 \\
x^2 + x - 1 \enclose{longdiv}{2x^4 + x^3 - 8x^2 - 4x + 5} \\
\underline{2x^4 + 2x^3 - 2x^2} \\
-x^3 - 6x^2 - 4x \\
\underline{-x^3 - x^2 + x} \\
-5x^2 - 5x + 5 \\
\underline{-5x^2 - 5x + 5} \\
0
\end{array}
$$

Therefore a complete factorization of our original polynomial looks like this

$$(x - 2)(x^2 + x - 1)(2x^2 - x - 5) = 0$$

This last factor can't be reduced so we get its roots from the formula and the complete set of roots is

$$x = 2, \quad \frac{-1 + \sqrt{5}}{2}, \quad \frac{-1 - \sqrt{5}}{2}, \quad \frac{1 + \sqrt{41}}{4}, \quad \frac{1 - \sqrt{41}}{4}$$

25. If 1/2, 2/5 and -3/4 are roots then working backwards gives us

$$x = 1/2 \qquad\qquad x = 2/5 \qquad\qquad x = -3/4$$

$$2x = 1 \qquad\qquad 5x = 2 \qquad\qquad 4x = -3$$

$$2x - 1 = 0 \qquad 5x - 2 = 0 \qquad 4x + 3 = 0$$

25. (Cont.)   or finally

$$(2x - 1)(5x - 2)(4x + 3) = 0$$

as the desired polynomial. Let's multiply them out

$$(10x^2 - 9x + 2)(4x + 3) = 0$$

or $40x^3 - 6x^2 - 19x + 6 = 0$ as required.

27. $x^4 - x^2 = 0$

29. If 1 is a root then $c + d - 3 = 0$.

1|	1	-4	c	d
		1	-3	c - 3
		1	-3	c-3	c+d-3

Also

2|	1	-4	c	d
		2	-4	2c - 8
		1	-2	c-4	2c+d-8

$2c + d - 8 = 0$.   Since $c + d - 3 = 0$, $d = 3 - c$ and substituting this into the second equation

$$2c + d - 8 = 0 \qquad \text{becomes}$$

$$2c + (3 - c) - 8 = 0$$

or $c - 5 = 0$

therefore c must equal 5, and $d = -2$. Try out $x^3 - 4x^2 + 5x - 2 = 0$ and see if 1 and 2 are roots.

31. $x - 2$ is a factor if $f(2) = 0$. Let's check

$$f(x) = x^n - n \cdot 2^{n-1}x + (n - 1)2^n$$

$$f(2) = 2^n - n \cdot 2^{n-1} \cdot 2 + (n - 1)2^n$$

adding the first and third terms gives

$$f(2) = (n - 1 + 1)2^n - n \cdot 2^{n-1+1}$$

31. (Cont.)

or $\qquad f(2) = n(2^n) - n(2^n) = 0$

Yes, $x - 2$ is a factor.

39. (a) Write the equation as $(x - r_1)(x - r_2)(x - r_3)(x - r_4) = 0$. When we expand the left-side here, we find that the coefficient of x^3 is $-(r_1 + r_2 + r_3 + r_4)$. But in the equation $x^4 + ax^2 + bx + c = 0$, the coefficient of x^3 is zero. Therefore $r_1 + r_2 + r_3 + r_4 = 0$, as required.

(b) The equation of a circle can be written in the form $x^2 + Ax + y^2 + By + C = 0$. Replacing y by x^2 in this equation yields $x^2 + Ax + x^4 + Bx^2 + C = 0$. This is a fourth degree equation containing no x^3 term. Assuming now that there are four solutions, it follows from part (a) that the sum of these four solutions is zero, as required.

EXERCISE SET 4.4

1. Factoring $x^2 - 2x - 3$ gives $(x - 3)(x + 1)$ which has the required form.

3. $4x^2 + 23x - 6$ will factor into $(4x - 1)(x + 6)$ but we must write the $(4x - 1)$ factor as $4(x - \frac{1}{4})$. The complete result is $4(x - \frac{1}{4})(x + 6)$.

5. $(x + \sqrt{5})(x - \sqrt{5})$ $\qquad\qquad\qquad$ 7. $[x - (5 + i)][x - (5 - i)]$

9. 6, multiplicity 2; $\quad$ -3, multiplicity 1

11. 0, multiplicity 6; $\quad$ -4, multiplicity 5

13. $f(x) = x^2(x - 4) = x^3 - 4x^2$

15. $(x - 3)^2$, $(x + 5)$, and $(x - 0)^4$ must appear as factors of $f(x)$. It can be written as $f(x) = x^4(x - 3)^2(x + 5)$ or multiplied out to get $f(x) = x^7 - x^6 - 21x^5 + 45x^4$.

17. The factors $(x + 5)$, $(x - 2)$, and $(x - 3)$ will appear in our solution.
     The equation will look like $f(x) = a_n(x + 5)(x - 2)(x - 3)$. We know that
     it passes through the point $(0,1)$ so

$$1 = a_n(0 + 5)(0 - 2)(0 - 3)$$

     or $a_n = 1/30$

     Therefore $f(x) = (1/30)(x + 5)(x - 2)(x - 3)$

     or $f(x) = (1/30)x^3 - (19/30)x + 1$

19. The table on page 214 tells us that for $x^2 + bx + c = 0$, the sum of the
     roots equals $-b$ and their product is c. We are given $r_1 = 9$ and
     $r_2 = -6$, so $b = -3$ and $c = -54$. The equation we want is therefore
     $x^2 - 3x - 54 = 0$.

21. $x^2 - 2x - 4 = 0$

23. The table says that $r_1 + r_2 + r_3 = -b$, so $-1 + 1 - 4 = -b$ and $b = 4$.
     In addition $r_1r_2 + r_2r_3 + r_3r_1 = c$ so $(-1)(1) + (1)(-4) + (-4)(-1) = c$
     and $c = -1$. Finally $r_1r_2r_3 = -d$ so $(-1)(1)(-4) = -d$ and $d = -4$.
     Using these values for b, c, and d our equation is

$$x^3 + 4x^2 - x - 4 = 0.$$

25. $x^3 + 6x^2 + 12x + 8 = 0$

27. Example 7 on page 215 uses the Identity Theorem and tells us that to
     establish this equation as an identity we need to show that
     $F(a) = F(b) = F(c) = 0$. So letting

$$F(x) = \frac{(x - a)(x - b)c^2}{(c - a)(c - b)} + \frac{(x - b)(x - c)a^2}{(a - b)(a - c)} + \frac{(x - c)(x - a)b^2}{(b - c)(b - a)} - x^2$$

     we will find $F(a)$, $F(b)$, and $F(c)$

$$F(a) = 0 + \frac{(a - b)(a - c)a^2}{(a - b)(a - c)} + 0 - a^2 = 0$$

     $F(b)$ and $F(c)$ will also $= 0$, and the identity is established.

33. We are told that two roots are equal so the equations in table 1 become

$$r_1 + r_2 + r_2 = -b \qquad \text{or} \quad r_1 + 2r_2 = 0$$

$$r_1r_2 + r_2r_2 + r_2r_1 = c \quad \text{or} \quad 2r_1r_2 + r_2^2 = -12$$

$$r_1r_2r_2 = -d \qquad \text{or} \quad r_1r_2^2 = -16$$

Substituting $r_1 = -2r_2$ from equation 1 into equation 2 gives

$$2(-2r_2)(r_2) + r_2^2 = -12$$

or

$$-4r_2^2 + r_2^2 = -12$$

$$-3r_2^2 = -12$$

$$r_2^2 = 4$$

$$r_2 = \pm 2$$

and

$$r_1 = -2r_2 = \pm 4$$

Let's be careful. Will both sets of roots work? Using $-4, 2,$ and 2 all three equations check. But, if we try $4, -2, -2$ then the third equation $r_1r_2^2 = -16$ is not satisfied,

$$4(-2)^2 \neq -16.$$

Direct substitution of $2, 2,$ and -4 in the original polynomial will confirm the fact that these are the required solutions.

35. Let $r_1 = r_2 = r$. Also, we have $b = 0$. So the equation $r_1 + r_2 + r_3 = -b$ yields $2r + r_3 = 0$, and consequently $r_3 = -2r$. The equation $r_1r_2r_3 = -d$ then becomes $r^2(-2r) = -d$. Therefore $r^3 = d/2$, or $r = \sqrt[3]{d/2}$. Since r is a root of the equation $x^3 + cx + d = 0$, we have:

$$d/2 + c\sqrt[3]{d/2} + d = 0$$

$$c\sqrt[3]{d/2} = -(3/2)d$$

$$(2c\sqrt[3]{d/2})^3 = (-3d)^3$$

$$8c^3(d/2) = -27d^3$$

35. (Cont.)

$$4c^3 = -27d^2$$

$$4c^3 + 27d^2 = 0, \quad \text{as required.}$$

39. In applying such a formula, the main difficulty is simply getting each number substituted in its proper place.

$$f(x) = \frac{10(x - 2)(x - 3)}{(-1 - 2)(-1 - 3)} + \frac{4(x + 1)(x - 3)}{(2 + 1)(2 - 3)} + \frac{14(x + 1)(x - 2)}{(3 + 1)(3 - 2)}$$

$$= \frac{10(x^2 - 5x + 6)}{(-3)(-4)} + \frac{4(x^2 - 2x - 3)}{(3)(-1)} + \frac{14(x^2 - x - 2)}{(4)(1)}$$

Let's use 12 for a common denominator

$$= \frac{10(x^2 - 5x + 6) - 16(x^2 - 2x - 3) + 42(x^2 - x - 2)}{12}$$

$$= \frac{36x^2 - 60x + 24}{12}$$

$$= 3x^2 - 5x + 2$$

We can check and show that the three given points satisfy this equation.

EXERCISE SET 4.5

1. Factors of $a_0 = 3$:   ±1, ±3

    Factors of $a_n = 4$:   ±1, ±2, ±4

    Possible Rational Roots: ±1, ±1/2, ±1/4, ±3, ±3/2, ±3/4

3. ±1, ±1/2, ±1/4, ±1/8, ±3, ±3/2, ±3/4, ±3/8, ±9, ±9/2, ±9/4, ±9/8

5. First let's multiply through by 15 to get integer coefficients.

    $$(2/3)x^3 - (4/5)x^2 - 5x + 2 = 0 \quad \text{becomes}$$

    $$10x^3 - 12x^2 - 75x + 30 = 0 \quad \text{now proceed.}$$

    Factors of $a_0 = 30$:   ±1, ±2, ±3, ±5, ±6, ±10, ±15, ±30

    Factors of $a_n = 10$:   ±1, ±2, ±5, ±10.

5. (Cont.)

Possible Rational Roots: ±1, ±1/2, ±1/5, ±1/10, ±2, ±2/5, ±3, ±3/2, ±3/5,

±3/10, ±5, ±5/2, ±6, ±6/5, ±10, ±15, ±15/2, ±30

7. From 9 comes ±1, ±3, ±9 as factors.

From 2 comes ±1, ±2 as possibilities.

So my possible rational roots are: ±1, ±1/2, ±3, ±3/2, ±9, ±9/2.

With ±1 it is sometimes easier to test by substituting to see if $f(\pm 1) = 0$,
but in general we use synthetic division until we find a zero remainder or
an upper bound. Let's try 1/2 for example.

```
1/2|    2   -5   -3    9

             1   -2  -5/2

        2   -4   -5   not zero
```

When we reach 3/2 we find

```
3/2|    2   -5   -3    9

             3   -3   -9

        2   -2   -6   Bingo!
```

So one root is x = 3/2. Now consider the depressed equation
$2x^2 - 2x - 6 = 0$ or more simply, upon dividing by 2, $x^2 - x - 3 = 0$. It
won't factor but the quadratic formula gives roots of $x = (1 \pm \sqrt{13})/2$. Our
complete solution set is therefore

$$\frac{3}{2}, \frac{1 \pm \sqrt{13}}{2}.$$

9. From 4 we have ±1, ±2, ±4 and from 3 we get ±1, ±3. So our possibilities
are ±1, ±3, ±2, ±2/3, ±4, ±4/3.

```
1|    3  -16   17   -4

           3  -13    4

      3  -13    4    0   First try!
```

In practice, however, it is usually easier to test f(1). Here it would be

9. (Cont.)

$$f(x) = 3x^3 - 16x^2 + 17x - 4$$

$$f(1) = 3 - 16 + 17 - 4 = 0$$

Our depressed equation is

$$3x^2 - 13x + 4 = 0 \quad \text{which factors}$$

$$(3x - 1)(x - 4) = 0 \quad \text{giving}$$

$$x = 1/3 \quad \text{and} \quad x = 4$$

Complete solution: x = 1/3, 1, 4.

11. 4, $\dfrac{-3 \pm \sqrt{13}}{4}$

13. The choices are: ±1, ±1/2, ±1/5, ±1/10, ±23, ±23/2, ±23/5, ±23/10.

Let's make a quick important observation. Since all the coefficients of the original equation are positive, no positive number can produce a zero. We have only to test negatives.

$$-1/2\big|\quad 10 \quad 107 \quad 301 \quad 171 \quad 23$$

$$\underline{\qquad\quad -5 \quad -51 \quad -125 \quad -23}$$

$$10 \quad 102 \quad 250 \quad 46 \quad 0 \quad \text{nice!}$$

Use the depressed equation which is now cubic.

$$-1/5\big|\quad 10 \quad 102 \quad 250 \quad 46$$

$$\underline{\qquad\quad -2 \quad -20 \quad -46}$$

$$10 \quad 100 \quad 230 \quad 0 \quad \text{again!}$$

We now have $10x^2 + 100x + 230 = 0$ or $x^2 + 10x + 23 = 0$ and the quadratic formula yields $-5 \pm \sqrt{2}$ to go with -1/2 and -1/5.

15. 1/2, 3/4, 2/3

17. Make the coefficients rational.

$$3x^3 - 17x^2 - 10x + 24 = 0$$

Our possibilities: $\pm 1, \pm 1/3, \pm 2, \pm 2/3, \pm 3, \pm 4, \pm 4/3, \pm 6, \pm 8, \pm 8/3, \pm 12, \pm 24$

But are we lucky, look at f(1). It's zero! Dividing we get

```
1|    3   -17   -10    24

           3   -14   -24

      3   -14   -24     0
```

Can we factor $3x^2 - 14x - 24 = 0$?

Yes. $(3x + 4)(x - 6)$

So our roots are 1, -4/3, and 6.

19. 1, 1, 1, $\pm\sqrt{2}$

21. Our possible roots here are $\pm 1, \pm 2, \pm 4, \pm 5, \pm 10, \pm 20$.

```
1|    1    2   -5    20

           1    3   -2

      1    3   -2    18    no luck


2|    1    2   -5    20

           2    8    6

      1    4    3    26
```

Notice that in the 3rd line of this last division all terms are positive.
2 must be an upper bound for roots. Now we consider f(-x)

$$f(-x) = (-x)^3 + 2(-x)^2 - 5(-x) + 20$$
$$= -x^3 + 2x^2 + 5x + 20$$

Our possible roots are the same, and we begin testing for a lower bound.
One observation first. If we use $-x^3 + 2x^2 + 5x + 20 = 0$ the first
element in the third line will always be -1 and we will never produce all
nonnegative terms. Instead we can multiply by -1 and use
$x^3 - 2x^2 - 5x - 20 = 0$ without changing roots.

21. (Cont.)

$\underline{1|}$ 1   -2   -5   -20

                   1   -1   -6
            _____

             1   -1   -6   -26

We continue with 2 and 4 until

$\underline{5|}$ 1   -2   -5   -20

                   5   15   50
            _____

             1   3   10   30

Since 5 is an upper bound for f(-x), -5 is a lower bound for f(x).

Final Results: 2 upper,   -5 lower.

23. Possible roots are: ±1, ±1/5, ±2, ±2/5, ±3, ±3/5, ±4, ±4/5, ±6, ±6/5, ±12,

                  ±12/5

Working up toward 2 we find

$\underline{2|}$ 5   0   0   -10   -12

                  10   20   40   60
            _____

             5   10   20   30   48

Therefore 2 is our least upper bound. Testing $f(-x) = 5x^4 + 10x - 12$
reveals -1 to be a lower bound for f(x).

25. 6 upper;   -2 lower

27. In this case, since ±1 are the only possible rational roots, our job is
easy. Neither f(1) or f(-1) is zero. In general we would test the
values within the limits of the bounds that we find.

35. The possibilities for rational roots are ±1, ±p. If x = 1, the equation
becomes $1^2 + 1 - p = 0$, or p = 2. If x = -1, the equation becomes
$(-1)^2 - 1 - p = 0$. This implies p = 0 which contradicts the fact that p
is a prime number. If x = p, the equation becomes $p^2 + p - p = 0$. Again,

35. (Cont.)   this implies $p = 0$, contrary to our hypothesis. Finally, if
$x = -p$, we have $(-p)^2 - p - p = 0$, or $p^2 - 2p = 0$. Therefore
$p(p - 2) = 0$, from which we conclude that $p = 0$ or $p = 2$. Again, we
discard the case $p = 0$. In summary now, $p = 2$ is the only prime for
which the equation $x^2 + x - p = 0$ has a rational root. (With $p = 2$, the
equation becomes $x^2 + x - 2 = 0$. The roots then are 1 and -2.)

37. (a) Suppose that $x = 1$ is a root. Then $1 + p - q = 0$. This is
equivalent to $q = p + 1$, which says that p and q are consecutive
integers. But 2 and 3 are (clearly) the only primes that are
consecutive integers. Thus $p = 2$, $q = 3$, as required. The equation
then becomes $x^3 + 2x - 3 = 0$. Using the fact that $x = 1$ is a root,
synthetic division can be used to rewrite the equation as
$(x - 1)(x^2 + x + 3) = 0$. The remaining roots are then found to be
$(-1 \pm 11i)/2$.

(b) With $x = -1$, the equation yields $-1 - p - q = 0$, or $p + q = -1$,
which is impossible. With $x = q$, the equation yields $q^2 + pq - q = 0$,
or $q(q^2 + p - 1) = 0$. This implies that $q = 0$ or $q^2 + p - 1 = 0$.
The case $q = 0$ is impossible. From the equation $q^2 + p - 1$, we have
$q^2 + p = 1$. This cannot occur since both q and p are larger than 1.
With $x = -q$, we have $-q^3 - pq - q = 0$, or $q(q^2 + p + 1) = 0$. Again,
the case $q = 0$ can be discarded immediately. Furthermore, the
equation $q^2 + p + 1 = 0$ is impossible, since q and p are both
positive.

EXERCISE SET 4.6

3. Since $x = 5 + 2i$ is a root, and complex roots occur in conjugate pairs,
$x = 5 - 2i$ is also a root. $[x - (5 + 2i)]$ and $[x - (5 - 2i)]$ are
factors and their product is

$$
\begin{array}{r}
x - 5 - 2i \\
x - 5 + 2i \\
\hline
x^2 - 5x - 2ix \\
-5x \qquad\quad + 25 + 10i \\
+ 2ix \qquad\quad - 10i - 4i^2 \\
\hline
x^2 - 10x \qquad + 25 \qquad\quad + 4
\end{array}
$$

3. (Cont.)   or $x^2 - 10x + 29$. This must be a factor. Dividing we get

$$
\begin{array}{r}
x \quad - \quad 3 \\
x^2 - 10x + 29 \overline{\big)\, x^3 - 13x^2 + 59x - 87} \\
\underline{x^3 - 10x^2 + 29x} \\
-3x^2 + 30x - 87 \\
\underline{-3x^2 + 30x - 87} \\
0
\end{array}
$$

So a complete factorization is $(x - 3)(x^2 - 10x + 29) = 0$, and the roots are 3, 5 + 2i, and 5 - 2i.

5. -2 - i,   -3 (double root)   7. 6 + 5i,   -1/4

9. The product $[x - (4 + \sqrt{2}\, i)][x - (4 - \sqrt{2}\, i)]$ gives us $x^2 - 8x + 18$ as one factor of our original equation. Long division is used to find the remaining quadratic factor

$$
\begin{array}{r}
4x^2 + \quad 9 \\
x^2 - 8x + 18 \overline{\big)\, 4x^4 - 32x^3 + 81x^2 - 72x + 162} \\
\underline{4x^4 - 32x^3 + 72x^2} \\
9x^2 - 72x + 162 \\
\underline{9x^2 - 72x + 162} \\
0
\end{array}
$$

Our original equation can be written as $(x^2 - 8x + 18)(4x^2 + 9) = 0$. Solving the depressed equation $4x^2 + 9 = 0$ we get

$$4x^2 + 9 = 0$$

$$4x^2 = -9$$

$$x^2 = -9/4$$

$$x = \pm(3/2)i$$

Our four roots are $4 \pm \sqrt{2}\, i$ and $\pm(3/2)i$.

. 10 - 2i, 1 ± √5   13. $\dfrac{1 - \sqrt{2}\, i}{3}$, $\dfrac{2}{5}$

15. $x = 3 - 2i$ being a root implies that $x = 3 + 2i$ is also. The same thing applies to $x = -1 - i$. Together with $x = 1$ we have five of the seven roots, and we set out to find the remaining quadratic factor which will yield the last two roots.

Multiply the first conjugate pair and divide to get a fifth degree depressed equation. Now multiply the second complex pair and divide to leave us with a third degree polynomial. Finally divide by $x - 1$ and arrive at our remaining quadratic factor, $x^2 - 2x - 1$. It won't factor but by the formula we find $x = -1 \pm \sqrt{2}$ as roots.

17. If $\left[x - \dfrac{4 + i}{3}\right]$ is a factor then so is $\left[x - \dfrac{4 - i}{3}\right]$ and their product will be an irreducible quadratic factor.

$$
\begin{array}{l}
x \;-\; \dfrac{4}{3} \;-\; \dfrac{i}{3} \\[4pt]
\underline{x \;-\; \dfrac{4}{3} \;+\; \dfrac{i}{3}} \\[4pt]
x^2 \;-\; \dfrac{4}{3}x \;-\; \dfrac{i}{3}x \\[4pt]
\quad\; -\dfrac{4}{3}x \qquad\quad +\dfrac{16}{9} + \dfrac{4}{9}i \\[4pt]
\qquad\quad \dfrac{i}{3}x \qquad\quad -\dfrac{4}{9}i - \dfrac{i^2}{9} \\[4pt]
\hline
x^2 \;-\; \dfrac{8}{3}x \qquad +\dfrac{16}{9} \qquad +\dfrac{1}{9}
\end{array}
$$

$x^2 - (8/3)x + 17/9$ is therefore a quadratic factor. We can multiply by 9 to get integer coefficients, $9x^2 - 24x + 17$. So we must have $f(x) = (9x^2 - 24x + 17)\cdot q(x)$ and we divide to find $q(x)$

$$
\begin{array}{r}
2x \;-\; 3 \\
9x^2 - 24x + 17 \;\overline{\big)\; 18x^3 - 75x^2 + 106x - 51} \\
\underline{18x^3 - 48x^2 + 34x} \\
-27x^2 + 72x - 51 \\
\underline{-27x^2 + 72x - 51} \\
0
\end{array}
$$

So $f(x) = (2x - 3)(9x^2 - 24x + 17)$

19. If $r_1 = 1 + \sqrt{6}$ then $r_2 = 1 - \sqrt{6}$. We will use the method of example 4.

$$r_1 + r_2 = 2 = -b$$

$$r_1 \cdot r_2 = -5 = c$$

and the quadratic is $x^2 - 2x - 5 = 0$.

21. $x^2 - (9/2)x + (61/16) = 0$

23. $f(x) = 2x^5 + 3x + 4$, no changes in sign and therefore no positive roots.

$f(-x) = -2x^5 - 3x + 4$, one change and therefore zero or one negative root.

But remember, complex roots occur in pairs and since we are required to
have 5 roots 4 must be complex and one negative.

25. $f(x) = 5x^4 + 2x - 7$ one change in sign.

$f(x) = 5x^4 - 2x - 7$ again one change.

We have four roots. Part c of Descarte's Rule says that if the number of
positive roots is less than the number of sign changes in $f(x)$, 1, it is
less by an even number. Therefore we have one positive root and therefore
one negative root by default. The other two roots are complex.

27. 1 positive, 2 complex or 1 positive, 2 negative

29. $f(x) = 3x^8 + x^6 - 2x^2 - 4$: 1 change

$f(-x) = 3x^8 + x^6 - 2x^2 - 4$: 1 change

By the same argument as problem 25, we will have one positive, one negative,
and six complex roots.

31. 1 positive; 8 complex

33. $f(x) = x^8 - 2$: 1 change

$f(-x) = x^8 - 2$: 1 change

The results must be exactly the same as #29.

35. 1 positive; 1 negative; 4 complex

39. If $\sqrt{3} + 2i$ is a root then so must be $\sqrt{3} - 2i$. We can multiply the factors $[x - (\sqrt{3} + 2i)][x - (\sqrt{3} - 2i)]$ or use the sum and product property to find a quadratic with these roots but it is $x^2 - 2\sqrt{3}x + 7$. Let's isolate the radical term and square both sides

$$x^2 + 7 = 2\sqrt{3}x$$
$$x^4 + 14x^2 + 49 = 4 \cdot 3x$$

and $f(x) = x^4 + 2x^2 + 49$ is the required polynomial.

41. If we follow the suggestion we have $x^4 + 16x^2 + 64 - 16x^2$ which can be written as $(x^2 + 8)^2 - 16x^2$, the difference of perfect squares. Factoring gives $(x^2 + 8 + 4x)(x^2 + 8 - 4x)$ or $(x^2 + 4x + 8)(x^2 - 4x + 8)$. Remember we can always multiply these and see if we in fact get $x^4 - 64$.

43. (a) Writing $x^6 + 1$ as $(x^2)^3 + 1$ we have a sum of cubes. Factoring gives $(x^2 + 1)(x^4 - x^2 + 1)$. The trinomial won't factor, but if we remember problem 41 we could write this as

$$(x^2 + 1)[(x^4 + 2x^2 + 1) - 3x^2]$$
$$(x^2 + 1)[(x^2 + 1)^2 - 3x^2]$$
$$(x^2 + 1)[(x^2 + 1) + \sqrt{3}x][(x^2 + 1) - \sqrt{3}x] \qquad \text{finally}$$
$$(x^2 + 1)(x^2 + \sqrt{3}x + 1)(x^2 - \sqrt{3}x + 1)$$

all quadratic. Remember we were asked only for real, not rational coefficients.

(b) Factoring (difficult) or using the quadratic formula on each of these quadratic factors will give me the linear factors. $x^2 + 1$ becomes $(x + i)(x - i)$ and other two also yield. My final list of linear factors is

$$(x + i)(x - i)\left(x + \frac{\sqrt{3} + i}{2}\right)\left(x + \frac{\sqrt{3} - i}{2}\right)\left(x - \frac{\sqrt{3} + i}{2}\right)\left(x - \frac{\sqrt{3} - i}{2}\right)$$

Exercise Set 4.7

1. By inspection $f(0) = -1$ and $f(1) = 1$ so there is a positive root
    between 0 and 1. The slope of a line from $(0,-1)$ to $(1,1)$ is $m = 2/1$ or
    2. In this relatively simple case we can see that such a line would cross
    the x-axis at $x = \frac{1}{2}$, and we will use that for our first approximation

    $$\underline{1/2|} \quad \begin{array}{cccc} 1 & 0 & 1 & -1 \\ & 1/2 & 1/4 & 5/8 \\ \hline 1 & 1/2 & 5/4 & \text{neg.} \end{array}$$

    Remember, this remainder is the same as $f(\frac{1}{2})$. It's still negative. Let's
    try $f(.6)$.

    $$\underline{.6|} \quad \begin{array}{cccc} 1 & 0 & 1 & -1 \\ & .6 & .36 & .798 \\ \hline 1 & .6 & 1.36 & \text{neg} \rightarrow \text{But closer to 0.} \end{array}$$

    $$\underline{.7|} \quad \begin{array}{cccc} 1 & 0 & 1 & -1 \\ & .7 & .49 & 1.043 \\ \hline 1 & .7 & 1.49 & \text{positive} \rightarrow \text{But not by much.} \end{array}$$

    The root must be between 0.6 and 0.7. We now investigate between these two
    values, noting that .7 almost gave us a zero remainder. Let's try 0.69.
    Again using a claculator and synthetic division we find a remainder of
    +.018. Trial with 0.68 yields $f(.68) = -.005$ and we have satisfied the
    initial charge.

3. Since $2^5 = 32$ and $3^5 = 243$, our root is between these. Why would you
    think it must be closer to two? (Sorry, but I can't pass up the opportunity
    to point out that I think it's closer to two, too.) In this case, it is
    probably easier just to use a calculator to test $(2.9)^5$, and we quickly zero
    in on 2.88 and 2.89 as our limits.

5. between 4.31 and 4.32

7. between -2.51 and -2.52

9. In dealing with $x^4 + 4x^3 - 6x^2 - 8x - 2 = 0$ our first problem is to
    isolate the whole number interval containing the negative root. $f(0)$ is
    negative as is $f(-1)$. Continuing in this way we find $f(-4)$ is -130 but
    $f(-5)$ is 13. We have found our first interval, and the root is much closer
    to -5 than -4. $f(-4.9)$ is still negative. Watch the calculation, again
    using a calculator.

-4.9⌋	1	4	-6	-8	-2
		-4.9	4.41	7.791	1.0241
	1	-.9	-1.59	-.209	-.9759

Although $f(-4.9)$ is negative, it's not by much. This is $f(-4.90)$, while
$f(-4.91)$ will be positive, and we have the necessary region.

11.

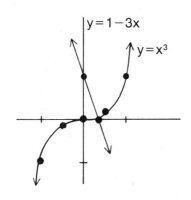

The graph shows these two functions
intersecting between x = 0 and 1.
Finding the point of intersection means
finding the value of x for which the two
y's are equal. In other words, where
does $x^3 = 1 - 3x$. This equation
$x^3 + 3x - 1 = 0$ has roots which can be
classified using Descarte's Rule of Signs.
$f(x)$ has one sign change. $f(-x)$ has no
sign changes. Conclusion: we <u>must</u> have
one positive root and a complex pair, but the graph already showed us that.
When we consider $f(x) = x^3 + 3x - 1$, we find $f(0) = -1$ and $f(1) = 3$.
The line connecting those points passes through the x axis at about x = .25.

.2⌋	1	0	3	-1
		.2	.04	.608
	1	.2	3.04	negative

.3⌋	1	0	3	-1
		.3	.09	.927
	1	.3	3.09	-.073

11. (Cont.)

```
.4│    1     0      3       -1
            .4    3.16    1.264
      1    .16           +.264
```

We can see the sign change and the relative size of the remainders says we are closer to .3 for a root.

```
.32│   1     0      3       -1
            .32   .1024    .9928
      1    .32   3.1024
```

This last calculation is as close as we can get to a zero remainder with two decimal places, and is the required answer.

13. x = 1.49

15. $x^4 - 2x^3 + 27x^2 - 126x + 144 = 0$. There are four sign changes in $f(x)$ and none in $f(-x)$. That means, by Descarte's Rule, that we have 4, 2 or no positive roots but no negative ones. Any positive rational root will be from the set of factors of 144 because $a_0 = 144$ and $a_n = 1$

```
1│    1    -2     27    -126     144
            1     -1     26     -100
      1    -1     26    -100      44    No luck

2│    1    -2     27    -126     144
            2      0     54     -144
      1     0     27     -72       0    Bingo
```

The depressed equation, $x^3 + 27x - 72 = 0$ will have one positive root. Testing 3 gives us a positive third time, hence it is an upper bound and we go shopping between 1 and 3 for the other root. We look there because $f(1)$ and $f(3)$ were positive and $f(2)$ was zero. Following the trial and error procedure of earlier problems we find the second root between 2.24 and 2.25.

17. 1:4;   third root between 1.16 and 1.17;   fourth root between -1.77 and -1.78;   fifth root between -3.39 and -3.40

19. (a) The distance from $P(a,b)$ to the origin is $\sqrt{(a - 0)^2 + (b - 0)^2} =$
$\sqrt{a^2 + b^2}$. Since P lies on the parabola $y = x^2$, we have $b = a^2$.
The expression for the distance then becomes $\sqrt{a^2 + a^4}$. We are given
that this distance is to be ab. Since $ab = a(a^2) = a^3$, we have:
$\sqrt{a^2 + a^4} = a^3$. By squaring both sides and rearranging, we obtain
$a^6 - a^4 - a^2 = 0$, or $a^4 - a^2 - 1 = 0$. By using the method shown in
Section 4.7, we find that $a = 1.27$, to two decimal places.

(b) Let $a^2 = t$. Then the equation becomes $t^2 - t - 1 = 0$. Applying the
quadratic formula, we find that the positive root here is:

$$t = \frac{1 + \sqrt{5}}{2} \quad . \quad \text{Thus} \quad a = \sqrt{\frac{1 + \sqrt{5}}{2}}$$

EXERCISE SET 4.8

1. yes   3. yes   5. no

7.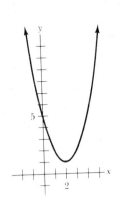

$y = (x - 2)^2 + 1$. This is our standard parabola shifted
2 units to the right and up 1 unit. There is no x
intercept because if $y = 0$, then $(x - 2)^2 = -1$ and
we can't take the square root. When $x = 0$, $y = 5$.

9.

11.

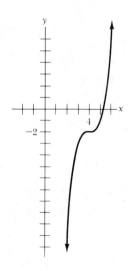

In this problem $y = x^3$ is moved around to get the desired graph. When $y = 0$,

$$(x - 4)^3 = 2$$

$$x - 4 = \sqrt[3]{2}$$

$$x = 4 + \sqrt[3]{2}, \quad \text{the x-intercept.}$$

The y-intercept is way down, but it is there. When $x = 0$, $y = -66$.

13.

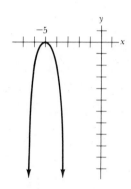

This is $y = x^4$ turned over and shifted five units left. It also is "skinny" because of the 2 coefficient. Instead of the usual over one down one over two down 16 ... pattern, it is over one down two and over two down 32. In every case, twice as much. The only intercept is (-5,0), or is it. Don't be fooled; this curve keeps opening. For $x = 0$, $y = -2(0 + 5)^4 = -1250$. It is way down, but it crosses the y-axis.

15.

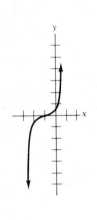

17.

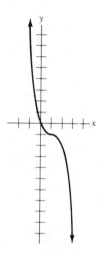

19. The roots can be found by inspection. If x = 2, then the (x - 2) factor
is zero. The roots of -1 and 1 can be found the same way. Near x = -1,

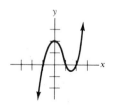

y is near (-1 - 2)(-1 - 1)(x + 1) or 6x + 6. It
rises fairly steeply to the right. At x = 1 the
curve is like the line y = -2x + 2 and near x = 2
it approximates y = 3x - 6. To complete the sketch
we need to pick points between the roots and get an
idea how high turn around points may be. Incidently,
such turn arounds are not necessarily half way
between roots, but they are usually in the general area. Here we might
choose to find f(0) (always a good choice) and f(3/2). f(0) = 2 and
f(3/2) = -5/8.

21.

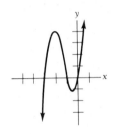

The roots of y = 2x(x + 1)(x + 3) are 0, -1, and
-3. We will also want to know when x = -2 and -½.
Again we look at the behavior of y near the roots.
For example when x is close to -3, y is like
12x + 36, rising steeply to the right.

23.

25.

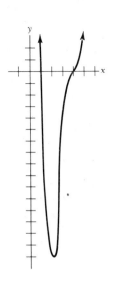

The roots are 1 and 4. Look at f(0). It's enormous!
f(0) = 2(0 - 1)(0 - 4)^3 = 128. The graph must be very
steep between x = 0 and x = 1. Let's find f(2) and
f(3) to help. We discover that the curve passes
through (2,-16) and (3,-4). Near x = 4 it behaves like
y = 6(x - 4)^3, a tall, thin version of y = x^3. Put it
together and you have a sketch like this one.

27.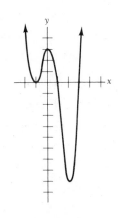

29. (not to scale)
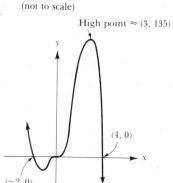
High point ≈ (3, 135)
(4, 0)
(−2, 0)

31. (not to scale)
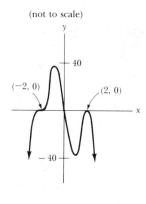
40
(−2, 0)
(2, 0)
−40

33. Remember that $y = (1/100)x^2$ is a parabola rising slowly as x increases, so it must eventually rise up to meet the line $y = x$. Where? When the y coordinates are equal, or when $x = (1/100)x^2$. Let's solve $(1/100)x^2 = x$.

$$x^2 = 100x$$
$$x^2 - 100x = 0$$
$$x(x - 100) = 0$$

$$x = 0 \mid x = 100$$

When $x = 100$ both y values will be 100.

37. zeros at 0, −1 (multiplicity 3)
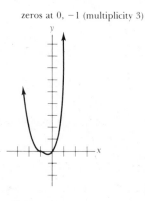

39. zeros at −4, −3, 1
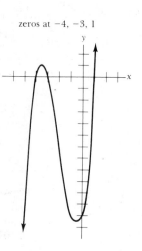

EXERCISE SET 4.9

1. A rational function is the quotient of two polynomials. It has the form
   $\frac{f(x)}{g(x)}$, so its domain will include all real numbers for which
   $g(x) \neq 0$ and its zeros or roots will be the zeros of $f(x)$. Here the
   domain will be all real numbers except $x = 1$ and the zeros will be
   $x = -6$ and $x = -4$.

3. domain: $\mathbb{R}$;   zeros: $\frac{-1 \pm \sqrt{41}}{4}$

5. Setting $2x - 1 = 0$ gives $x = \frac{1}{2}$ and letting $4x + 3 = 0$ gives $x = -3/4$.
   These are the only real numbers excluded from the domain. Factoring the
   numerator we have

$$6x^3 - 13x^2 - 5x$$

$$x(6x^2 - 13x - 5)$$

$$x(3x + 1)(2x - 5)$$

   and the zeros of the function are 0, -1/3, and 5/2.

7. (a) The graph of $y = \frac{3}{x + 2}$ has the same basic shape as $y = 1/x$,
      shifted two units to the left. Plotting some other points helps us
      fill in and smooth out the curve

x	-5	-4	-3	-1	0	1
y	-1	$-\frac{3}{2}$	-3	3	$\frac{3}{2}$	1

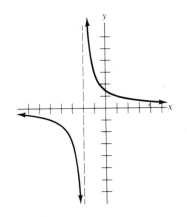

(b)

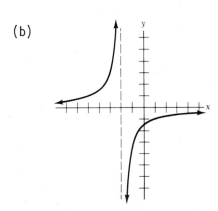

7. (b) To take the negative of the original function, we ismply reflect the
         graph of part (a) across the x-axis.

9.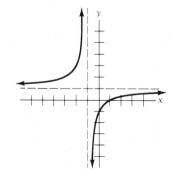

Following example 4 on page 246 we divide x - 1
by x + 1 and get 1 - 2/(x + 1) and we
conclude that the graph can be obtained by moving
the graph of y = -2/(x + 1) up one unit. We
start with y = 1/x, move it one unit left. The
graph of y = 2/(x + 1) has the same basic shape,
and we can sketch it by picking several x
values to fill out the curve. The switch to
y = -2/(x + 1) simply reflects the original
across the x axis. That curve is finally moved up one unit. This all
sounds rather confusing, but it is much easier after you have worked through
the process several times.

11.

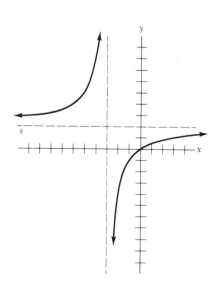

13.

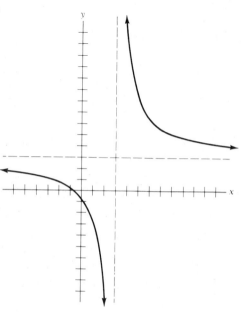

15. (a)

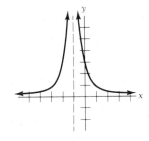

Page 247 discussed the basic form of $y = 1/x^n$. The graph of $y = 3/(x + 1)^2$ simply shifts $y = 1/x^2$ one unit left and changes the shape slightly. $x = -1$ becomes a vertical asymplote. y will never equal zero. Plot a few points to fill in the basic shape.

(b)

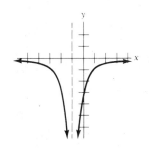

This is the negative of our graph from part (a). It is reflected across the x axis.

17.

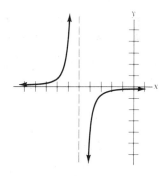

19.

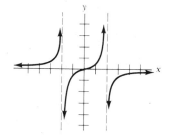

The factors in the denominator give us 2 and -2 for vertical asymptotes and the only root comes from $-x = 0$ in the numerator. Close to -2 the function behaves like

$$y = \frac{-(-2)}{(x + 2)(-2 - 2)} = \frac{\frac{1}{2}}{x + 2}$$

Near $x = 0$ it approximates

$$y = \frac{-x}{(0 + 2)(0 - 2)} = \frac{1}{4}x ,$$

and as x gets near +2, y looks like

$$y = \frac{-2}{(2 + 2)(x - 2)} = \frac{-\frac{1}{2}}{x - 2}$$

If we write the equation as $y = -x/(x^2 - 4)$ and divide x^2 we get

19. (Cont.)

$$y = \frac{-\dfrac{1}{x}}{1 - \dfrac{4}{x^2}}$$

and we see that as $|x|$ gets large y hets close to zero. In other words $y = 0$ is a horizontal asymptote. If we add to this analysis by calculating y for selected x's, such as

x	-4	-3	-1	1	3	4
y	$\dfrac{1}{3}$	$\dfrac{3}{5}$	$-\dfrac{1}{3}$	$\dfrac{1}{3}$	$-\dfrac{3}{5}$	$-\dfrac{1}{3}$

we get a smooth graph.

21.

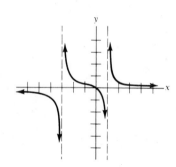

23.

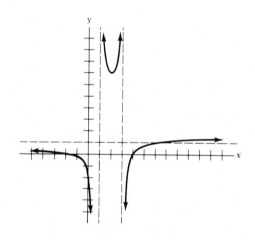

Zeros at $x = 4$ and -2. Vertical asymptotes at $x = 1$ and 3. If we multiply we have

$$y = \frac{x^2 - 2x - 8}{x^2 - 4x + 3} \qquad \text{or}$$

$$y = \frac{1 - \dfrac{2}{x} - \dfrac{8}{x^2}}{1 - \dfrac{4}{x} + \dfrac{3}{x^2}}$$

and as $|x|$ gets large y gets close to 1. As is almost always

23. (Cont.) true we will finish off our rough ideas by judicious selection of some other x values and calculation of corresponding y's. Here choose perhaps x = -3, -1, 0, 1/2, 3/2, 2, 5/2, 7/2, 5, 6. All of these are not necessary, but each helps that much more. One more interesting thing to note; the curve crosses y = 1 out near x = 6 or 7 and then settles back down asymptotically as x moves on out. Note the same behavior in problem 25.

25.

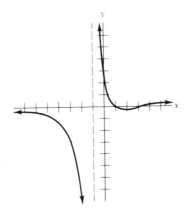

Chapter 5   Exponential and Logarithmic Functions

1. (a) Example 1 told us that $2^{10} \simeq 10^3$. Therefore $2^{20} = (2^{10})^2 = (10^3)^2 = 10^6$.

   (b) $2^{50} = (2^{10})^5 = (10^3)^5 = 10^{15}$

   (c) $2^{21} = 2 \cdot 2^{20} = 2 \cdot 10^6$

   (d) $2^{59} = 2^{-1} \cdot 2^{60} = 2^{-1} \cdot 10^{18} = \frac{1}{2} \cdot 10^{18}$

3. $\dfrac{(2^{-2})^4}{2^{-3}} = \dfrac{2^{-8}}{2^{-3}} = \dfrac{1}{2^5} = \dfrac{1}{32}$

5. $8^{2/3} = \sqrt[3]{8^2}$ or alternatively $(\sqrt[3]{8})^2$

         $= \sqrt[3]{64}$ $= (2)^2$

         $= 4$ $= 4$

The second alternative is generally easier.

7. $\dfrac{10^{50}}{10^{48}} = 10^2 = 100$

9. $\left(\dfrac{2}{3}\right)^{-3} = \dfrac{2^{-3}}{3^{-3}} = \dfrac{3^3}{2^3} = \dfrac{27}{8}$

There are generally several approaches to simplifying these expressions. Here is a second method.

$$\left(\dfrac{2}{3}\right)^{-3} = \dfrac{1}{\left(\dfrac{2}{3}\right)^3} = \dfrac{1}{\dfrac{8}{27}} = \dfrac{27}{8}$$

11. 1100

13. $\dfrac{111}{100}$

15. $(a^{-3}b^4)^2 = a^{-6}b^8 = b^8/a^6$

17. $\left(\dfrac{x^6 y^{-3} z^{-8}}{3x^{-2}y^5}\right)^{-1}$ Again there are several ways to procede. I'll choose this one.

$= \dfrac{x^{-6}y^3 z^8}{3^{-1}x^2 y^{-5}} = \dfrac{3y^8 z^8}{x^8}$

19. $\dfrac{y^{7/3}}{8}$

21. $(x^{-1} + y^{-1})^{-2}$ BE CAREFUL!

The common mistake is to think this is $x^2 + y^2$, but there is no such distributive property for exponents over addition or subtraction. First we work inside.

$$\left(\dfrac{1}{x} + \dfrac{1}{y}\right)^{-2} = \left(\dfrac{y + x}{xy}\right)^{-2} = \dfrac{(x + y)^{-2}}{(xy)^{-2}} = \dfrac{x^2 y^2}{(x + y)^2}$$

23. $\dfrac{1}{a}$

25. (a) $a^4 + \dfrac{4}{a^{-4}}$ We need a common denominator to add these terms so we multiply the first term by a^{-4}/a^{-4} getting

25. (a) (Cont.)

$$\frac{a^0 + 4}{a^{-4}} = \frac{1 + 4}{a^{-4}} = 5a^4$$

A simpler way would be to write the expression as $a^4 + 4a^4 = 5a^4$.

(b) $\dfrac{2x^{-1}}{2x^{-1}} \cdot x^{-2} - \dfrac{1}{2x^{-1}}$

$= \dfrac{2x^{-3} - 1}{2x^{-1}}$ now let's factor x^{-3} out of the numerator

$= \dfrac{x^{-3}(2 - x^3)}{2x^{-1}}$ now we will cancel

$= \dfrac{2 - x^3}{2x^2}$

(c) $-x^{-1} - \dfrac{x^{-1}}{x^{-2}} = -\dfrac{1}{x} - x = \dfrac{-1 - x^2}{x}$

27. Here we will factor the smallest power of $(1 - 2x)$ namely $(1 - 2x)^{-3}$ from each term.

$$3x(1 - 2x)^{-3} - (1 - 2x)^{-2} = (1 - 2x)^{-3}[3x - (1 - 2x)^1] = \frac{5x - 1}{(1 - 2x)^3}$$

29. $(1 - x^2)^{\frac{1}{2}} - x^2(1 - x^2)^{-\frac{1}{2}} = (1 - x^2)^{-\frac{1}{2}}[(1 - x^2) - x^2] = \dfrac{1 - 2x^2}{(1 - x^2)^{\frac{1}{2}}}$

31. (a) $\sqrt[7]{\sqrt{x}} = (\sqrt{x})^{1/7} = (x^{1/2})^{1/7} = x^{1/14}$

(b) $\sqrt[3]{a^6} = a^{6/3} = a^2$

(c) $\dfrac{\sqrt{3}}{\sqrt[3]{3}} = \dfrac{3^{1/2}}{3^{1/3}} = 3^{1/2 - 1/3} = 3^{1/6}$

(d) $\sqrt[5]{x} \cdot \sqrt[6]{x} = x^{1/5} \cdot x^{1/6} = x^{1/5 + 1/6} = x^{11/30}$

31. (e) $\sqrt{5\sqrt{5}} = \sqrt{5 \cdot 5^{1/2}} = \sqrt{5^{3/2}} = (5^{3/2})^{1/2} = 5^{3/4}$

33. $(x^2 + a)^{2/3} - 5(x^2 + a)^{-1/3} = 0$ Factoring $(x^2 + a)^{-1/3}$ we get

$(x^2 + a)^{-1/3}[(x^2 + a) - 5] = 0$ or

$$\frac{x^2 + a - 5}{(x^2 + a)^{1/3}} = 0$$

This will equal zero when the numerator is zero, so we have

$$x^2 + a - 5 = 0$$
$$x^2 = 5 - a$$
$$x = \pm\sqrt{5 - a}$$

35. (a) $3^{2x} = 27$

In these cases we must write both sides with similar bases and then equate exponents

$3^{2x} = 27$ becomes

$3^{2x} = 3^3$ and therefore

$2x = 3$ and

$x = 3/2$

(b) $2^{2x+1} = 64$ (c) $2^{3x+1} = 1/64$

$2^{2x+1} = 2^6$ $2^{3x+1} = 2^{-6}$

$2x + 1 = 6$ $3x + 1 = -6$

$2x = 5$ $3x = -7$

$x = 5/2$ $x = -7/3$

(d) $10^{t^2+3t+4} = 100$

$t^2 + 3t + 4 = 2$ equating exponents

$t^2 + 3t + 2 = 0$ factoring

35. (d) (Cont.)

    $(t + 2)(t + 1) = 0$ so

    $t = -1$ or -2 are solutions

39. 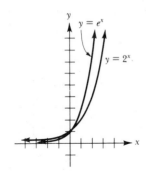 $\sqrt[x]{x^{(x^2-x)}} = x^{x^2-x}{}^{1/x} = x^{[(x^2-x)/x]} = x^{(x-1)}$

45. (a) $2^{1/2} = \sqrt{2}$ (b) $(\sqrt{2})^2 = 2$

EXERCISE SET 5.2

1. (a) no   (b) yes   (c) yes   (d) no   (e) no

   (f) yes   (g) no   (h) no

3.

5.

x	x^2	2^x	Which is larger?
0	0	1	2^x
1	1	2	2^x
2	4	4	equal
3	9	8	x^2
4	16	16	equal
5	25	32	2^x
6	36	64	2^x
10	100	1024	2^x

7. (a) domain: $\mathbb{R}$,   range: $y < 1$,
        intercepts: $(0,0)$,   asymptote: $y = 1$

   (b) domain: $\mathbb{R}$,   range: $y < 2$,
        intercepts: $(0,1)$, $(1,0)$,   asymptote: $y = 2$

   We know the graph of $y = 2^x$. Here it is reflected
   across the x axis to get $y = -2^x$ and then that is
   raised one and two units for parts (a) and (b)
   respectively.

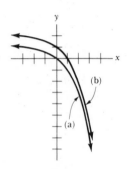

9. (a) domain: $\mathbb{R}$,   range: $y < 1$,
      intercepts: $(0,0)$,   asymptote: $y = 1$

   (b) domain: $\mathbb{R}$,   range: $y < e$,
      intercepts: $(0, e-1)$, $(1,0)$,   asymptote: $y = e$

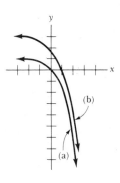

These graphs are the negatives of $y = e^x$, reflected across the x-axis and then raised 1 unit in part (a) and "e" units in part (b).

11. (a) domain: $\mathbb{R}$,   range: $y > 0$,
      intercept: $(0,3)$,   asymptote: $y = 0$

   (b) domain: $\mathbb{R}$,   range: $y > 1$,
      intercept: $(0,4)$,   asymptote: $y = 1$

   (c) domain: $\mathbb{R}$,   range: $y < 0$,
      intercept: $(0,-3)$,   asymptote: $y = 0$

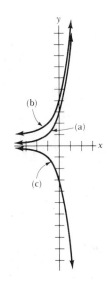

See how important memorizing basic graphs like $y = 3^x$ or $y = e^x$ is? You can always fall back on plotting points, but it is easier to realize that given $f(x)$, $f(x + 1)$ is the same graph shifted one unit left.

13. (a) domain: $\mathbb{R}$,   range: $y > 0$,
      intercept: $(0,e)$,   asymptote: $y = 0$

   (b) domain: $\mathbb{R}$,   range: $y < 0$,
      intercept: $(0,-e)$,   asymptote: $y = 0$

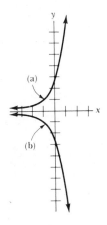

15. (a) domain: $\mathbb{R}$,   range: $y > 0$;
         intercept: $(0,1)$,   asymptote: $y = 0$

    (b) domain: $\mathbb{R}$,   range: $y > 0$;
         intercept: $(0,1)$, asymptote: $y = 0$

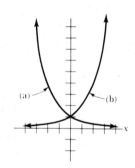

17. (a) $x^2 e^x - 16e^x = 0$ factor

         $e^x(x^2 - 16) = 0$

         $e^x(x + 4)(x - 4) = 0$

         but since e^x never equals zero, (remember the graph of $y = e^x$) our
         roots are 4 and -4.

    (b) $3e^x - 5xe^x + 2e^2 e^x = 0$

         $e^x(3 - 5x + 2x^2) = 0$

         $e^x(3 - 2x)(1 - x) = 0$

         and we have $x = 1$ and $3/2$ for roots.

19. $x = 5$

21. (a) Given the growth law $N = N_0 e^{kt}$ and the initial conditions, we can
         write

$$3 \times 10^4 = 2 \times 10^4 e^{k \cdot 8}$$

$$3/2 = e^{8k}$$

$$\sqrt[8]{3/2} = e^k$$

         So now we want N when $t = 9$

$$N = 2 \times 10^4 e^{k \cdot 9}$$

$$N = 2 \times 10^4 (3/2)^{9/8}$$

         We need a calculator to raise 1.5 to the 9/8 power. Then times
         2×10^4 gives us about 31,600 bacteria.

21. (b) When 24 hours have elapsed

$$N = 2 \times 10^4 \, (3/2)^{24/8} \qquad \text{(much easier)}$$

$$N = 2 \times 10^4 \, (27/8)$$

and N = about 67,500 bacteria

23. Remember half-life is the time necessary for half of an original sample to decompose. Here the half-life is 5 days.

(a) In 5 days we go from 8 to 4 grams.

(b) Half again to 2 grams

(c) 1 gram

(d) ½ gram

(e) 1/128 gram. It was halved 6 more times.

25. (a) $10(1/2)^{1/28} \approx 9.8$ gram

(b) $10(1/2)^{5/14} \approx 7.8$ gram

27. We could simply calculate the number of 10 second intervals in 5 min (30) and them go from 50% to 25% to 12½% and so on 30 times. But, let's look at the problem from a growth and decay standpoint. We know

$$\tfrac{1}{2}N_0 = N_0 e^{k \cdot 10 \text{ sec}}$$

$$e^{10k} = \tfrac{1}{2} \qquad \text{dividing by } N_0$$

$$e^k = (\tfrac{1}{2})^{1/10}$$

So we want $N = N_0 (\tfrac{1}{2})^{(1/10) \cdot 300} \qquad$ (300 seconds)

$$N = N_0 (\tfrac{1}{2})^{30}$$

And N turns out to be about 9.3×10^{-8} percent of N_0. Please use a calculator to raise ½ to the 30th power.

31.

x	S(x)
−3	−10.0
−2	−3.6
−1	−1.2
0	0
1	1.2
2	3.6
3	10.0

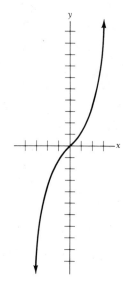

33. (c)

x	x + 1	e^x
1	2	2.71828
.5	1.5	1.64872
.1	1.1	1.10517
.01	1.01	1.01005
.001	1.001	1.001005
.0001	1.0001	1.000100005

35. (a)

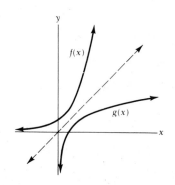

We know the graph of $y = 2^x$ but lets list a few typical points in a table

x	-3	-2	-1	0	1	2	3
y	$\frac{1}{8}$	$\frac{1}{4}$	$\frac{1}{2}$	1	2	4	8

Then the graph of g, the inverse of f, should contain these points with the x and y coordinates interchanged. G(x) will be f(x) reflected across the line y = x.

(b) Domain: x > 0

Range: $\mathbb{R}$

Intercept: x only, at (1,0)

Asymptote: x = 0 (the negative y-axis)

37. (a) Since $N = N_0 e^{kt}$

$N = 1\, e^{k \cdot t}$ using $N_0 = 1$ billion and

$2 = e^{k \cdot 50}$

$e^k = 2^{1/80}$

so N in 1980 should be given by

$N = (2^{1/80})^{130}$

$N = 2^{13/8}$ or about 3.08 billion

(b) It's too low

41. (a)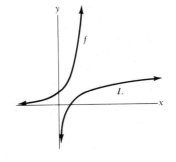

(b) Domain: $x > 0$

Range: $\mathbb{R}$

Intercept: $(1,0)$

Asymptote: $x = 0$

(c)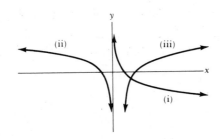

(i) intercept: $(1,0)$

asymptote: $x = 0$

(ii) intercept: $(-1,0)$

asymptote: $x = 0$

(iii) intercept: $(2,0)$

asymptote: $x = 1$

Exercise Set 5.3

1. (a) No, because a horizontal line can intersect the parabola twice.

    (b) Yes

3. (a) yes   (b) no

5. (a) yes

    (b) No, be cafeful here because a horizontal line hits this at $(-1,1)$ and $(0,1)$. Its inverse will not be a function.

7. (a) $\log_3 9 = 2$ (b) $\log_{10} 1000 = 3$

    (c) $\log_7 343 = 3$ (d) $\log_2 \sqrt{2} = \frac{1}{2}$

9. (a) $2^5 = 32$ (b) $10^0 = 1$

    (c) $e^{\frac{1}{2}} = \sqrt{e}$ (d) $3^{-4} = 1/81$

    (e) $t^v = u$

11. $\log_5 30$ represents the power to which 5 must be raised to get 30. It is clearly greater than 2, since $5^2 = 25$. $\log_8 60$ is less than 2 since $8^2 = 64$. Hence $\log_5 30$ is larger.

13. (a) $\log_9 27$ is the power to which 9 must be raised to get 27. We can see it's between 1 and 2 since $9^1 = 9$ while $9^2 = 81$. To find it let $\log_9 27 = n$ then $9^n = 27$ in exponential form and $3^{2n} = 3^3$. So, $2n = 3$ and $n = 3/2$.

    (b) If $\log_4(1/32) = n$ then $4^n = 1/32$ or $2^{2n} = 2^{-5}$. So $2n = -5$, and $n = -5/2$. $\log_4(1/32) = -5/2$ as required.

13. (c) Follow the same steps. If $\log_5(5\sqrt{5}) = n$ then

$$5^n = 5\sqrt{5}$$

$$5^n = 5^{3/2}$$

and $\qquad n = 3/2$

15. (a) $\log_x 256 = 8$

so $\quad x^8 = 256 = 2^8$

and $\quad x = 2$

(b) $\log_5 x = -1$

so $\quad 5^{-1} = x$

and $\quad x = 1/5$

The solution to problems of this type frequently depends on our ability to move back and forth between logarithmic and exponential form.

17. (a) $x = 1,4$

19. $\log_8 2 + (1/3)\log_a a^5$

The $\log_8 2$ is 1/3 because $8^{1/3} = 2$, but what does the definition say about $\log_a a^5$. It stands for that power that the base a must be raised to to get a^5. That must be the 5th power. Therefore

$$(1/3)\log_a a^5 = (1/3)(5) = 5/3$$

And the sum is 6/3 or 2.

21. (a) Domain: $x > -1$, range: $\mathbb{R}$,
intercept: $(0,0)$, asymptote: $x = -1$

(b) Domain: $x > -1$, range: $\mathbb{R}$,
intercepts: $(0,0)$, asymptote: $x = -1$

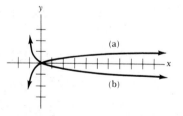

21. (cont)

Here agian if we know the graph of $y = \log_{10}x$ then $\log_{10}(x + 1)$ shifts
to the left one unit. Our old asymptote was the y-axis, now it's $x = -1$.
In the same way the intercept of $(1,0)$ has moved to $(0,0)$. And, the
negative simply reflects part (a) across the x-axis.

23. (a) Domain: $x > 0$,   range: $\mathbb{R}$,
          intercept: $(1,0)$,   asymptote: $x = 0$

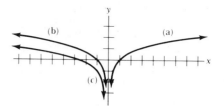

     (b) Domain: $x < 0$,   range: $\mathbb{R}$,
          intercept: $(-1,0)$,   asymptote: $x = 0$

     (c) Domain: $x < 0$,   range: $\mathbb{R}$,
          intercept: $(-e,0)$,   asymptote: $x = 0$

The general comments from problem 21 apply equally here. Familiarity with
$y = \ln x$ makes parts (b) and (c) much easier.

25. (a) 4   (b) -1   (c) ½

27. (a) We are asked to solve $10^{(x^2)} = 40$ and to get the x^2 out of its
          position in the exponent. We will take the $\log_{10}$ of both sides.

          If $$10^{(x^2)} = 40$$

          then $$\log_{10}10^{(x^2)} = \log_{10}40$$

          and $$x^2 = \log_{10}40$$

          so $$x = \pm\sqrt{\log_{10}40}$$

     (b) If $$(10^x)^2 = 40$$

          then $$10^x = \sqrt{40}$$

          and $$x = \log_{10}\sqrt{40}$$

27. (c) Since $\log_{10} 40$ is between 1 and 2, its square root is also greater than 1. But, $\sqrt{40}$ is between 6 and 7 and the $\log_{10}$ of such a number is less than 1. THerefore, the answer from part (a) is larger.

31. If $e^{4t^2-1} = 6$ then taking the natural logarithm of both sides gives

$$\ln e^{4t^2-1} = \ln 6$$

or
$$4t^2 - 1 = \ln 6$$

$$4t^2 = 1 + \ln 6$$

$$t^2 = \frac{1 + \ln 6}{4}$$

$$t = \frac{\sqrt{1 + \ln 6}}{2}$$

33. (a) $k = \dfrac{\ln .5}{4.5 \times 10^9} \approx -1.54 \times 10^{-10}$

(b) 99.9999846%

35. (a) Starting with $N = N_0 e^{kt}$ we have

$$\tfrac{1}{2}N_0 = N_0 e^{k \cdot 1}$$

$$e^k = \tfrac{1}{2} \qquad \text{and taking the ln of both sides}$$

$$k = \ln \tfrac{1}{2}$$

(b) If 90% is gone that will leave 10% or .4 gm, and we have

$$.4 = 4e^{(\ln .5)t}$$

$$.1 = e^{(\ln .5)t}$$

$$\ln .1 = \ln(e^{(\ln .5)t})$$

$$\ln .1 = (\ln .5)t$$

35. (b) (cont)

$$t = \frac{\ln .1}{\ln .5}, \quad \text{about 3.32 years}$$

37. (a) We start with

$$3 \times 10^8 = 2 \times 10^7 \, e^{k \cdot 2}$$

$$e^{2k} = 15$$

or $$2k = \ln 15$$

$$k = \frac{\ln 15}{2}$$

so $$2N_0 = N_0 e^{\frac{\ln 15}{2} \cdot t}$$

$$2 = e^{\frac{\ln 15}{2} \cdot t}$$

$$\ln 2 = \frac{\ln 15}{2} \cdot t$$

$$t = \frac{2 \ln 2}{\ln 15} \approx .51 \text{ hours}$$

(b) Since 1 billion = 10^9 we want

$$10^9 = 2 \times 10^7 \, e^{\frac{\ln 15}{2} \cdot t}$$

or $$t = \frac{2 \ln 50}{15} \approx 2.89 \text{ hours}$$

39. Our rule for finding inverses was to interchange x and y and then solve
    for y so

$$f(x) = e^{x+1}$$

or $$y = e^{x+1}$$

becomes $$x = e^{y+1}$$

$$\ln x = \ln(e^{y+1})$$

$$\ln x = y + 1$$

39. (cont)

$$y = -1 + \ln x$$

or $f^{-1}(x) = -1 + \ln x$

A word of caution here. Be careful about writing an answer like this as
ln x - 1. It can incorrectly be read as ln(x - 1) instead of (ln x) - 1.
The form of our answer avoids this problem.

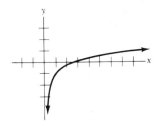

The intercept will be (e,0)
and the negative y-axis is an
asymptote.

41.

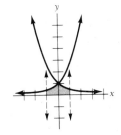

43. (a) In the decay law $N = N_0 e^{kt}$, we replace t by T and N by $\frac{1}{2}N_0$.
         This yields $\frac{1}{2}N_0 = N_0 e^{kT}$, or $\frac{1}{2} = e^{kT}$. Therefore $kT = \ln \frac{1}{2}$, and
         consequently $k = (\ln \frac{1}{2})/T$, as required.

     (b) $k = \dfrac{\ln \frac{1}{2}}{2} = \dfrac{\ln \frac{1}{2}}{3.8}$. (A calculator shows that this value is
                                        approximately -0.182.)

     (c) $t = \dfrac{(3.8)\ln(0.01)}{\ln(0.5)} \approx 25$ days

45. $e^{2x} - 5e^x - 6 = 0$ has the form of a quadratic in e^x. To see this let $e^x = n$, then the equation becomes $n^2 - 5n - 6 = 0$ and we factor

$$(e^x - 6)(e^x + 1) = 0$$

If $e^x - 6 = 0$ then $e^x = 6$ and $x = \ln 6$, but e^x can never equal -1 so there is no root for this factor and $x = \ln 6$ is the only solution.

47. $x = 10^{30}$

51. (a) $\ln(\ln x)$ will exist only for $\ln x > 0$ which means $x > 1$.

   (b) $y = \ln(\ln x)$ becomes

                $x = \ln(\ln y)$ and solving we have

                $e^x = e^{\ln(\ln y)}$

                $e^x = \ln y$

                $e^{e^x} = e^{\ln y}$

                $y = e^{e^x}$ so $f^{-1}(x) = e^{e^x}$

Exercise Set 5.4

1. $\log_{10}70 - \log_{10}7 = \log_{10} \frac{70}{7} = \log_{10}10 = 1$

3. $\log_7\sqrt{7} = \log_7 7^{\frac{1}{2}} = \frac{1}{2} \log_7 7 = \frac{1}{2}$

5. $\log_3 108 + \log_3(3/4) = \log_3(108)(3/4) = \log_3 81 = \log_3 3^4 = 4$

7. $-\frac{1}{2} + \ln\sqrt{e} = -\frac{1}{2} + \ln e^{\frac{1}{2}} = -\frac{1}{2} + \frac{1}{2} = 0$

9. $2^{\log_2 5} - 3 \log_5 \sqrt[3]{5} = 5 - 3 \log_5 5^{1/3} = 5 - 3(1/3) = 5 - 1 = 4$

11. $\log_{10}30 + \log_{10}2 = \log_{10}60$

13. $\log_5 20$

15. (a) $\ln 3 - 2 \ln 4 + \ln 32 = \ln 3 - \ln 4^2 + \ln 32 = \ln \dfrac{3 \cdot 32}{4^2} = \ln 6$

     (b) $\ln 3 - 2(\ln 4 + \ln 32) = \ln 3 - 2(\ln 4 \cdot 32) = \ln 3 - 2 \ln 128$

$$= \ln 3 - \ln 128^2 = \ln \frac{3}{128^2}$$

17. $\log_b 4 \left[\dfrac{(1 + x)}{\sqrt{1 - x}} \right]^3$

19. $4 \log_{10}3 - 6 \log_{10}(x^2 + 1) + \frac{1}{2} \left\lceil \log_{10}(x + 1) - 2 \log_{10}3 \right\rceil$

$$= \log_{10}3^4 - \log_{10}(x^2 + 1)^6 + \frac{1}{2}\left[\log_{10}(x + 1) - \log_{10}3^2 \right]$$

$$= \log_{10}81 - \log_{10}(x^2 + 1)^6 + \frac{1}{2}\left[\log_{10} \frac{x + 1}{9} \right]$$

$$= \log_{10}81 - \log_{10}(x^2 + 1)^6 + \log_{10} \left(\frac{x + 1}{9} \right)^{\frac{1}{2}}$$

$$= \log_{10} \frac{81 \dfrac{\sqrt{x + 1}}{3}}{(x^2 + 1)^6}$$

$$= \log_{10} \frac{27\sqrt{x + 1}}{(x^2 + 1)^6}$$

21. (a) $\log_{10} \dfrac{x^2}{1 + x^2} = \log_{10}x^2 - \log_{10}(1 + x^2) = 2 \log_{10}x - \log_{10}(1 + x^2)$

     (b) $\ln \dfrac{x^2}{\sqrt{1 + x^2}} = \ln x^2 - \ln \sqrt{1 + x^2} = 2 \ln x - \frac{1}{2} \ln(1 + x^2)$

23. (a) $\frac{1}{2} \log_{10}(9 - x^2)$

23. (b) $\frac{1}{2} \ln(4 - x^2) - \ln(x - 1) - \frac{3}{2} \ln(x + 1)$

25. (a) $\log_b \sqrt{x/b} = \frac{1}{2} \log_b(x/b) = \frac{1}{2}(\log_b x - \log_b b) = \frac{1}{2}(\log_b x - 1) = \frac{1}{2} \log_b x - \frac{1}{2}$

     (b) $2 \ln \sqrt{(1 + x^2)(1 + x^4)(1 + x^6)} = \ln(1 + x^2) + \ln(1 + x^4) + \ln(1 + x^6)$

27. (a) $a + 2b + 3c$ (b) $\frac{1}{2}(a + b + c)$

     (c) $a - \frac{1}{2}(b + c)$ (d) $2a - 4b - (1/3)c$

     (e) $5(a + b) - c$ (f) $(2/3)a + b - (1/3)c$

29. Taking the ln of both sides we have

$$\ln 5 = \ln 2 + \ln e^{2x-1}$$
$$\ln 5 = \ln 2 + (2x - 1)$$
$$\ln 5 = \ln 2 + 2x - 1$$
$$2x = \ln 5 - \ln 2 + 1$$
$$x = \frac{\ln 5 - \ln 2 + 1}{2}$$

31. $t = \ln 2 - \ln 3 - 1$

33. If $2^x = 9$

     then $\ln 2^x = \ln 9$

     and $x \ln 2 = \ln 9$

     finally $x = \frac{\ln 9}{\ln 2}$ (this is not $\ln \frac{9}{2}$.)

35. $x = \frac{\ln 10}{\ln 5 - \ln 2}$

37. $\log_9(x + 1) = \frac{1}{2} + \log_9 x$

$\log_9(x + 1) - \log_9 x = \frac{1}{2}$

$\log_9 \dfrac{x + 1}{x} = \frac{1}{2}$ Now go to exponential form

$9^{\frac{1}{2}} = \dfrac{x + 1}{x}$

$3 = \dfrac{x + 1}{x}$

$3x = x + 1$

$2x = 1$

$x = \frac{1}{2}$

39. $x = 3$

41. $\log_{10}(x + 3) - \log_{10}(x - 2) = 2$

$\log_{10} \dfrac{x + 3}{x - 2} = 2$

$10^2 = \dfrac{x + 3}{x - 2}$

$100(x - 2) = x + 3$

$100x - 200 = x + 3$

$99x = 203$

$x = \dfrac{203}{99}$

43. $x = 3$

45. $\log_{10}(x - 6) + \log_{10}(x + 3) = 1$

$\log_{10}(x - 6)(x + 3) = 1$

so $10^1 = (x - 6)(x + 3)$

$x^2 - 3x - 18 = 10$

45. (cont)

$$x^2 - 3x - 28 = 0$$

$$(x - 7)(x + 4) = 0$$

$x = 7$ and $x = -4$ are roots of this quadratic.

However, we must check to make sure both roots work in the original equation. 7 does, but when we try -4 we have $\log_{10}(-10)$ and $\log_{10}(-1)$, both of which are not defined.

47. (a) $\log_{10}x - y = \log_{10}(3x - 1)$

$$\log_{10}x - \log_{10}(3x - 1) = y$$

$$\log_{10} \frac{x}{3x - 1} = y$$

$$10^y = \frac{x}{3x - 1}$$

$$10^y(3x - 1) = x$$

$$3(10^y)x - 10^y = x$$

$$3(10^y)x - x = 10^y$$

$$x[3(10^y) - 1] = 10^y$$

$$x = \frac{10^y}{3(10^y) - 1}$$

(b) $\log_{10}(x - y) = \log_{10}(3x - 1)$ is easier to solve, for we can conclude directly that

$$x - y = 3x - 1$$

$$-2x = y - 1$$

$$x = \frac{y - 1}{-2} \quad \text{or} \quad \frac{1 - y}{2}$$

49. There is a formula which shows us how to convert to logs in any base, but let's do one the longer way and review how the formula is derived.

(a) (i) Given $\log_2 5$, we are asked to write it as a base 10 log

$$\log_2 5 = N$$

so

$$2^N = 5$$

and

$$\log_{10} 2^N = \log_{10} 5$$

or

$$N \cdot \log_{10} 2 = \log_{10} 5$$

finally

$$N = \frac{\log_{10} 5}{\log_{10} 2}$$

or

$$\log_2 5 = \frac{\log_{10} 5}{\log_{10} 2}$$

(ii) $\log_5 10$. In general we have seen that

$$\log_a x = \frac{\log_b x}{\log_b a}$$

so

$$\log_5 10 = \frac{\log_{10} 10}{\log_{10} 5} = \frac{1}{\log_{10} 5}$$

(iii) ln 3 or $\log_e 3 = \frac{\log_{10} 3}{\log_{10} e}$

(iv) $\log_b 2 = \frac{\log_{10} 2}{\log_{10} b}$

(v) $\log_2 b = \frac{\log_{10} b}{\log_{10} 2}$

49. (b)   (i) Again using the formula,

$$\log_{10} 6 = \frac{\log_e 6}{\log_e 10} = \frac{\ln 6}{\ln 10}$$

(ii) $\log_2 10 = \dfrac{\ln 10}{\ln 2}$

(iii) $\log_{10}(\log_{10} x) = \log_{10}\left(\dfrac{\ln x}{\ln 10}\right) = \dfrac{\ln\left(\dfrac{\ln x}{\ln 10}\right)}{\ln 10}$.

51. (a) true   (b) true   (c) true

    (d) false   (e) true   (f) false

    (g) true   (h) false   (i) true

    (j) false   (k) false   (l) true

    (m) true

57. $b^{3 \log_b x} = b^{\log_b x^3}$

By the rules for logs number 4 on page 286 this is equal to x^3, but let's see if we can reason why. $\log_b x^3$ menas the power to which b must be raised to get x^3. So we have b raised to the power to which it must be raised to get x^3, and therefore it must equal x^3.

59. $\log_2 \sqrt[5]{4\sqrt{2}} = \log_2 \sqrt[5]{2^2 \cdot 2^{\frac{1}{2}}} = \log_2 \sqrt[5]{2^{5/2}} = \log_2 2^{(5/2)\cdot(1/5)} = \log_2 2^{\frac{1}{2}} = \frac{1}{2}$

65. $(\log_2 3)(\log_3 4)(\log_4 5)$

Using the change of base formula

$$\log_3 4 = \frac{\log_2 4}{\log_2 3} \quad \text{and} \quad \log_4 5 = \frac{\log_2 5}{\log_2 4}$$

Substituting, our original product becomes

65. (cont)

$$(\log_2 3)\left(\frac{\log_2 4}{\log_2 3}\right)\left(\frac{\log_2 5}{\log_2 4}\right) \quad \text{or just} \quad \log_2 5.$$

69. $f(x) = \ln(x + \sqrt{x^2 + 1}$

The inverse will be

$$x = \ln(y + \sqrt{y^2 + 1})$$

$$e^x = e^{\ln(y+\sqrt{y^2+1})}$$

$$e^x = y + \sqrt{y^2 + 1} \qquad \text{let's isolate the radical}$$

$$e^x - y = \sqrt{y^2 + 1} \qquad \text{and squaring both sides we have}$$

$$e^{2x} - 2e^x y + y^2 = y^2 + 1$$

$$-2e^x y = 1 - e^{2x}$$

$$y = \frac{e^{2x} - 1}{2e^x}$$

EXERCISE SET 5.5

1. For annual compounding of money we use the formula from page 296.

$$A = P(1 + r)^t$$

We want A when P = $800, r = 6%, and t is 4 years

$$A = 800(1 + .06)^4$$

$$= 800(1.06)^4$$

$$= 800(1.2624) \quad \text{(using a calculator)}$$

$$= \$1009.98.$$

3. 8.45%

5. Again, $A = 500(1 + .05)^4 = \$607.75$, but now we take this amount to a new

bank and redeposit it. So,

5. (cont) $A = 607.75(1 + .06)^4$

                $A = \$767.27$ after four years in the second bank.

7. (a) $\$3869.68$

    (b) $\$4006.39$

9. For compounding other than annually we need the more general formula on page 297.

$$A = P(1 + \frac{r}{n})^{nt}$$

So here $P = \$100$, $r = 6\%$ and we have $n = 4$ compoundings per year.
We want the value of t for which $A \geq \$120$.

$$120 \leq 100(1 + \frac{.06}{4})^{4t}$$

$$1.2 \leq (1.015)^{4t}   \text{(taking the ln)}$$

$$\ln 1.2 \leq 4t \ln(1.015)$$

$$4t \geq \frac{\ln 1.2}{\ln 1.015}$$

$$t \geq \frac{\ln 1.2}{4 \ln 1.015}$$

$$t \geq 3.06$$

This is slightly over 3 years, and so   13   quarters will be required.

11. $\$3487.50$

13. For continuous compounding $A = Pe^{rt}$,   and here we want to find a P which
     will yield an A of $\$5000$ in 10 years at $6\frac{1}{2}\%$.   So,

$$5000 = Pe^{.065(10)}$$

$$5000 = Pe^{.65}$$

$$P = \frac{5000}{e^{.65}}   \text{(using a calculator)}$$

$$P = \frac{5000}{1.9155}$$

$$P = \$2610.23$$

15. 5.83%

17. Let's take the 6% investment first.

$$A = 10,000(1 + .06)^5$$

$$= 10,000(1.3382)$$

$$= \$13382.26$$

The second choice will be

$$A = 10,000e^{.05(5)}$$

$$= 10,000e^{.25}$$

$$= \$12840.25, \quad \text{considerably less.}$$

19. (b) 13.86 years

21. Here

$$A = 1000e^{(.08)300}$$

$$A = 1000e^{24}$$

$$A = 1000(2.65 \times 10^{10})$$

$$A \approx \$2.65 \times 10^{13}$$

That's 26½ trillion, a nice inheritance.

25.

	World Population Projections				
	1975 Population (billions)	% Population in 1975	Growth Rate (% per year)	Year 2000 Population (billions)	% of World Population in 2000
World	4.090	100	1.8	6.414	100
More Developed Regions	1.131	27.7	0.6	1.314	20.5
Less Developed Regions	2.959	72.3	2.1	5.002	78.0

The growth problems are solved by assuming an exponential growth rate,

$$N = N_0 e^{kt}.$$

First, we find the percent distribution by dividing the total population into each of the two regions.

$$\frac{1.131}{4000} \approx 27.7\% \quad \text{for more developed regions.}$$

25. (cont)

Applying the growth formula to total world population we have

$$N = N_0 e^{kt}$$
$$N = 4.090e^{.018(15)}$$
$$N = 4.090e^{.45}$$
$$N \approx 6.414 \quad \text{billion}$$

The other calculations are similar to these two.

27.

World Population Estimates and Projections			
1975 Population (billions)	Growth Rate (% per year)	Year 2000 Population (billions)	% Increase in Population
Low	4.043	1.5	5.883	45.5
Medium	4.090	1.8	6.414	56.8
High	4.134	2.0	6.816	64.9

29. (a) k = .0200

    (b) 170,853,565

    (c) slower

31. (a) k = .0068 = .68%/year

    (b) k = .0096 = .96%/year

    (c) 19,751,512

    (d) higher

33. (a)   (b)

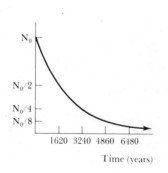

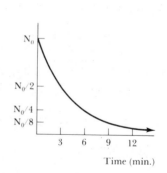

35. (a) $N = N_0 e^{kt}$

   $\frac{1}{2}N_0 = N_0 e^{k \cdot 13}$ because after 13 years N will be one-half of the original amount. So, dividing by N_0, we get

   $e^{13k} = .5$ taking the ln of both sides

   $13k = \ln .5$

   $k = \frac{\ln .5}{13} \approx -.0533$

   Once we understand this, it will be convenient for us to remember that k always equals $\ln .5$ divided by the length of a half life for decay problems.

   (b) $N = N_0 e^{(-.0533)(10)}$

   $N \approx .587 N_0$ or about 58.7% of N_0 after 10 years.

   If $t = 100$ $N \approx .5\%$ of N_0.

37. (a) $k = -.0248$

   (b) $t = 279$ years

39. $t = 416$ years

41. (a) Let's go back and look at example 10 on page 306.

   Taking the equation $M = \log_{10} \frac{A}{A_0}$ and writing it in exponential form

   we have $\frac{A}{A_0} = 10^m$ or $A = 10^m A_0$.

   If A is the strength of a quake, then $A_1 = 10^5 A_0$ and $A_2 = 10^4 A_0$.

   Comparing the two as a ratio we have

   $$\frac{A_1}{A_2} = \frac{10^5 A_0}{10^4 A_0} = \frac{10^5}{10^4} = 10^{5-4} = 10.$$

   The second quake was therefore 10 times as great.

   (b) The solution simply requires careful use of the laws of exponents. The ratio here will be

41. (b) (cont) $\dfrac{A_1}{A_2} = \dfrac{10^{M+D}A_0}{10^M A_0} = 10^{M+D-M} = 10^D$ as required.

43. (a) 2020
    (b) 2035
    (c) 2019

45. (a) $122.49

    (b) 2.6 generations

47. (a) First we will multiply both sides by $\dfrac{k}{A_0}$ and we get

    $$\dfrac{Ak}{A_0} = e^{kT} - 1$$

    so

    $$e^{kT} = \dfrac{Ak}{A_0} + 1.$$

    Now taking the natural logarithm of both sides we have

    $$kT = \ln\left(\dfrac{Ak}{A_0} + 1\right)$$

    or finally

    $$T = \dfrac{\ln\left(\dfrac{Ak}{A_0} + 1\right)}{k} \quad \text{as required.}$$

    (b)   (i) Here

    $$T = \dfrac{\ln\left[\dfrac{(1661)(.01)}{21.7} + 1\right]}{.01}$$

    $$= \dfrac{\ln(1.77)}{.01}$$

    which is about 57 years.

    (ii) Proceeding in the same manner using $k = .02$ we find the life expectancy to be 46 years.

    (iii) Here it is 39 years.

47. (cont)

(c)
$$T = \frac{\ln\left[\frac{(8493)(.02)}{50} + 1\right]}{.02}$$

$$= \frac{\ln(4.40)}{.02}$$

or about 74 years.

49. In each case here we start with
$$T = \frac{\ln\left[\frac{A \cdot k}{A_0} + 1\right]}{k}.$$

fluorine	1989
silver	1992
tin	2006
copper	2012
phosphate	2026
aluminum	2038

For flourine we have

$$T = \frac{\ln\left[\frac{(37)(.0458)}{2.1} + 1\right]}{.0458}$$

and T is about 12.9 years. The depletion date is therefore 12.9 + 1976 or about 1989. The same technique is applied to each of the minerals to complete the data in the table.

53. 3.87×10^9 years

57. 4877 years

59. 1992 years

Chapter 6 Trigonometric Functions of Angles

1. (a) $8^2 + 15^2 = 17^2$

     $64 + 225 = 289$ ✓

   (b) $\sin \theta = \dfrac{\text{opposite}}{\text{hypotenuse}} = \dfrac{15}{17}$

     $\cos \beta = \dfrac{\text{adjacent}}{\text{hypotenuse}} = \dfrac{15}{17}$

   (c) $\cos \theta = \dfrac{\text{adjacent}}{\text{hypotenuse}} = \dfrac{8}{17}$

     $\sin \beta = \dfrac{\text{opposite}}{\text{hypotenuse}} = \dfrac{8}{17}$

   (d) $\tan \theta = \dfrac{\text{opposite}}{\text{adjacent}} = \dfrac{15}{8}$

     $\csc \theta = \dfrac{\text{hypotenuse}}{\text{opposite}} = \dfrac{17}{15}$

     $\sec \theta = \dfrac{\text{hypotenuse}}{\text{adjacent}} = \dfrac{17}{8}$

     $\cot \theta = \dfrac{\text{adjacent}}{\text{opposite}} = \dfrac{8}{15}$

     $\tan \beta = \dfrac{\text{opposite}}{\text{adjacent}} = \dfrac{8}{15}$

     $\csc \beta = \dfrac{\text{hypotenuse}}{\text{opposite}} = \dfrac{17}{8}$

1. (d) (cont.)

$$\sec \beta = \frac{\text{hypotenuse}}{\text{adjacent}} = \frac{17}{15}$$

$$\cot \beta = \frac{\text{adjacent}}{\text{opposite}} = \frac{15}{8}$$

3. 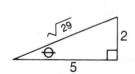   (a) $\sin \theta = \frac{2}{\sqrt{29}}$ $\left(\frac{2\sqrt{29}}{29}\right)$

$$\cos \theta = \frac{5}{\sqrt{29}}   \left(\frac{5\sqrt{29}}{29}\right)$$

(b) $\sin^2 \theta + \cos^2 \theta = \left(\frac{2}{\sqrt{29}}\right)^2 + \left(\frac{5}{\sqrt{29}}\right)^2 = \frac{4}{29} + \frac{25}{29} = 1$

(c) $\tan \theta = \frac{2}{5}$

$$\frac{\sin \theta}{\cos \theta} = \frac{\frac{2}{\sqrt{29}}}{\frac{5}{\sqrt{29}}} = \frac{2}{\sqrt{29}} \cdot \frac{\sqrt{29}}{5} = \frac{2}{5}$$

Tan θ always equals $\frac{\sin \theta}{\cos \theta}$.

(d) $\csc \theta = \frac{\sqrt{29}}{2}$

$$\sec \theta = \frac{\sqrt{29}}{5}$$

$$\cot \theta = \frac{5}{2}$$

5. There are two simple ways to solve the problem. First, using the 45°-45°-90° property, we see that the other leg must be 6 cm. and the hypotenuse is $6\sqrt{2}$ cm. Also, we can write $\tan 45° = \frac{6}{x}$ or $x = \frac{6}{\tan 45°} = \frac{6}{1} = 6$ and $\sin 45° = \frac{6}{\text{hypotenuse}}$ so hypotenuse $= \frac{6}{\sin 45°} = \frac{6}{\frac{\sqrt{2}}{2}} = 6\sqrt{2}$.

Both sets of answers are the same.

7. 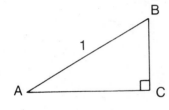   Since $\sec B = \frac{\text{hypotenuse}}{\text{adjacent}}$

$$\frac{3}{2} = \frac{1}{\overline{BC}}$$

$$\overline{BC} = \frac{2}{3}$$

9. $\csc A = \frac{29}{21}$

13. 1000 tan 29° ft or 554 ft

15. Using the sin function we have that $\sin \angle SEM = \dfrac{\overline{MS}}{\overline{SE}}$ so

$$\sin 21.16° = \frac{\overline{MS}}{93,000,000}$$

and $\overline{MS}$ is about 34 million miles.

17. (a) $\frac{3}{2}$ sq units

 (b) 11.3 sq units

 (c) 21.2 sq units

19.

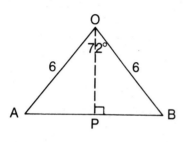

Following the hint, we will draw a perpendicular from O to AB. Call the point of intersection P. Since the triangle OAB is isosceles, $\overline{PA} = \overline{PB}$. $\angle AOP$ is now 36° and

$$\sin 36° = \frac{AP}{6} .$$

So   AP = 6 · sin 36°

                                     = 6(.0578) = 3.527

and $\overline{AB}$ = 7.05 in.

21. 10,657 ft

23. $\cos \alpha = \dfrac{OA}{OB}$, so $\overline{OA} = OB \cdot \cos \alpha$

                                     = 1 · cos α

                                     = cos α

Using the same reasoning we have

$$\sin \alpha = \frac{AB}{OB} \quad \text{and} \quad \overline{AB} = \sin \alpha .$$

Also $\tan \alpha = \dfrac{DC}{OC}$ so $\overline{DC} = \tan \alpha .$

25. 136 m

27. $\overline{OA} = \sqrt{2}$, $\alpha = 45°$;

$\overline{OB} = \sqrt{3}$, $\beta \approx 35°$;

$\overline{OC} = 2$, $\gamma = 30°$;

$\overline{OD} = \sqrt{5}$, $\delta \approx 27°$;

$\overline{OE} = \sqrt{6}$, $\varepsilon \approx 24°$

29. Since $\sec \beta = \sqrt{1 + a^2}$ and in general, $\sec \beta = \dfrac{\text{hypotenuse}}{\text{adjacent}}$, we can draw the following figure. Pythagoras tells us that opposite $\angle \beta$ must be a, and by inspection

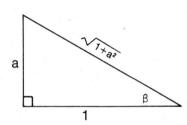

$\sin \beta = \dfrac{a}{\sqrt{1 + a^2}}$ $\cos \beta = \dfrac{\sqrt{1 + a^2}}{a}$

$\cos \beta = \dfrac{1}{\sqrt{1 + a^2}}$ $\sec \beta = \sqrt{1 + a^2}$

$\tan \beta = a$ $\cot \beta = \dfrac{1}{a}$

31. Examine the similar triangles having AB and BC as hypotenuses, and notice that θ is also the angle at B in the smaller triangle. We will write trigonometric relationships for each triangle, solve for AB and BC, and then add to get $\overline{AC}$.

$$\sin \theta = \frac{5}{\overline{BC}} \quad \text{so} \quad \overline{BC} = \frac{5}{\sin \theta}$$

and

$$\cos \theta = \frac{4}{\overline{AB}} \quad \text{or} \quad \overline{AB} = \frac{4}{\cos \theta}$$

Now $\overline{AC} = \overline{AB} + \overline{BC}$ and therefore $\overline{AC} = \dfrac{4}{\cos \theta} + \dfrac{5}{\sin \theta}$ or

$$= \frac{4 \sin \theta + 5 \cos \theta}{\sin \theta \cos \theta}$$

which can also be written as

$$4 \sec \theta + 5 \csc \theta. \quad \text{(Why?)}$$

33. First observe that the figure $x^2 + y^2 = 1$ is a circle with a radius of

     one. Then any segment which is a radius can be replaced by one. In each

     case we will look for a trigonometric relationship involving the required

     segment.

     (a) $\sin \theta = \dfrac{\overline{DE}}{\overline{OD}}$ so, $\overline{DE} = \sin \theta$

     (b) $\cos \theta = \dfrac{\overline{OE}}{\overline{OD}}$ so, $\overline{OE} = \cos \theta$

     (c) $\tan \theta = \dfrac{\overline{CF}}{\overline{OF}}$ so, $\overline{CF} = \tan \theta$

     (d) $\sec \theta = \dfrac{\overline{OC}}{\overline{OF}}$ so, $\overline{OC} = \sec \theta$

     Going to $\triangle OAB$, $\angle B = \theta$ and

     (e) $\csc \theta = \dfrac{\overline{OB}}{\overline{OA}}$ so, $\overline{OB} = \csc \theta$

     (f) $\cot \theta = \dfrac{\overline{AB}}{\overline{OA}}$ so, $\overline{AB} = \cot \theta$

     These segments are sometimes called the line values of the six trigonometric

     functions.

39. (b)

n	5	10	50	100	1000	5000	10,000
An	2.38	2.94	3.1333	3.1395	3.141572	3.1415918	3.1415924

43. 1076 mi

Exercise Set 6.2

1. (a) $(1 - \cos \theta)^2 = 1^2 - 2(1)(\cos \theta) + (\cos \theta)^2$

     $$= 1 - 2 \cos \theta + \cos^2 \theta$$

     (b) $(\sin \theta + \cos \theta)^2 = \sin^2 \theta + 2 \sin \theta \cos \theta + \cos^2 \theta$

     $$= (\sin^2 \theta + \cos^2 \theta) + 2 \sin \theta \cos \theta$$

     $$= 1 + 2 \sin \theta \cos \theta$$

1. (cont)

(c) $\cos \theta + \dfrac{1}{\sin \theta} = \dfrac{\cos \theta}{1} + \dfrac{1}{\sin \theta}$

$\qquad\qquad\quad = \dfrac{\sin \theta \cos \theta}{\sin \theta} + \dfrac{1}{\sin \theta}$

$\qquad\qquad\quad = \dfrac{\sin \theta \cos \theta + 1}{\sin \theta}$

(d) $(\sin A + \cos A)(\csc A + \sec A) = \sin A \csc A + \sin A \sec A + \cos A \csc A$

$\qquad\qquad\qquad\qquad\qquad\qquad\qquad\qquad\qquad + \cos A \sec A$

$\qquad\qquad\qquad\qquad\qquad = \dfrac{\sin A}{\sin A} + \dfrac{\sin A}{\cos A} + \dfrac{\cos A}{\sin A} + \dfrac{\cos A}{\cos A}$

$\qquad\qquad\qquad\qquad\qquad = 1 + \dfrac{\sin A}{\cos A} + \dfrac{\cos A}{\sin A} + 1$

$\qquad\qquad\qquad\qquad\qquad = 2 + \tan A + \cot A$

(e) $(\sin^2 B + 1)(\cos^2 B + 1) = \sin^2 B \cos^2 B + \sin^2 B + \cos^2 B + 1$

$\qquad\qquad\qquad\qquad\qquad = \sin^2 B \cos^2 B + 1 + 1$

$\qquad\qquad\qquad\qquad\qquad = \sin^2 B \cos^2 B + 2$

3. (a) $(\tan \theta - 6)(\tan \theta + 1)$

(b) $(\sin B + \cos B)(\sin B - \cos B)$

(c) $(\cos A + 1)^2$

(d) $3 \sin \theta (\cos^2 \theta + 2)$

(e) $(\csc \alpha - 3)(\csc \alpha + 1)$

(f) $(3 \sin \theta + 2)(2 \sin \theta + 1)$

5. $\dfrac{1 - \tan \theta}{\dfrac{\sin \theta}{\cos \theta} - 1} = \dfrac{1 - \tan \theta}{\tan \theta - 1}$

$\qquad\qquad = -1 \quad \text{(because in general we always have } \dfrac{A - B}{B - A} = -1)$

7. (a) $\sin^2 \theta \cos \theta \csc^3 \theta \sec \theta = \dfrac{\sin^2 \theta \cos \theta}{\sin^3 \theta \cos \theta}$

$\qquad\qquad\qquad\qquad\qquad = \dfrac{1}{\sin \theta}$

$\qquad\qquad\qquad\qquad\qquad = \csc \theta$

(b) $\sin \theta \csc \theta \tan \theta = (\sin \theta)(1/\sin \theta)\tan \theta$

$\qquad\qquad\qquad\qquad = 1 \cdot \tan \theta = \tan \theta$

7. (cont)

    (c) $\cot B \sin^2 B \cot B = \dfrac{\cos B}{\sin B} \cdot \sin^2 B \cdot \dfrac{\cos B}{\sin B}$

$$= (\cos B)(\cos B)$$

$$= \cos^2 B$$

9. (a) $\sin^2 \theta + \cos^2 \theta = (4/5)^2 + (3/5)^2 = \dfrac{16}{25} + \dfrac{9}{25} = \dfrac{25}{25} = 1$

    (b) $\sin^2 \theta + \cos^2 \beta = \dfrac{16}{25} + \dfrac{16}{25} = \dfrac{32}{25} \neq 1$

    (c) $\dfrac{\sin \theta}{\cos \theta} = \dfrac{4/5}{3/5} = \dfrac{4}{3} = \tan \theta$

    (d) $\sin \theta = 4/5$ and $\cos \beta = 4/5$. Therefore $\sin \theta = \cos \beta$. Similarly,

        we have $\cos \theta = 3/5$ and $\sin \beta = 3/5$; thus $\cos \theta = \sin \beta$.

11. $\sin \theta = \sqrt{1 - \cos^2 \theta} = \sqrt{1 - (5/13)^2}$

$$= \sqrt{1 - \dfrac{25}{169}} = \sqrt{\dfrac{144}{169}} = \dfrac{12}{13} \ .$$

Having found now that $\sin \theta = 12/13$, we can calculate $\tan \theta$ as follows:

$$\tan \theta = \dfrac{\sin \theta}{\cos \theta}$$

$$= \dfrac{12/13}{5/13} = 12/5$$

13. $\sin \theta = \dfrac{3}{5}$; $\tan \theta = \dfrac{3}{4}$; $\csc \theta = \dfrac{5}{3}$; $\sec \theta = \dfrac{5}{4}$; $\cot \theta = \dfrac{4}{3}$

15. (a) First compute $\sin^2 18°$:

$$\sin^2 18° = \left[\dfrac{1}{4} (\sqrt{5} - 1) \right]^2 = \dfrac{1}{16} (5 - 2\sqrt{5} + 1)$$

$$= \dfrac{1}{16} (6 - 2\sqrt{5})$$

Then since $\cos 18° = \sqrt{1 - \sin^2 18°}$ we have

15. (cont)

$$\cos 18° = \sqrt{1 - \frac{6 - 2\sqrt{5}}{16}}$$

$$= \sqrt{\frac{16}{16} - \frac{6 - 2\sqrt{5}}{16}} = \sqrt{\frac{16 - (6 - 2\sqrt{5})}{16}}$$

$$= \sqrt{\frac{10 + 2\sqrt{5}}{16}} = \frac{\sqrt{10 + 2\sqrt{5}}}{4}$$

Thus $\cos 18° = \frac{1}{4}\sqrt{10 + 2\sqrt{5}}$.

(b) Use part (a) along with the facts that $\sin 72° = \cos 18°$ and

$\cos 72° = \sin 18°$.

17. $\sin \theta \cos \theta \sec \theta \csc \theta = \dfrac{\sin \theta \cos \theta}{\cos \theta \sin \theta} = 1$

19. $\dfrac{\sin \theta \sec \theta}{\tan \theta} = \dfrac{\sin \theta (1/\cos \theta)}{\sin \theta / \cos \theta}$

$$= \frac{\sin \theta}{\cos \theta} \times \frac{\cos \theta}{\sin \theta}$$

$$= 1$$

21. $\sec x - 5 \tan x = \dfrac{1}{\cos x} - \dfrac{5 \sin x}{\cos x}$

$$= \frac{1 - 5 \sin x}{\cos x}$$

23. $\cos A(\sec A - \cos A) = \cos A \sec A - \cos^2 A$

$$= 1 - \cos^2 A$$

$$= \sin^2 A$$

25. $(1 - \sin \theta)(\sec \theta + \tan \theta) = \sec \theta + \tan \theta - \sin \theta \sec \theta - \sin \theta \tan \theta$

$$= \frac{1}{\cos \theta} + \frac{\sin \theta}{\cos \theta} - \frac{\sin \theta}{\cos \theta} - \frac{\sin \theta \sin \theta}{\cos \theta}$$

$$= \frac{1}{\cos \theta} - \frac{\sin^2 \theta}{\cos \theta}$$

$$= \frac{1 - \sin^2 \theta}{\cos \theta} = \frac{\cos^2 \theta}{\cos \theta} = \cos \theta$$

27. $(\sec \alpha - \tan \alpha)^2 = \left(\dfrac{1}{\cos \alpha} - \dfrac{\sin \alpha}{\cos \alpha} \right)^2$

$$= \left(\dfrac{1 - \sin \alpha}{\cos \alpha} \right)^2$$

$$= \dfrac{(1 - \sin \alpha)^2}{\cos^2 \alpha}$$

$$= \dfrac{(1 - \sin \alpha)^2}{1 - \sin^2 \alpha}$$

$$= \dfrac{(1 - \sin \alpha)^2}{(1 - \sin \alpha)(1 + \sin \alpha)} = \dfrac{1 - \sin \alpha}{1 + \sin \alpha}$$

29. Using the abbreviations $S = \sin A$ and $C = \cos A$, we have

$$\dfrac{\sin A}{1 - \cot A} - \dfrac{\cos A}{\tan A - 1} = \dfrac{S}{1 - \dfrac{C}{S}} - \dfrac{C}{\dfrac{S}{C} - 1}$$

$$= \dfrac{S}{S} \cdot \dfrac{S}{1 - \dfrac{C}{S}} - \dfrac{C}{C} \cdot \dfrac{C}{\dfrac{S}{C} - 1}$$

$$= \dfrac{S^2}{S - C} - \dfrac{C^2}{S - C}$$

$$= \dfrac{S^2 - C^2}{S - C}$$

$$= \dfrac{(S - C)(S + C)}{S - C}$$

$$= S + C = \sin A + \cos A$$

31. $\csc^2 \theta + \sec^2 \theta = \dfrac{1}{\sin^2 \theta} + \dfrac{1}{\cos^2 \theta}$

$$= \dfrac{\cos^2 \theta + \sin^2 \theta}{\sin^2 \theta \cos^2 \theta}$$

$$= \dfrac{1}{\sin^2 \theta \cos^2 \theta}$$

$$= \dfrac{1}{\sin^2 \theta} \cdot \dfrac{1}{\cos^2 \theta} = \csc^2 \theta \sec^2 \theta$$

33.
$$\frac{2 \sin^3 \beta}{1 - \cos \beta} = \frac{2 \sin \beta \sin^2 \beta}{1 - \cos \beta}$$

$$= \frac{2 \sin \beta (1 - \cos^2 \beta)}{1 - \cos \beta}$$

$$= \frac{2 \sin \beta (1 - \cos \beta)(1 + \cos \beta)}{1 - \cos \beta}$$

$$= 2 \sin \beta (1 + \cos \beta)$$

$$= 2 \sin \beta + 2 \sin \beta \cos \beta$$

35.
$$\frac{\sin^3 \theta + \cos^3 \theta}{\sin \theta + \cos \theta} = \frac{(\sin \theta + \cos \theta)(\sin^2 \theta - \sin \theta \cos \theta + \cos^2 \theta)}{\sin \theta + \cos \theta}$$

$$= \sin^2 \theta - \sin \theta \cos \theta + \cos^2 \theta$$

$$= (\sin^2 \theta + \cos^2 \theta) - \sin \theta \cos \theta$$

$$= 1 - \sin \theta \cos \theta$$

37.
$$\frac{\sec \theta - \csc \theta}{\sec \theta + \csc \theta} = \frac{\dfrac{1}{\cos \theta} - \dfrac{1}{\sin \theta}}{\dfrac{1}{\cos \theta} + \dfrac{1}{\sin \theta}} \cdot \frac{\sin \theta}{\sin \theta}$$

$$= \frac{\dfrac{\sin \theta}{\cos \theta} - 1}{\dfrac{\sin \theta}{\cos \theta} + 1}$$

$$= \frac{\tan \theta - 1}{\tan \theta + 1}$$

39. $r^2 \sin^2 \theta \cos^2 \phi + r^2 \sin^2 \theta \sin^2 \phi + r^2 \cos^2 \theta$

$$= r^2 \sin^2 \theta (\cos^2 \phi + \sin^2 \phi) + r^2 \cos^2 \theta$$

$$= r^2 \sin \theta (1) + r^2 \cos^2 \theta$$

$$= r^2 (\sin^2 \theta + \cos^2 \theta)$$

$$= r^2 (1) = r^2$$

EXERCISE SET 6.3

1. (a)

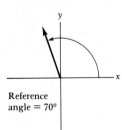

Reference
angle = 70°

(b)

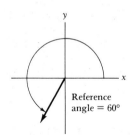

Reference
angle = 60°

(c)

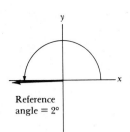

Reference
angle = 2°

(d)

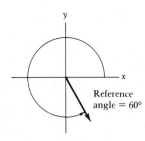

Reference
angle = 60°

(e)

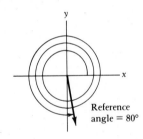

Reference
angle = 80°

(f)

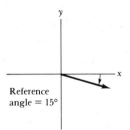

Reference
angle = 15°

5. If the y-coordinate of P is $\frac{2}{3}$ then we can find x from the equation of
    the circle, $x^2 + y^2 = 1$

$$x^2 + \left(\frac{2}{3}\right)^2 = 1$$
$$x^2 = 1 - \frac{4}{9}$$
$$x^2 = \frac{5}{9}$$
$$x = \pm \frac{\sqrt{5}}{3}$$

but we reject the positive value because P is a 2nd quadrant point.

Now

$$\cot \theta = \frac{x}{y}$$
$$= \frac{-\frac{\sqrt{5}}{3}}{\frac{2}{3}} = -\frac{\sqrt{5}}{2}$$

7. In each case we will follow a three step procedure: find the reference angle, recall the value of the trigonometric function for that angle and then apply a positive or negative value depending on the quadrant.

(a) sin 315°: reference angle is 45°,

$$\sin 45 = \frac{\sqrt{2}}{2},$$

4th quadrant therefore negative

so $\sin 315° = -\frac{\sqrt{2}}{2}.$

(b) cos 300°: reference angle is 60°,

$$\cos 60° = \frac{1}{2}$$

4th quadrant, so it's positive

We find $\cos 300° = \frac{1}{2}.$

Using a similar process we find

(c) $\tan 330° = -\tan 30° = -\frac{\sqrt{3}}{3}$

(d) $\cos 210° = -\cos 30° = -\frac{\sqrt{3}}{2}$

(e) $\sec 210° = -\sec 30° = -\frac{2\sqrt{3}}{3}$

(f) $\csc 225° = -\csc 45° = -\sqrt{2}$

(g) $\tan 135° = -\tan 45° = -1$

(h) $\cot 120° = -\cot 60° = \frac{\sqrt{3}}{3}$

(i) $\cot 480° = -\cot 60° = -\frac{\sqrt{3}}{3}$

9. $\sin \theta = -\frac{\sqrt{2}}{2}$; $\tan \theta = -1$; $\csc \theta = \sqrt{2}$; $\cos \theta = \frac{\sqrt{2}}{2}$; $\csc \theta = -\sqrt{2}$;

$\cot \theta = -1$

11. (a)

θ	0°	90°	180°	270°	360°	450°	540°	630°	720°
$\sin \theta$	0	1	0	−1	0	1	0	−1	0
$\cos \theta$	1	0	−1	0	1	0	−1	0	1

11. (cont)

   (b)

θ	30°	60°	90°	120°	150°	180°	210°	240°	270°	300°	330°	360°
$\sin\theta$	$\frac{1}{2}$	$\frac{\sqrt{3}}{2}$	1	$\frac{\sqrt{3}}{2}$	$\frac{1}{2}$	0	$-\frac{1}{2}$	$-\frac{\sqrt{3}}{2}$	-1	$\frac{-\sqrt{3}}{2}$	$-\frac{1}{2}$	0

13.

	Terminal side of angle θ lies in			
	Quadrant I	**Quadrant II**	**Quadrant III**	**Quadrant IV**
$\sin\theta$	positive	positive	negative	negative
$\cos\theta$	positive	negative	negative	positive
$\tan\theta$	positive	negative	positive	negative

15. Example 6 suggests substituting in the identity $\sin^2\theta + \cos^2\theta = 1$.

$$\sin^2\theta + (-\tfrac{3}{5})^2 = 1$$
$$\sin^2\theta = 1 - \frac{9}{25}$$
$$\sin^2\theta = \frac{16}{25}$$
$$\sin\theta = \pm\frac{4}{5}$$

and we choose the negative root because θ is a third quadrant angle.

17. Since $\sec\beta = \dfrac{1}{\cos\beta}$

$$(\tfrac{1}{4})^2 + \cos^2\beta = 1$$
$$\cos^2\beta = 1 - \frac{1}{16}$$
$$\cos^2\beta = \frac{15}{16}$$
$$\cos\beta = -\frac{\sqrt{15}}{4} \quad \text{(2nd quadrant)}$$

   Therefore $\sec\beta = -\dfrac{4\sqrt{15}}{15}$, as required.

19. $120°, 240°, -120°$

21. $A = \dfrac{3}{2}\sin 120° = \dfrac{3}{2}\cdot\dfrac{\sqrt{3}}{2} \approx 1.3$ sq. units

23. Some of these can be done directly. For example:

(a) $\sin 195° = -\sin 15°$ (reference angle)

$$= -\frac{1}{4} (\sqrt{6} - \sqrt{2})$$

(b) $\cos 162° = -\cos 18°$ (reference angle)

$$= -\frac{1}{4} (\sqrt{5} - 1).$$

But, to find $\tan 345°$ I need not only $\sin 15°$ but $\cos 15°$ as well.

(c) $\sin^2 \theta + \cos^2 \theta = 1$

$$\cos^2 15° = 1 - \left(\frac{\sqrt{6} - \sqrt{2}}{4}\right)^2$$

$$= 1 - \left(\frac{6 - 4\sqrt{3} + 2}{16}\right)$$

$$= \frac{16 - 6 + 4\sqrt{3} - 2}{16}$$

$$= \frac{8 + 4\sqrt{3}}{16} \quad \text{or} \quad \frac{2 + \sqrt{3}}{4}$$

so taking the square root of both sides

$$\cos 15° = \frac{\sqrt{2 + \sqrt{3}}}{2}$$

Finally

$$\tan 345° = -\tan 15°$$

$$= -\frac{\sin 15°}{\cos 15°}$$

$$= -\frac{\frac{(\sqrt{6} - \sqrt{2})}{4}}{\frac{\sqrt{2 + \sqrt{3}}}{2}}$$

$$= -\frac{\sqrt{6} - \sqrt{2}}{2\sqrt{2 + \sqrt{3}}}$$

(d) $\sin -15° = -\sin 15°$ (reference angle)

$$= -\frac{1}{4} (\sqrt{6} - \sqrt{2})$$

23. (cont)

(e)   cos - 18° = cos 18°

$$= \frac{1}{4} (\sqrt{5} - 1)$$

(f)   cos 918° = cos 198° = -cos 18°

$$= - \frac{1}{4} (\sqrt{5} - 1)$$

(g)   The theorem from 6.2 page 335 proves very useful here. Recall that

sin(90° - θ) - cos θ and cos(90° - θ) = sin θ. By direct application

$$\cos 75° = \sin 15°$$

$$= \frac{1}{4} (\sqrt{6} - \sqrt{2})$$

(h)   sin 72° = cos 18°

$$= \frac{1}{4} (\sqrt{5} - 1)$$

(i)   Let's juggle.

$$\sec 105° = \frac{1}{\cos 105°}$$

$$= - \frac{1}{\cos 15°}$$

$$= - \frac{1}{\frac{\sqrt{6} - \sqrt{2}}{4}} \quad \text{(from g)}$$

$$= - \frac{4}{\sqrt{6} - \sqrt{2}} \quad \text{now rationalize to get}$$

$$= -(\sqrt{6} + \sqrt{2})$$

(j)   The same slight of hand we used in part (i) will give us

csc(-108°) = -($\sqrt{5}$ + 1) here.

(k) and (1) You are welcome to substitute and multiply it out, but my

sense of "constructive laziness" reminds me that these both have the

form of $\sin^2 θ + \cos^2 θ$ and are therefore equal to 1.

27. (a)   30°

(b)   270°

29. (a) P is $(\cos \theta, \sin \theta)$ and Q is $(\cos \phi, \sin \phi)$.

   (b) Applying the distance formula to segment $\overline{PQ}$ we get

$$\overline{PQ} = \sqrt{(\cos \theta - \cos \phi)^2 + (\sin \theta - \sin \phi)^2}$$

$$\overline{P\theta} = \sqrt{\cos^2 \theta - 2 \cos \theta \cos \phi + \cos^2 \phi + \sin^2 \theta - 2 \sin \theta \sin \phi + \sin^2 \phi}$$

using the $\sin^2 x + \cos^2 x = 1$ identity twice we get

$$\overline{P\theta} = \sqrt{2 - 2 \cos \theta \cos \phi - 2 \sin \theta \sin \phi}$$

which is

$$\sqrt{2} \cdot \sqrt{1 - \cos \theta \cos \phi - \sin \theta \sin \phi}$$

as required.

EXERCISE SET 6.4

1. (a) Here we can write $\dfrac{x}{\sin 45°} = \dfrac{12}{\sin 60°}$. Solving we have

$$x = \frac{12(\sin 45°)}{\sin 60°}$$

$$= \frac{12 \cdot \frac{\sqrt{2}}{2}}{\frac{\sqrt{3}}{2}}$$

$$= \frac{12\sqrt{2}}{\sqrt{3}} = 4\sqrt{6} \text{ cm.}$$

Notice that the Law of Sines was given as $\dfrac{\sin A}{a} = \dfrac{\sin B}{b}$, but it is also true that $\dfrac{a}{\sin A} = \dfrac{b}{\sin B}$. This latter form is used here because it puts the unknown in the numerator and requires less algebraic manipulation. Think about things like this before you attack.

   (b) How can we find the angle opposite x? It is the supplement of $15° + 30°$, or $135°$. So, $\dfrac{x}{\sin 135°} = \dfrac{4}{\sin 30°}$ and

$$x = \frac{4(\sin 135°)}{\sin 30°}$$

$$= \frac{4\left(\frac{\sqrt{2}}{2}\right)}{\frac{1}{2}}$$

$$= 4\sqrt{2} \text{ in.}$$

(c) $\dfrac{x}{\sin 45°} = \dfrac{3}{\sin 30°}$

$$x = \frac{3 \cdot \sin 45°}{\sin 30°} = 3\sqrt{2} \text{ cm.}$$

3. Since the angle at the top is 120°,

$$\frac{b}{\sin 30°} = \frac{x}{\sin 120°}$$

$$b = \frac{x \cdot \sin 30°}{\sin 120°}$$

$$= \frac{x \cdot \frac{1}{2}}{\frac{\sqrt{3}}{2}}$$

$$= \frac{x}{\sqrt{3}} \quad \text{or} \quad \frac{x\sqrt{3}}{3} \quad \text{units.}$$

The triangle is isosceles, and therefore b = c.

5. Make a sketch - always do this if one is not provided.

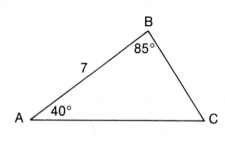

The formula for the area of a general triangle is $A = \frac{1}{2} ab \sin C$. It requires two sides and the included angle, so we need to find sin AC or BC.

$$\frac{\overline{AC}}{\sin 85°} = \frac{7}{55°}$$

$$\overline{AC} = \frac{7 \cdot \sin 85°}{\sin 55°} \qquad \text{These are not nice angles. We need a calculator or the tables.}$$

$$\overline{AC} = \frac{7(.9962)}{(.8192)} = 8.513$$

5. (cont)

So, $A = \frac{1}{2}$ (7)(8.513)(sin 40°)

A is about 19.15 sq. in.

7. (a)

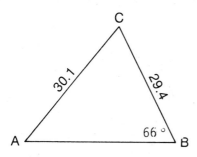

We will stick with the Law of Sines for now.

$$\frac{\sin \angle A}{29.4} = \frac{\sin 66°}{30.1}$$

$$\sin \angle A = \frac{29.4(\sin 66°)}{30.1}$$

so sin $\angle$ A = .8923 and $\angle$ A = 63° to the nearest degree. We can conclude that

$\angle$ C = 180 - 66 - 63

   = 51°

Finally for side c,

$$\frac{c}{\sin 51°} = \frac{30.1}{\sin 66°}$$

$$c = \frac{30.1(\sin 51°)}{\sin 66°}$$

$$c = 25.6$$

(b)

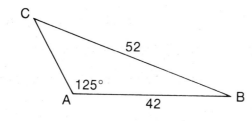

Don't expect your sketch to be perfect in advance.

First $\angle$ C

$$\frac{\sin \angle C}{42} = \frac{\sin 125°}{52}$$

$$\sin \angle C = .6616$$

and $\angle$ C = 41°. So $\angle$ B must be 14° because that's all that's left over.

For side b,

$$\frac{b}{\sin 14°} = \frac{52}{\sin 125°}$$

$$b = 15$$

7. (b) (cont)

        Accuracy in these calculations was not our main objective. We are

        careful not to produce answers which purport to be more accurate than

        the given information.

9. (c) $\angle$ C = 105°, c = 1.93

    (d) $\angle$ C = 15°, c = .52

11. (a) x = 21 cm

     (b) x = 5.4"

13.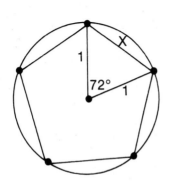

The Law of Cosines applied here to find side x,

says,

$$x^2 = 1^2 + 1^2 - 2(1)(1)(\cos\ 72°)$$

$$= 2 - 2\ \cos\ 72°$$

$$= 2 - .6180$$

$$= 1.382$$

So x = $\sqrt{1.38}$ ≈ 1.76 and 5x, the perimeter of the entire pentagon is

5.88 units.

15.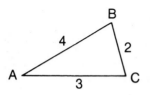

We will use the Law of Cosines, but let's solve

for the angle first.

$$a^2 = b^2 + c^2 - 2bc\ \text{Cos}\ A$$

$$2bc\ \text{Cos}\ A = b^2 + c^2 - a^2$$

$$\text{Cos}\ A = \frac{b^2 + c^2 - a^2}{2bc} \qquad \text{now substitute}$$

$$\text{Cos}\ A = \frac{3^2 + 4^2 - 2^2}{2(3)(4)}$$

$$= \frac{21}{24} = \frac{7}{8}$$

If Cos A = .875, $\angle$ A = 28.96°.

The same thing happens when we look for a different angle.

15.   (cont)

$$b^2 = a^2 + c^2 - 2ac \; Cos \; B$$

and

$$cos \; B = \frac{a^2 + c^2 - b^2}{2ac} \; ,$$

from which we find $\angle$ B = 46.57. As a great check on ourselves, we can find $\angle$ C two ways. We can repeat this process or recall that $\angle$ A + $\angle$ B + $\angle$ C = 180°.

17.   Well,

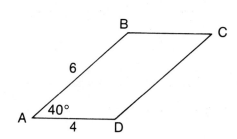

$$\overline{BD}^2 = 6^2 + 4^2 - 2(6)(4)Cos \; 40°$$

$$= 52 - 48(.7760)$$

$$= 15.23 \; units$$

and

$$\overline{BD} = 3.90.$$

Now, the other angle, say $\angle$ B, must be 140°. So

$$\overline{AC}^2 = 6^2 + 4^2 - 2(6)(4)cos \; 140$$

$$= 52 - 48(-.7760)$$

$$= 88.77$$

and

$$AC = 9.42 \; units.$$

19. $\overline{PQ}$ = 160 ft

29.   (c) $\frac{1}{2} \sqrt{2 + \sqrt{3}}$ or $\frac{\sqrt{6} + \sqrt{2}}{4}$;

      (d) $\frac{1}{2} \sqrt{2 + \sqrt{3}}$ or $\frac{\sqrt{6} + \sqrt{2}}{4}$

Chapter 7 Trigonometric Functions of Real Numbers

Exercise Set 7.1

1. Remember, to convert from degrees to radians, multiply by $\frac{\pi}{180°}$.

    (a) $60° \cdot \frac{\pi}{180°} = \frac{\pi}{3}$ radians

    (b) $225° \cdot \frac{\pi}{180°} = \frac{5\pi}{4}$ radians

    (c) $36° \cdot \frac{\pi}{180°} = \frac{\pi}{5}$ radians

    (d) $450° \cdot \frac{\pi}{180°} = \frac{5\pi}{2}$ radians

    (e) $0° = 0$ radians

3. (a) $35° \cdot \frac{\pi}{180°} = \frac{7}{36}\pi$

    (b) $22.5° \cdot \frac{\pi}{180°} = \frac{\pi}{8}$

    (c) $2° \cdot \frac{\pi}{180°} = \frac{\pi}{90}$

    (d) $100° \cdot \frac{\pi}{180°} = \frac{5}{9}\pi$

5. Since $90° = \frac{\pi}{2}$ or about $\frac{3.14}{2}$ radians, $\frac{3}{2}$ radians is less than a right angle.

7.

θ	0	$\frac{\pi}{2}$	π	$\frac{3\pi}{2}$	2π
$\cos \theta$	1	0	-1	0	1

9. In each case s = rθ, but make sure the central angle φ, θ, is in radians.

(a) s = rθ

$$s = 2 \cdot \frac{\pi}{4} = \frac{\pi}{2} \text{ cm.}$$

(b) $s = 1 \cdot \frac{5}{6} \pi = \frac{5}{6} \pi$ in.

(c) $s = 3 \cdot \frac{4}{3} \pi = 4\pi$ ft.

11. If s = rθ, then $\theta = \frac{s}{r}$. So $\theta = \frac{4}{4} = 1$ radian.

13. $A = \frac{1}{2} r^2 \theta$, so $\theta = \frac{2A}{r^2}$

$$\theta = \frac{2(\frac{\pi}{5})}{1^2}$$

$$\theta = \frac{2\pi}{5} \text{ radians}$$

15. A = θ + sin θ

17. (a) $\frac{2\pi}{3}$

(b) $\frac{\pi}{12}$

19. 135π ft.

21. (b) $\theta = \frac{\pi}{2}$

Exercise Set 7.2

1.

θ	$\sin \theta$	$\cos \theta$	$\tan \theta$	$\csc \theta$	$\sec \theta$	$\cot \theta$
0	0	1	0	undef.	1	undef.
$\frac{\pi}{6}$	$\frac{1}{2}$	$\frac{\sqrt{3}}{2}$	$\frac{\sqrt{3}}{3}$	2	$\frac{2\sqrt{3}}{3}$	$\sqrt{3}$
$\frac{\pi}{4}$	$\frac{\sqrt{2}}{2}$	$\frac{\sqrt{2}}{2}$	1	$\sqrt{2}$	$\sqrt{2}$	1
$\frac{\pi}{3}$	$\frac{\sqrt{3}}{2}$	$\frac{1}{2}$	$\sqrt{3}$	$\frac{2\sqrt{3}}{3}$	2	$\frac{\sqrt{3}}{3}$
$\frac{\pi}{2}$	1	0	undef.	1	undef.	0
$\frac{2\pi}{3}$	$\frac{\sqrt{3}}{2}$	$-\frac{1}{2}$	$-\sqrt{3}$	$\frac{2\sqrt{3}}{3}$	-2	$-\frac{\sqrt{3}}{3}$
$\frac{3\pi}{4}$	$\frac{\sqrt{2}}{2}$	$-\frac{\sqrt{2}}{2}$	-1	$\sqrt{2}$	$-\sqrt{2}$	-1
$\frac{5\pi}{6}$	$\frac{1}{2}$	$-\frac{\sqrt{3}}{2}$	$-\frac{\sqrt{3}}{3}$	2	$-\frac{2\sqrt{3}}{3}$	$-\sqrt{3}$
π	0	-1	0	undef.	-1	undef.

3. Since $\sin \theta = -\frac{3}{5}$

$$(-\frac{3}{5})^2 + \cos^2 \theta = 1$$

$$\cos^2 \theta = 1 - \frac{9}{25}$$

$$\cos^2 \theta = \frac{16}{25}$$

$$\cos \theta = \pm \frac{4}{5}$$

We choose $-\frac{4}{5}$ because for $\pi < \theta < \frac{3\pi}{2}$, $\cos \theta$ is negative.

To find $\tan \theta$, use

$$\tan \theta = \frac{\sin \theta}{\cos \theta}$$

$$= \frac{-\frac{3}{5}}{-\frac{4}{5}} = \frac{3}{4} \text{ as required.}$$

5. $\tan t = -\frac{\sqrt{3}}{\sqrt{13}} = -\frac{\sqrt{39}}{13}$

7. $\tan \theta = \frac{12}{5}$ so

$$1 + (\frac{12}{5})^2 = \sec^2 \theta$$

$$1 + \frac{144}{25} = \sec^2 \theta$$

$$\frac{169}{25} = \sec^2 \theta$$

$$\pm \frac{13}{5} = \sec \theta$$

and since $\cos \theta > 0$ so is $\sec \theta$. So we pick $\sec \theta = \frac{13}{5}$.
Its reciprocal, $\cos \theta$, will be $\frac{5}{13}$. To find $\sin \theta$ use
$\sin^2 \theta + \cos^2 \theta = 1$

$$\sin^2 \theta = 1 - (\frac{5}{13})^2$$

$$= \frac{144}{169}$$

So $\sin \theta = \frac{12}{13}$. Why do we take the positive value? Where are both the
tangent and cosine positive?

9. Substituting we have

$$\sqrt{9 - x^2} = \sqrt{9 - (3 \sin \theta)^2}$$
$$= \sqrt{9 - 9 \sin^2 \theta}$$
$$= \sqrt{9(1 - \sin^2 \theta)}$$
$$= \sqrt{9 \cos^2 \theta}$$
$$= 3 \cos \theta \quad (\text{positive since } 0 < \theta < \frac{\pi}{2})$$

13.

$$\frac{1}{\sqrt{u^2 + 7}} = \frac{1}{\sqrt{(\sqrt{7} \tan \theta)^2 + 7}}$$
$$= \frac{1}{\sqrt{7(\tan^2 \theta + 1)}}$$
$$= \frac{1}{\sqrt{7 \sec^2 \theta}}$$
$$= \frac{1}{\sqrt{7} \sec \theta}$$
$$= \frac{\sqrt{7}}{7} \cos \theta$$

15. (a) We will need to find $\sin \theta$ first.

$$\sin^2 \theta + (-\frac{1}{3})^2 = 1$$
$$\sin^2 \theta = 1 - \frac{1}{9}$$
$$\sin^2 \theta = \frac{8}{9}$$
$$\sin \theta = \pm \frac{2\sqrt{2}}{3}$$

and since θ is a second quadrant number $\sin \theta$ will be positive.

Also recall from page 378 that $\sin(-\theta) = -\sin \theta$ and $\cos(-\theta) = \cos \theta$.

So

$$\sin(-\theta) + \cos(-\theta) = -\frac{2\sqrt{2}}{3} + (-\frac{1}{3})$$
$$= \frac{-(2\sqrt{2} + 1)}{3} .$$

15. (cont)

(b) Work if you want to, but I remember that $\sin^2 ☆ + \cos^2 ☆ = 1$.

17. Page 379 pointed out that $\sin(\theta + 2\pi k) = \sin \theta$ and $\cos(\theta + 2\pi k) = \cos \theta$. We use that here.

(a) $\cos(\frac{\pi}{4} + 2\pi) = \cos \frac{\pi}{4} = \frac{\sqrt{2}}{2}$

(b) $\sin(\frac{\pi}{3} + 2\pi) = \sin \frac{\pi}{3} = \frac{\sqrt{3}}{2}$

(c) $\sin(\frac{\pi}{2} - 6\pi) = \sin \frac{\pi}{2} = 1$

19. In this unit circle we can find the y-coordinate or $\sin \theta$ at point P.

$$x^2 + y^2 = 1$$

$$(-\frac{8}{17})^2 + y^2 = 1$$

$$y^2 = 1 - \frac{64}{289}$$

$$y^2 = \frac{225}{289}$$

$$y = +\frac{15}{17} \qquad \text{Why the positive?}$$

(a) Here we go.

$$\sin \theta = y = \frac{15}{17} \qquad\qquad \csc \theta = \frac{1}{\sin \theta} = \frac{17}{15}$$

$$\cos \theta = x = -\frac{8}{17} \qquad\qquad \sec \theta = \frac{1}{\cos \theta} = -\frac{17}{8}$$

$$\tan \theta = \frac{y}{x} = -\frac{15}{8} \qquad\qquad \cot \theta = \frac{1}{\tan \theta} = -\frac{8}{15}$$

(b) The coordinates for $(-\theta)$ will be $(-\frac{8}{17}, -\frac{15}{17})$, and the signs of the sin, tan, csc, and cot will change. Their magnitudes will remain the same.

23. (a) $\sin \theta = \frac{2}{\sqrt{5}}$, $\cos \theta = \frac{1}{\sqrt{5}}$

(b) $9y^2 - x^2$

25.

θ	$\theta - \frac{\theta^3}{6}$	$\sin \theta$
.1	.099833 $\cdots$	.099833 $\cdots$
.2	.198666 $\cdots$	.198669 $\cdots$
.3	.295500 $\cdots$	.295520 $\cdots$
1.0	.833333 $\cdots$	.841470 $\cdots$

27. $\sin \theta = \pm \dfrac{\sqrt{\sec^2 \theta - 1}}{\sec \theta}$; $\cos \theta = \dfrac{1}{\sec \theta}$; $\tan \theta = \pm \sqrt{\sec^2 \theta - 1}$;

$\csc \theta = \dfrac{\sec \theta}{\pm \sqrt{\sec^2 \theta - 1}}$; $\cot \theta = \dfrac{1}{\pm \sqrt{\sec^2 \theta - 1}}$

29.

θ	$\sin \theta$	which is larger, θ or $\sin \theta$?
.1	.0998	θ
.2	.1987	θ
.3	.2955	θ
.4	.3894	θ
.5	.4794	θ

EXERCISE SET 7.3

1. (a) $\sin(\theta - \dfrac{3\pi}{2}) = \sin \theta \cos \dfrac{3\pi}{2} - \cos \theta \sin \dfrac{3\pi}{2}$

$= (\sin \theta)(0) - (\cos \theta)(-1)$

$= \cos \theta$

(b) $\cos(\theta + \pi) = \cos \theta \cos \pi - \sin \theta \sin \pi$

$= (\cos \theta)(-1) - (\sin \theta)(0)$

$= - \cos \theta$

(c) $\cos(\dfrac{3\pi}{2} + \theta) = \cos \dfrac{3\pi}{2} \cos \theta - \sin \dfrac{3\pi}{2} \sin \theta$

$= (0)(\cos \theta) = (-1)(\sin \theta)$

$= \sin \theta$

(d) $\sin(\theta - \pi) = \sin \theta \cos \pi - \cos \theta \sin \pi$

$= (\sin \theta)(-1) = (\cos \theta)(0)$

$= -\sin \theta$

3. $\cos 75° = \cos(30° + 45°)$

                        $= \cos 30° \cos 45° - \sin 30° \sin 45°$

                        $= (\frac{\sqrt{3}}{2})(\frac{\sqrt{2}}{2}) - (\frac{1}{2})(\frac{\sqrt{2}}{2})$

                        $= \frac{\sqrt{6} - \sqrt{2}}{4}$

5. $\sin \frac{7\pi}{12} = \sin(\frac{3\pi}{12} + \frac{4\pi}{12})$

                        $= \sin(\frac{\pi}{4} + \frac{\pi}{3})$

                        $= \sin \frac{\pi}{4} \cos \frac{\pi}{3} + \cos \frac{\pi}{4} \sin \frac{\pi}{3}$

                        $= (\frac{\sqrt{2}}{2})(\frac{1}{2}) + (\frac{\sqrt{2}}{2})(\frac{\sqrt{3}}{2})$

                        $= \frac{\sqrt{2} + \sqrt{6}}{4}$

7. (a) First we need to compute $\cos \alpha$ and $\sin \beta$. Since the terminal side of α lies in the second quadrant, $\cos \alpha$ is negative and we have

                $\cos \alpha = -\sqrt{1 - \sin^2 \alpha}$

                        $= -\sqrt{1 - \frac{144}{169}} = -\sqrt{\frac{169}{169} - \frac{144}{169}}$

                        $= -\sqrt{\frac{25}{169}} = -\frac{5}{13}$.

Since the terminal side of β lies in the fourth quadrant, $\sin \beta$ is negative and we have

                $\sin \beta = -\sqrt{1 - \cos^2 \beta}$

                        $= -\sqrt{1 - \frac{9}{25}} = -\sqrt{\frac{25}{25} - \frac{9}{25}}$

                        $= -\sqrt{\frac{16}{25}} = -\frac{4}{5}$.

Now we can compute $\sin(\alpha + \beta)$:

7. (a) (cont)

$$\sin(\alpha + \beta) = \sin \alpha \cos \beta + \cos \alpha \sin \beta$$

$$= (\tfrac{12}{13})(\tfrac{3}{5}) + (-\tfrac{5}{13})(-\tfrac{4}{5})$$

$$= \tfrac{36}{65} + \tfrac{20}{65}$$

$$= \tfrac{56}{65}$$

(b)

$$\sin(\alpha - \beta) = \sin \alpha \cos \beta - \cos \alpha \sin \beta$$

$$= (\tfrac{12}{13})(\tfrac{3}{5}) - (-\tfrac{5}{13})(-\tfrac{4}{5})$$

$$= \tfrac{36}{65} - \tfrac{20}{65}$$

$$= \tfrac{16}{65}$$

(c)

$$\cos(\alpha + \beta) = \cos \alpha \cos \beta - \sin \alpha \sin \beta$$

$$= (-\tfrac{5}{13})(\tfrac{3}{5}) - (\tfrac{12}{13})(-\tfrac{4}{5})$$

$$= \tfrac{-15}{65} + \tfrac{48}{65}$$

$$= \tfrac{33}{65}$$

(d)

$$\cos(\alpha - \beta) = \cos \alpha \cos \beta + \sin \alpha \sin \beta$$

$$= (-\tfrac{5}{13})(\tfrac{3}{5}) + (\tfrac{12}{13})(-\tfrac{4}{5})$$

$$= \tfrac{-15}{65} - \tfrac{48}{65}$$

$$= -\tfrac{63}{65}$$

(e)

$$\tan(\alpha + \beta) = \frac{\sin(\alpha + \beta)}{\cos(\alpha + \beta)}$$

$$= \frac{56/65}{33/65}$$

$$= \frac{56}{33}$$

7. (cont)

    (f) $\tan(\alpha - \beta) = \dfrac{\sin(\alpha - \beta)}{\cos(\alpha - \beta)}$

                                                     $= \dfrac{16/65}{-63/65}$

                                                     $= -\dfrac{16}{63}$

9. (a) Since the terminal side of θ lies in the fourth quadrant, $\sin \theta$

         is negative and we have

                        $\sin \theta = -\sqrt{1 - \cos^2 \theta}$

                              $= -\sqrt{1 - \dfrac{144}{169}} = -\sqrt{\dfrac{169}{169} - \dfrac{144}{169}}$

                              $= -\sqrt{\dfrac{25}{169}} = -\dfrac{5}{13}$

    Thus $\sin \theta = -5/13$.

    (b) $\cos 2\theta = \cos(\theta + \theta)$

                                       $= \cos \theta \cos \theta - \sin \theta \sin \theta$

                                       $= \cos^2 \theta - \sin^2 \theta$

                                       $= \dfrac{144}{169} - \dfrac{25}{169}$

                                       $= \dfrac{119}{169}$

11. We first need to compute the values of sine and cosine for the angles β
    and θ. Since $\csc \beta = 2$, we immediately have $\sin \beta = \dfrac{1}{2}$. Furthermore
    since $0 < \beta < \dfrac{\pi}{2}$, our experience with the $30° - 60°$ right triangle
    tells us that $\cos \beta = \sqrt{3}/2$. Next, since $\tan \theta = -2/3$ we have

                    $\sec^2 \theta = 1 + \tan^2 \theta = 1 + \dfrac{4}{9} = \dfrac{13}{9}$

    Thus $\sec \theta = -\dfrac{\sqrt{13}}{3}$. (Notice that the negative value is appropriate
    here since the terminal side of the angle θ lies in the second quadrant.
    Now since $\sec \theta = -\sqrt{13}/3$, we have $\cos \theta = -3/\sqrt{13}$. From this we can

11. (cont)

calculate sin θ as follows:

$$\sin \theta = \pm \sqrt{1 - \cos^2 \theta}$$

$$= \pm \sqrt{1 - \frac{9}{13}} = \pm \sqrt{\frac{4}{13}}$$

$$= \pm \frac{2}{\sqrt{13}}$$

We want the positive value in this case, because $\frac{\pi}{2} < \theta < \pi$. Thus sin θ = $2/\sqrt{13}$. At this point we are prepared to calculate sin(θ + β) and cos(β - θ). We have

$$\sin(\theta + \beta) = \sin \theta \cos \beta + \cos \theta \sin \beta$$

$$= (2/\sqrt{13})(\sqrt{3}/2) + (-3/\sqrt{13})(\frac{1}{2})$$

$$= \frac{\sqrt{3}}{\sqrt{13}} - \frac{3}{2\sqrt{13}}$$

$$= \frac{2\sqrt{3} - 3}{2\sqrt{13}}$$

Thus $\sin(\theta + \beta) = \dfrac{2\sqrt{3} - 3}{2\sqrt{13}}$. To compute cos(β - θ) we have

$$\cos(\beta - \theta) = \cos \beta \cos \theta + \sin \beta \sin \theta$$

$$= (\sqrt{3}/2)(-3/\sqrt{13}) + (\frac{1}{2})(2/\sqrt{13})$$

$$= -\frac{3\sqrt{3}}{2\sqrt{13}} + \frac{1}{\sqrt{13}}$$

$$= -\frac{3\sqrt{3}}{2\sqrt{13}} + \frac{1}{\sqrt{13}} \cdot \frac{2}{2}$$

$$= \frac{2 - 3\sqrt{3}}{2\sqrt{13}}$$

13. We have $\overline{AB} = 1$ and $\overline{BD} = 2 + 1 = 3$. Therefore $\overline{AD} = \sqrt{1^2 + 3^2}$; $\overline{AD} = \sqrt{10}$. Also $\overline{AC} = \sqrt{1^2 + 2^2} = \sqrt{5}$; $\overline{AC} = \sqrt{5}$. Now we compute cos(α + β):

13. (cont)

$$\cos(\alpha + \beta) = \cos \alpha \cos \beta - \sin \alpha \sin \beta$$

$$= (\overline{BC}/\overline{AC})(\overline{BD}/\overline{AD}) - (\overline{AB}/\overline{AC})(\overline{AB}/\overline{AD})$$

$$= (2/\sqrt{5})(3/\sqrt{10}) - (1/\sqrt{5})(1/\sqrt{10})$$

$$= \frac{6}{\sqrt{50}} - \frac{1}{\sqrt{50}} = \frac{5}{\sqrt{50}}$$

$$= \frac{5}{\sqrt{25}\ \sqrt{2}} = \frac{5}{5\sqrt{2}} = \frac{1}{\sqrt{2}}$$

$$= \frac{\sqrt{2}}{2}$$

We now have found that $\cos(\alpha + \beta) = \sqrt{2}/2$. Since this is positive, it follows that $0 < \alpha + \beta < \frac{\pi}{2}$ and consequently $\alpha + \beta = \frac{\pi}{4}$.

15. $\cos(\theta + \frac{\pi}{3}) + \cos(\theta - \frac{\pi}{3})$

$$= \cos \theta \cos \frac{\pi}{3} - \sin \theta \sin \frac{\pi}{3} + \cos \theta \cos \frac{\pi}{3} + \sin \theta \sin \frac{\pi}{3}$$

$$= (\cos \theta)(\frac{1}{2}) - (\sin \theta)(\frac{\sqrt{3}}{2}) + (\cos \theta)(\frac{1}{2}) + (\sin \theta)(\frac{\sqrt{3}}{2})$$

$$= \frac{1}{2} \cos \theta + \frac{1}{2} \cos \theta$$

$$= \cos \theta$$

17. $\cos(\alpha + \beta)\cos(\alpha - \beta) = (\cos \alpha \cos \beta - \sin \alpha \sin \beta)(\cos \alpha \cos \beta + \sin \alpha \sin \beta)$

$$= \cos^2 \alpha \cos^2 \beta - \sin^2 \alpha \sin^2 \beta$$

$$= (\cos^2 \alpha)(1 - \sin^2 \beta) - (1 - \cos^2 \alpha)\sin^2 \beta$$

$$= \cos^2 \alpha - \cos^2 \alpha \sin^2 \beta - \sin^2 \beta + \cos^2 \alpha \sin^2 \beta$$

$$= \cos^2 \alpha - \sin^2 \beta$$

19. (a) $\sin(A + B) = \sin(180° - C)$

$$= \sin 180° \cos C - \cos 180° \sin C$$

$$= 0 - (-1)\sin C$$

$$= \sin C$$

19. (cont)

(b) $$\cos(A + B) = \cos(180° - C)$$

$$= \cos 180° \cos C + \sin 180° \sin C$$

$$= (-1)\cos C + 0$$

$$= -\cos C$$

(c) $$\tan(A + B) = \frac{\sin(A + B)}{\cos(A + B)} = \frac{\sin C}{-\cos C} = -\tan C$$

21. (a) $$\sin 2\theta = \sin(\theta + \theta)$$

$$= \sin \theta \cos \theta + \cos \theta \sin \theta$$

$$= \sin \theta \cos \theta + \sin \theta \cos \theta$$

$$= 2 \sin \theta \cos \theta$$

(b) $$\cos 2\theta = \cos(\theta + \theta)$$

$$= \cos \theta \cos \theta - \sin \theta \sin \theta$$

$$= \cos^2 \theta - \sin^2 \theta$$

(c) $$\sin 3\theta = \sin(\theta + 2\theta)$$

$$= \sin \theta \cos 2\theta + \cos \theta \sin 2\theta$$

$$= (\sin \theta)(\cos^2 \theta - \sin^2 \theta) + (\cos \theta)(2 \sin \theta \cos \theta)$$

$$= \sin \theta \cos^2 \theta - \sin^3 \theta + 2 \sin \theta \cos^2 \theta$$

$$= 3 \sin \theta \cos^2 \theta - \sin^3 \theta$$

(d) $$\cos 3\theta = \cos(\theta + 2\theta)$$

$$= \cos \theta \cos 2\theta = \sin \theta \sin 2\theta$$

$$= (\cos \theta)(\cos^2 \theta - \sin^2 \theta) - \sin \theta(2 \sin \theta \cos \theta)$$

$$= \cos^3 \theta - \cos \theta \sin^2 \theta - 2 \cos \theta \sin^2 \theta$$

$$= \cos^3 \theta - 3 \cos \theta \sin^2 \theta$$

23. Using the hint that is given, we have

$$\tan(\alpha + \beta) = \frac{\tan \alpha + \tan \beta}{1 - \tan \alpha \tan \beta}$$

$$= \frac{\dfrac{a}{a + 1} + \dfrac{1}{2a + 1}}{1 - (\dfrac{a}{a + 1})(\dfrac{1}{2a + 1})} \cdot \frac{(a + 1)(2a + 1)}{(a + 1)(2a + 1)}$$

$$= \frac{a(2a + 1) + 1(a + 1)}{(a + 1)(2a + 1) - a(1)}$$

$$= \frac{2a^2 + 2a + 1}{2a^2 + 2a + 1}$$

$$= 1$$

Now since $\tan(\alpha + \beta) = 1$ and $0 < \alpha + \beta < \pi$ it follows that $\alpha + \beta = \frac{\pi}{4}$, as required.

Exercise Set 7.4

1. (a) $\tan(\beta + s) = \dfrac{\tan \beta + \tan s}{1 - \tan \beta \tan s}$

$$= \frac{(4/3) + (3/2)}{1 - (4/3)(3/2)} \cdot \frac{6}{6}$$

$$= \frac{8 + 9}{6 - 12}$$

$$= -\frac{17}{6}$$

(b) $\tan(\beta - s) = \dfrac{\tan \beta - \tan s}{1 + \tan \beta \tan s}$

$$= \frac{(4/3) - (3/2)}{1 + (4/3)(3/2)} \cdot \frac{6}{6}$$

$$= \frac{8 - 9}{6 + 12}$$

$$= -\frac{1}{18}$$

(c) $\tan(\alpha - s) = \dfrac{\tan \alpha - \tan s}{1 + \tan \alpha \tan s}$

$$= \frac{(3/4) - (3/2)}{1 + (3/4)(3/2)} \cdot \frac{8}{8}$$

$$= \frac{6 - 12}{8 + 9}$$

1. (c) (cont) $= -\dfrac{6}{17}$

   (d) $\tan(\alpha - \beta) = \dfrac{\tan \alpha - \tan \beta}{1 + \tan \alpha \tan \beta}$

$$= \dfrac{(3/4) - (4/3)}{1 + (3/4)(4/3)} \cdot \dfrac{12}{12}$$

$$= \dfrac{9 - 16}{12 + 12}$$

$$= -\dfrac{7}{24}$$

3. (a) $\tan 2\alpha = \dfrac{2 \tan \alpha}{1 - \tan^2 \alpha}$

$$= \dfrac{2(3/4)}{1 - (3/4)^2} = \dfrac{3/2}{1 - \dfrac{9}{16}} \cdot \dfrac{16}{16}$$

$$= \dfrac{24}{16 - 9}$$

$$= \dfrac{24}{7}$$

   (b) $\tan 2\beta = \dfrac{2 \tan \beta}{1 - \tan^2 \beta}$

$$= \dfrac{2(4/3)}{1 - (4/3)^2} = \dfrac{8/3}{1 - (16/9)} \cdot \dfrac{9}{9}$$

$$= \dfrac{24}{9 - 16}$$

$$= -\dfrac{24}{7}$$

   (c) $\tan 2s = \dfrac{2 \tan s}{1 - \tan^2 s}$

$$= \dfrac{2(3/2)}{1 - (3/2)^2} = \dfrac{3}{1 - (9/4)} \cdot \dfrac{4}{4}$$

$$= \dfrac{12}{4 - 9}$$

$$= -\dfrac{12}{5}$$

3. (d)
$$\tan 2t = \frac{2 \tan t}{1 - \tan^2 t}$$

$$= \frac{2(2/3)}{1 - (2/3)^2} = \frac{4/3}{1 - (4/9)} \cdot \frac{9}{9}$$

$$= \frac{12}{9 - 4}$$

$$= \frac{12}{5}$$

5. (a)
$$\sin \frac{\alpha}{2} = \sqrt{\frac{1 - \cos \alpha}{2}}$$

$$= \sqrt{\frac{1 - (4/5)}{2}} = \sqrt{\frac{1/5}{2}}$$

$$= \sqrt{1/10} = \frac{1}{\sqrt{10}} \quad \left(\text{or} \quad \frac{\sqrt{10}}{10} \right)$$

$$\cos \frac{\alpha}{2} = \sqrt{\frac{1 + \cos \alpha}{2}}$$

$$= \sqrt{\frac{1 + (4/5)}{2}} = \sqrt{\frac{9/5}{2}}$$

$$= \sqrt{9/10} = \frac{3}{\sqrt{10}} \quad \left(\text{or} \quad \frac{3\sqrt{10}}{10} \right)$$

(b)
$$\sin \frac{s}{2} = \sqrt{\frac{1 - \cos s}{2}}$$

$$= \sqrt{\frac{1 - (2/\sqrt{13})}{2}} = \sqrt{\frac{1 - (2/\sqrt{13})}{2} \cdot \frac{\sqrt{13}}{\sqrt{13}}}$$

$$= \sqrt{\frac{\sqrt{13} - 2}{2\sqrt{13}}}$$

$$\cos \frac{s}{2} = \sqrt{\frac{1 + \cos s}{2}}$$

$$= \sqrt{\frac{1 + (2/\sqrt{13})}{2}} = \sqrt{\frac{1 + (2/\sqrt{13})}{2} \cdot \frac{\sqrt{13}}{\sqrt{13}}}$$

$$= \sqrt{\frac{\sqrt{13} + 2}{2\sqrt{13}}}$$

5. (cont)

(c) $\sin(\alpha + \frac{s}{2}) = \sin\alpha \cos\frac{s}{2} + \cos\alpha \sin\frac{s}{2}$

$$= (3/5)\sqrt{\frac{\sqrt{13} + 2}{2\sqrt{13}}} + (4/5)\sqrt{\frac{\sqrt{13} - 2}{2\sqrt{13}}}$$

$$= \frac{3\sqrt{\sqrt{13} + 2}}{5\sqrt{2\sqrt{13}}} + \frac{4\sqrt{\sqrt{13} - 2}}{5\sqrt{2\sqrt{13}}}$$

$$= \frac{3\sqrt{\sqrt{13} + 2} + 4\sqrt{\sqrt{13} - 2}}{5\sqrt{2\sqrt{13}}}$$

(d) First we calculate the values of $\cos\frac{\beta}{2}$ and $\sin\frac{\beta}{2}$ as follows:

$$\cos\frac{\beta}{2} = \sqrt{\frac{1 + \cos\beta}{2}}$$

$$= \sqrt{\frac{1 + (3/5)}{2}} = \sqrt{\frac{8/5}{2}}$$

$$= \sqrt{4/5} = 2/\sqrt{5} = 2\sqrt{5}/5$$

$$\sin\frac{\beta}{2} = \sqrt{\frac{1 - \cos\beta}{2}}$$

$$= \sqrt{\frac{1 - (3/5)}{2}} = \sqrt{\frac{2/5}{2}}$$

$$= \sqrt{1/5} = 1/\sqrt{5} = \sqrt{5}/5$$

We've found that $\cos\frac{\beta}{2} = 2\sqrt{5}/5$ and $\sin\frac{\beta}{2} = \sqrt{5}/5$. Using these values
we then have

$$\cos(\frac{\beta}{2} - t) = \cos\frac{\beta}{2}\cos t + \sin\frac{\beta}{2}\sin t$$

$$= \frac{2\sqrt{5}}{5} \cdot \frac{3}{\sqrt{13}} + \frac{\sqrt{5}}{5} \cdot \frac{2}{\sqrt{13}}$$

$$= \frac{6\sqrt{5}}{5\sqrt{13}} + \frac{2\sqrt{5}}{5\sqrt{13}}$$

$$= \frac{8\sqrt{5}}{5\sqrt{13}} \cdot \frac{\sqrt{13}}{\sqrt{13}}$$

$$= \frac{8\sqrt{65}}{65}, \quad \text{as required.}$$

7. (a) $$\tan \frac{\alpha}{2} = \frac{\sin \alpha}{1 + \cos \alpha}$$

$$= \frac{3/5}{1 + (4/5)} \cdot \frac{5}{5}$$

$$= \frac{3}{5 + 4} = \frac{3}{9} = \frac{1}{3}$$

Thus $\tan \frac{\alpha}{2} = \frac{1}{3}$.

(b) First we compute $\tan \frac{\beta}{2}$:

$$\tan \frac{\beta}{2} = \frac{\sin \beta}{1 + \cos \beta} = \frac{4/5}{1 + (3/5)} \cdot \frac{5}{5}$$

$$= \frac{4}{5 + 3} = \frac{4}{8} = \frac{1}{2}$$

Thus $\tan \frac{\beta}{2} = \frac{1}{2}$. Now with this value of $\tan \frac{\beta}{2}$, we compute $\tan(\frac{\beta}{2} + \frac{\pi}{4})$ as follows:

$$\tan(\frac{\beta}{2} + \frac{\pi}{4}) = \frac{\tan \frac{\beta}{2} + \tan \frac{\pi}{4}}{1 - \tan \frac{\beta}{2} \tan \frac{\pi}{4}}$$

$$= \frac{(1/2) + 1}{1 - (1/2)(1)} = \frac{3/2}{1/2} = 3$$

Thus $\tan(\frac{\beta}{2} + \frac{\pi}{4}) = 3$.

9. $$\tan \frac{\pi}{8} = \tan \frac{\pi/4}{2}$$

$$= \frac{\sin(\pi/4)}{1 + \cos(\pi/4)}$$

$$= \frac{\sqrt{2}/2}{1 + (\sqrt{2}/2)} \cdot \frac{2}{2}$$

$$= \frac{\sqrt{2}}{2 + \sqrt{2}} \cdot \frac{2 - \sqrt{2}}{2 - \sqrt{2}}$$

$$= \frac{2\sqrt{2} - 2}{4 - 2} = \frac{2(\sqrt{2} - 1)}{2}$$

$$= \sqrt{2} - 1, \text{ as required.}$$

11. First we use the Pythagorean Theorem to compute the length of the hypotenuse in the given right triangle. Calling that length h, we have

$$h = \sqrt{(2ab)^2 + (a^2 - b^2)^2}$$

$$= \sqrt{4a^2b^2 + a^4 - 2a^2b^2 + b^4}$$

$$= \sqrt{a^4 + 2a^2b^2 + b^4} = \sqrt{(a^2 + b^2)^2}$$

$$= a^2 + b^2.$$

Thus we have $h = a^2 + b^2$ and consequently $\sin \theta = 2ab/(a^2 + b^2)$, $\cos \theta = (a^2 - b^2)/(a^2 + b^2)$, $\sin \phi = (a^2 - b^2)/(a^2 + b^2)$, and $\cos \phi = 2ab/(a^2 + b^2)$. Now we're prepared to compute $\tan \frac{\theta}{2}$ and $\tan \frac{\phi}{2}$. We have

$$\tan \frac{\theta}{2} = \frac{\sin \theta}{1 + \cos \theta}$$

$$= \frac{2ab/(a^2 + b^2)}{1 + [(a^2 - b^2)/(a^2 + b^2)]} \cdot \frac{a^2 + b^2}{a^2 + b^2}$$

$$= \frac{2ab}{a^2 + b^2 + a^2 - b^2} = \frac{2ab}{2a^2}$$

$$= \frac{b}{a}$$

$$\tan \frac{\phi}{2} = \frac{\sin \phi}{1 + \cos \phi}$$

$$= \frac{(a^2 - b^2)/(a^2 + b^2)}{1 + [2ab/(a^2 + b^2)]} \cdot \frac{a^2 + b^2}{a^2 + b^2}$$

$$= \frac{a^2 - b^2}{a^2 + b^2 + 2ab} = \frac{(a - b)(a + b)}{(a + b)^2}$$

$$= \frac{a - b}{a + b}.$$

In summary now, we've determined that $\tan \frac{\theta}{2} = \frac{b}{a}$ and $\tan \frac{\phi}{2} = (a - b)/(a + b)$.

13. (a) Since $\sec \theta = z$, $0 < \theta < \frac{\pi}{2}$, we have $\cos \theta = \frac{1}{z}$ and

$$\sin \theta = \sqrt{1 - \cos^2 \theta}$$

$$= \sqrt{1 - (1/z^2)} = \sqrt{(z^2 - 1)/z^2}$$

$$= \frac{\sqrt{z^2 - 1}}{z} \ .$$

Now we can compute $\sin \frac{\theta}{2}$:

$$\sin \frac{\theta}{2} = \sqrt{\frac{1 - \cos \theta}{2}}$$

$$= \sqrt{\frac{1 - (1/z)}{2}} = \sqrt{\frac{1 - (1/z)}{2} \cdot \frac{z}{z}}$$

$$= \sqrt{\frac{z - 1}{2z}}$$

(b) $\sin 2\theta = 2 \sin \theta \cos \theta = 2 \left(\frac{\sqrt{z^2 - 1}}{z} \right) \left(\frac{1}{z} \right)$

Thus $\sin 2\theta = \frac{2\sqrt{z^2 - 1}}{z^2}$.

(c) $\cos 2\theta = \cos^2 \theta - \sin^2 \theta$

$$= (1/z)^2 - (\sqrt{z^2 - 1}/z)^2$$

$$= \frac{1}{z^2} - \frac{z^2 - 1}{z^2} = \frac{1 - (z^2 - 1)}{z^2}$$

$$= \frac{2 - z^2}{z^2}$$

15. $\dfrac{1 - \tan^2 s}{1 + \tan^2 s} = \dfrac{1 - \tan^2 s}{\sec^2 s}$,

$$= \frac{1}{\sec^2 s} - \frac{\tan^2 s}{\sec^2 s}$$

$$= \cos^2 s - \frac{(\sin^2 s)/(\cos^2 s)}{1/\cos^2 s}$$

$$= \cos^2 s - \sin^2 s$$

$$= \cos 2s$$

17.
$$\sin \theta = \sin[2(\tfrac{\theta}{2})]$$

$$= 2 \sin \tfrac{\theta}{2} \cos \tfrac{\theta}{2}$$

19.
$$\frac{\sin 2\theta}{\sin \theta} - \frac{\cos 2\theta}{\cos \theta} = \frac{2 \sin \theta \cos \theta}{\sin \theta} - \frac{2 \cos^2 \theta - 1}{\cos \theta}$$

$$= 2 \cos \theta - (2 \cos \theta - \frac{1}{\cos \theta})$$

$$= \frac{1}{\cos \theta} = \sec \theta.$$

21.
$$\sin 3\theta = \sin(\theta + 2\theta)$$

$$= \sin \theta \cos 2\theta + \cos \theta \sin 2\theta$$

$$= \sin \theta(\cos^2 \theta - \sin^2 \theta) + \cos \theta(2 \sin \theta \cos \theta)$$

$$= \sin \theta \cos^2 \theta - \sin^3 \theta + 2 \sin \theta \cos^2 \theta$$

$$= 3 \sin \theta \cos^2 \theta - \sin^3 \theta$$

23.
$$\cos 2\theta = \cos^2 \theta - \sin^2 \theta$$

$$= (1 - \sin^2 \theta) - \sin^2 \theta$$

$$= 1 - 2 \sin^2 \theta$$

25. From the identity $\cos^2 t - \sin^2 t = \cos 2t$ we obtain

$$(1 - \sin^2 t) - \sin^2 t = \cos 2t$$

$$1 - 2 \sin^2 t = \cos 2t$$

$$-2 \sin^2 t = -1 + \cos 2t$$

$$\sin^2 t = \frac{1 - \cos 2t}{2}$$

Now since this last equation holds for all values of t, we may replace t by $\theta/2$ to obtain

25.   (cont) $\sin^2(\theta/2) = \dfrac{1 - \cos[2(\theta/2)]}{2}$

                                 $\sin^2(\theta/2) = \dfrac{1 - \cos\theta}{2}$

                                 $\sin\theta = \pm\sqrt{\dfrac{1 - \cos\theta}{2}}$,   as required.

27.   The identity to be established is $2\csc 2\theta = \dfrac{\csc^2\theta}{\cot\theta}$.   [Note: In the first

      printing of the text, the denominator on the right side of the equation

      incorrectly appears as $\cot^2\theta$.]   We have

$$2\csc 2\theta = \frac{2}{\sin 2\theta} = \frac{2}{2\sin\theta\cos\theta}$$

$$= \frac{1}{\sin\theta\cos\theta} \cdot \frac{\sin\theta}{\sin\theta}$$

$$= \frac{1}{\sin^2\theta} \cdot \frac{\sin\theta}{\cos\theta}$$

$$= \csc^2\theta\tan\theta$$

$$= \frac{\csc^2\theta}{\cot\theta}$$

29. $\dfrac{1 + \cos 2\theta}{\sin 2\theta} = \dfrac{2\cos^2\theta}{\sin 2\theta}$ using identity (c) on page 391

$$= \frac{2\cos^2\theta}{2\sin\theta\cos\theta}$$

$$= \frac{\cos\theta}{\sin\theta}$$

$$= \cot\theta$$

31. $\tan\theta + \cot\theta = \dfrac{\sin\theta}{\cos\theta} + \dfrac{\cos\theta}{\sin\theta}$

$$= \frac{\sin^2\theta + \cos^2\theta}{\cos\theta\sin\theta}$$

$$= \frac{1}{\cos\theta\sin\theta} \cdot \frac{2}{2}$$

$$= \frac{2}{\sin 2\theta}$$

$$= 2\csc 2\theta$$

33. $$(\sin \theta - \cos \theta)^2 = \sin^2 \theta - 2 \sin \theta \cos \theta + \cos^2 \theta$$

$$= (\sin^2 \theta + \cos^2 \theta) - \sin 2\theta$$

$$= 1 - \sin 2\theta$$

35. $\tan(\frac{\pi}{4} + \theta) - \tan(\frac{\pi}{4} - \theta) = \dfrac{\tan \frac{\pi}{4} + \tan \theta}{1 - \tan \frac{\pi}{4} \tan \theta} - \dfrac{\tan \frac{\pi}{4} - \tan \theta}{1 + \tan \frac{\pi}{4} \tan \theta}$

$$= \frac{1 + \tan \theta}{1 - \tan \theta} - \frac{1 - \tan \theta}{1 + \tan \theta}$$

$$= \frac{(1 + \tan \theta)^2 - (1 - \tan \theta)^2}{(1 - \tan \theta)(1 + \tan \theta)}$$

$$= \frac{1 + 2 \tan \theta + \tan^2 \theta - (1 - 2 \tan \theta + \tan^2 \theta)}{1 - \tan^2 \theta}$$

$$= \frac{4 \tan \theta}{1 - \tan^2 \theta} = 2\left(\frac{2 \tan \theta}{1 - \tan^2 \theta}\right)$$

$$= 2 \tan 2\theta$$

37. $$\tan \frac{\theta}{2} = \frac{\sin \theta}{1 + \cos \theta} \cdot \frac{1 - \cos \theta}{1 - \cos \theta}$$

$$= \frac{\sin \theta(1 - \cos \theta)}{1 - \cos^2 \theta}$$

$$= \frac{\sin \theta(1 - \cos \theta)}{\sin^2 \theta}$$

$$= \frac{1 - \cos \theta}{\sin \theta}$$

39. (a) First we compute $\tan(60° - \theta)$ and $\tan(60° + \theta)$.

$$\tan(60° - \theta) = \frac{\tan 60° - \tan \theta}{1 + \tan 60° \tan \theta}$$

$$= \frac{\sqrt{3} - \tan \theta}{1 + \sqrt{3} \tan \theta}$$

$$\tan(60° + \theta) = \frac{\tan 60° + \tan \theta}{1 - \tan 60° \tan \theta}$$

$$= \frac{\sqrt{3} + \tan \theta}{1 - \sqrt{3} \tan \theta}$$

Next we compute the product $\tan(60° - \theta)\tan(60° + \theta)$:

39. (a) (cont)

$$\tan(60° - \theta)\tan(60° + \theta) = \frac{\sqrt{3} - \tan \theta}{1 + \sqrt{3} \tan \theta} \cdot \frac{\sqrt{3} + \tan \theta}{1 - \sqrt{3} \tan \theta}$$

$$= \frac{3 - \tan^2 \theta}{1 - 3 \tan^2 \theta}$$

From this it follows that

$$\tan \theta \tan(60° - \theta)\tan(60° + \theta) = \frac{\tan \theta (3 - \tan^2 \theta)}{1 - 3 \tan^2 \theta} .$$

Next we consider $\tan 3\theta$. We have

$$\tan 3\theta = \tan(\theta + 2\theta)$$

$$= \frac{\tan \theta + \tan 2\theta}{1 - \tan \theta \tan 2\theta}$$

$$= \frac{\tan \theta + \dfrac{2 \tan \theta}{1 - \tan^2 \theta}}{1 - \tan \theta \left(\dfrac{2 \tan \theta}{1 - \tan^2 \theta}\right)} \cdot \frac{1 - \tan^2 \theta}{1 - \tan^2 \theta}$$

$$= \frac{\tan \theta - \tan^3 \theta + 2 \tan \theta}{1 - \tan^2 \theta - 2 \tan^2 \theta}$$

$$= \frac{3 \tan \theta - \tan^3 \theta}{1 - 3 \tan^2 \theta}$$

$$= \frac{\tan \theta (3 - \tan^2 \theta)}{1 - 3 \tan^2 \theta}$$

The required identity follows now since both sides are equal to the quantity $\dfrac{\tan \theta (3 - \tan^2 \theta)}{1 - 3 \tan^2 \theta}$.

(b) In the identity from part (a), let $\theta = 20°$. This yields

$$\tan 20° \tan(60° - 20°)\tan(60° + 20°) = \tan[3(20°)]$$

$$\tan 20° \tan 40° \tan 80° = \tan 60°$$

$$\tan 20° \tan 40° \tan 80° = \sqrt{3}$$

41. (a) $\cos 3\theta = \cos(\theta + 2\theta)$

$= \cos \theta \cos 2\theta - \sin \theta \sin 2\theta$

$= \cos \theta (2 \cos^2 \theta - 1) - \sin \theta (2 \sin \theta \cos \theta)$

$= 2 \cos^3 \theta - \cos \theta - 2 \cos \theta (\sin^2 \theta)$

$= 2 \cos^3 \theta - \cos \theta - 2 \cos \theta (1 - \cos^2 \theta)$

$= 2 \cos^3 \theta - \cos \theta - 2 \cos \theta + 2 \cos^3 \theta$

$= 4 \cos^3 \theta - 3 \cos \theta$,   as required.

(b)   (i) Since $36° + 54° = 90°$ we have

$\sin 36° = \cos(90° - 36°) = \cos 54°.$

That is, $\sin 36° = \cos 54°$, as required.

(ii) Since $2 \sin \theta \cos \theta = \sin 2\theta$ we have

$2 \sin 18° \cos 18° = \sin 36°$

$= \cos 54°$

$= \cos[3(18°)]$

$= 4 \cos^3 18° - 3 \cos 18°$

(iii) Dividing each side of the last equation in (ii) by $\cos 18°$
yields

$2 \sin 18° = 4 \cos^2 18° - 3$

(c) $2 \sin 18° = 4 \cos^2 18° - 3$

$2 \sin 18° = 4(1 - \sin^2 18°) - 3$

$2 \sin 18° = 4 - 4 \sin^2 18° - 3$

$4 \sin^2 18° + 2 \sin 18° - 1 = 0$

This is a quadratic equation in $\sin 18°$. Applying the quadratic
formula yields

$$\sin 18° = \frac{-2 \pm \sqrt{4 - 4(4)(-1)}}{2(4)}$$

$$= \frac{-2 \pm \sqrt{20}}{8} = \frac{-2 \pm 2\sqrt{5}}{8}$$

$$= \frac{-1 \pm \sqrt{5}}{4}$$

We choose the positive root here because $\sin 18° > 0$. Thus $\sin 18° = \frac{1}{4}(-1 + \sqrt{5})$, as required.

(d) See the solution for 15(a) in Exercise Set 6.2 (page   of this manual).

43. Since $z = \tan \theta$, we have $1 + z^2 = 1 + \tan^2 \theta = \sec^2 \theta$. Thus $1/(1 + z^2) = \cos^2 \theta$. From this we can compute $\sin^2 \theta$:

$$\sin^2 \theta = 1 - \cos^2 \theta$$

$$= 1 - \frac{1}{1 + z^2}$$

$$= \frac{1 + z^2 - 1}{1 + z^2} = \frac{z^2}{1 + z^2} .$$

Now we have

$$\cos 2\theta = \cos^2 \theta - \sin^2 \theta$$

$$= \frac{1}{1 + z^2} - \frac{z^2}{1 + z^2}$$

$$= \frac{1 - z^2}{1 + z^2} , \quad \text{as required.}$$

Next we compute $\sin 2\theta$. One way to do this is as follows. From page 392 in the text we have

$$\tan \quad = \frac{\sin 2\theta}{1 + \cos 2\theta} .$$

Replacing $\tan \theta$ by z and $\cos 2\theta$ by $\dfrac{1 - z^2}{1 + z^2}$, we obtain

$$z = \frac{\sin 2\theta}{1 + \dfrac{1 - z^2}{1 + z^2}} .$$

Thus

$$\sin 2\theta = z + \frac{z(1 - z^2)}{1 + z^2}$$

$$= \frac{z(1 + z^2) + z(1 - z^2)}{1 + z^2}$$

$$= \frac{z + z^3 + z - z^3}{1 + z^2}$$

$$= \frac{2z}{1 + z^2} , \quad \text{as required.}$$

45. (a) $4 \sin 6\theta \cos 2\theta = 4(\frac{1}{2})[\sin(6\theta + 2\theta) + \sin(6\theta - 2\theta)]$

$$= 2(\sin 8\theta + \sin 4\theta)$$

(b) $2 \sin A \sin 3A = 2(\frac{1}{2})[\cos(A - 3A) - \cos(A + 3A)]$

$$= \cos(-2A) - \cos 4A$$

$$= \cos 2A - \cos 4A$$

(c) $\cos 4\theta \cos 2\theta = \frac{1}{2}[\cos(4\theta + 2\theta) + \cos(4\theta - 2\theta)]$

$$= \frac{1}{2}(\cos 6\theta + \cos 2\theta)$$

47. (a) $\sin(A + B)\sin(A - B) = \frac{1}{2}\{\cos[(A + B) - (A - B)] - \cos[(A + B) + (A - B)]\}$

$$= \frac{1}{2}\{\cos 2B - \cos 2A\}$$

$$= \frac{1}{2}\{1 - 2 \sin^2 B - (1 - 2 \sin^2 A)\}$$

$$= \frac{1}{2}(2 \sin^2 A - 2 \sin^2 B)$$

$$= \sin^2 A - \sin^2 B$$

(b) $\cos(A + B)\cos(A - B) = \frac{1}{2}\{\cos[(A + B) + (A - B)] + \cos[(A + B) - (A - B)]\}$

$$= \frac{1}{2}\{\cos 2A + \cos 2B\}$$

$$= \frac{1}{2}[(2 \cos^2 A - 1) + (1 - 2 \sin^2 B)]$$

$$= \cos^2 A - \sin^2 B$$

51.
$$\frac{\sin \theta + \sin 3\theta}{\cos \theta + \cos 3\theta} = \frac{2 \sin \frac{\theta + 3\theta}{2} \cos \frac{\theta - 3\theta}{2}}{2 \cos \frac{\theta + 3\theta}{2} \cos \frac{\theta - 3\theta}{2}}$$

$$= \frac{\sin 2\theta \cos(-\theta)}{\cos 2\theta \cos(-\theta)}$$

$$= \frac{\sin 2\theta}{\cos 2\theta}$$

$$= \tan 2\theta$$

53.
$$\frac{\sin 2x + \sin 2y}{\cos 2x + \cos 2y} = \frac{2 \sin\left(\frac{2x + 2y}{2}\right) \cos\left(\frac{2x - 2y}{2}\right)}{2 \cos\left(\frac{2x + 2y}{2}\right) \cos\left(\frac{2x - 2y}{2}\right)}$$

$$= \frac{\sin(x + y)}{\cos(x + y)}$$

$$= \tan(x + y)$$

55. (a) The areas of the two smaller triangles are $\frac{1}{2}$ af sin $\frac{C}{2}$ and $\frac{1}{2}$ bf sin $\frac{C}{2}$, respectively. The area of triangle BCA is $\frac{1}{2}$ ab sin C. Since the sum of the areas of the two smaller triangles equals the area of triangle BCA, we have

$$\frac{1}{2} \text{ af sin } \frac{C}{2} + \frac{1}{2} \text{ bf sin } \frac{C}{2} = \frac{1}{2} \text{ ab sin C.}$$

(b) Multiplying both sides of the equation given in part (a) by 2 yields

$$\text{af sin } \frac{C}{2} + \text{bf sin } \frac{C}{2} = \text{ab sin C}$$

$$\text{f sin } \frac{C}{2} (a + b) = \text{ab sin C}$$

$$f = \frac{\text{ab sin C}}{(\sin \frac{C}{2})(a + b)}$$

$$f = \frac{\text{ab}(2 \sin \frac{C}{2} \cos \frac{C}{2})}{(\sin \frac{C}{2})(a + b)}$$

$$f = \frac{2 \text{ ab cos } \frac{C}{2}}{a + b}$$

55. (c) $\cos \dfrac{C}{2} = \sqrt{\dfrac{1 + \cos C}{2}}$ $\left[\begin{array}{l}\text{The positive root is appropriate}\\[4pt]\text{here because } 0° < \dfrac{C}{2} < 90°.\end{array}\right]$

$= \sqrt{\dfrac{1 + (a^2 + b^2 - c^2)/2ab}{2} \cdot \dfrac{2ab}{2ab}}$

$= \sqrt{\dfrac{2ab + a^2 + b^2 - c^2}{4ab}} = \dfrac{1}{2}\sqrt{\dfrac{(a + b)^2 - c^2}{ab}}$

$= \dfrac{1}{2}\sqrt{\dfrac{(a + b - c)(a + b + c)}{ab}}$ $\left[\begin{array}{l}\text{We used difference}\\\text{of squares factoring.}\end{array}\right]$

(d)   Now we substitute the result obtained in part (c) into the expression for f that was found in part (b). This yields

$f = \dfrac{2ab\left[\dfrac{1}{2}\sqrt{\dfrac{(a + b - c)(a + b + c)}{ab}}\right]}{a + b}$

$= \dfrac{\dfrac{ab}{\sqrt{ab}}\sqrt{(a + b - c)(a + b + c)}}{a + b}$

$= \dfrac{\dfrac{\sqrt{ab}\,\sqrt{ab}}{\sqrt{ab}}\sqrt{(a + b - c)(a + b + c)}}{a + b}$

$= \dfrac{\sqrt{ab}}{a + b}\sqrt{(a + b - c)(a + b + c)},$ as required.

[Remark: This formula for the length of an angle bisector can be used to prove the Steiner-Lehmus Theorem. The statement of this theorem is as follows. If two angle bisectors in a triangle are equal (each bisector being measured from a vertex to the opposite side), then the triangle is isosceles.]

Exercise Set 7.5

1. (a) Since the graph repeats its pattern every 10 units, that is the period.

    The max is 12, while the min is 0 and $\dfrac{12 - 0}{2} = 6$, the amplitude.

    (b) period = 6, amplitude = $\dfrac{-3 - (-6)}{2} = 1.5$.

    (c) period = 4, amplitude = $\dfrac{5 - (-5)}{2} = 5$.

    (d) period = $\dfrac{2}{5}\pi$, amplitude = $\dfrac{2 - (-2)}{2} = 2$.

3. (a)

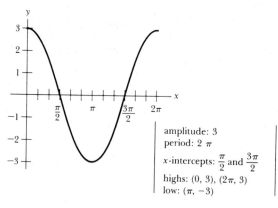

amplitude: 3
period: 2π
x-intercepts: $\dfrac{\pi}{2}$ and $\dfrac{3\pi}{2}$
highs: $(0, 3)$, $(2\pi, 3)$
low: $(\pi, -3)$

(b)

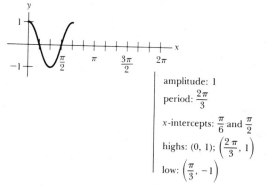

amplitude: 1
period: $\dfrac{2\pi}{3}$
x-intercepts: $\dfrac{\pi}{6}$ and $\dfrac{\pi}{2}$
highs: $(0, 1)$; $\left(\dfrac{2\pi}{3}, 1\right)$
low: $\left(\dfrac{\pi}{3}, -1\right)$

Note here that the 3 as a coefficient for cos x effects the amplitude, while 3 as a coefficient for x effects the period.

(c)

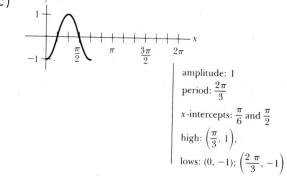

amplitude: 1
period: $\dfrac{2\pi}{3}$
x-intercepts: $\dfrac{\pi}{6}$ and $\dfrac{\pi}{2}$
high: $\left(\dfrac{\pi}{3}, 1\right)$,
lows: $(0, -1)$; $\left(\dfrac{2\pi}{3}, -1\right)$

5. (a)

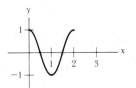

amplitude: 1
period: 2
x-intercepts: $\frac{1}{2}$ and $\frac{3}{2}$
highs: (0, 1); (2, 1)
low: (1, −1)

Remember that for

$y = \cos bx$, the period

is $\frac{2\pi}{b}$. In this case,

$\frac{2\pi}{\pi} = 2$ is the period.

Also note how the one

added to the equation in

part (b) raises its graph

to generate part (c).

(b)

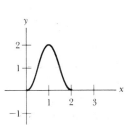

amplitude: 1
period: 2
x-intercepts: $\frac{1}{2}$ and $\frac{3}{2}$
high: (1, 1)
lows: (0, −1); (2, −1)

(c)

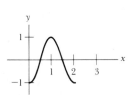

amplitude: 1
period: 2
x-intercepts: 0 and 2
high: (1, 2)
lows: (0, 0); (2, 0)

7. (a)

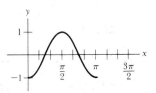

amplitude: 1
period: π
x-intercepts: $\frac{\pi}{4}$ and $\frac{3\pi}{4}$
high: $\left(\frac{\pi}{2}, 1\right)$
lows: (0, −1); (π, −1)

(b)

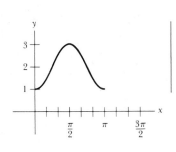

amplitude: 1
period: π
x-intercepts: none
high: $\left(\frac{\pi}{2}, 3\right)$
lows: (0, 1); (π, 1)

9.   (a)   (b)

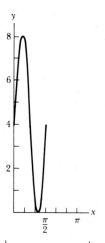

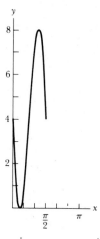

amplitude: 4

period: $\frac{\pi}{2}$

x-intercept: $\frac{3\pi}{8}$

high: $\left(\frac{\pi}{8}, 8\right)$

low: $\left(\frac{3}{8}\pi, 0\right)$

amplitude: 4

period: $\frac{\pi}{2}$

x-intercept: $\frac{\pi}{8}$

high: $\left(\frac{3\pi}{8}, 8\right)$

low: $\left(\frac{\pi}{8}, 0\right)$

11.

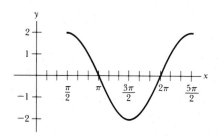

amplitude: 2

period: 2π

phase shift: $\frac{\pi}{2}$

x-intercepts: π and 2π

highs: $\left(\frac{\pi}{2}, 2\right)$; $\left(\frac{5\pi}{2}, 2\right)$

low: $\left(\frac{3}{2}\pi, -2\right)$

Here we compare $y = 2\cos\left(x - \frac{\pi}{2}\right)$ to $y = A\cos(Bx + c)$ and observe an amplitude of 2 a period of $\frac{2\pi}{1}$ or 2π and a phase shift of $-\frac{C}{B}$ which is $-\frac{-\pi}{2}$ or $\frac{\pi}{2}$ units. We choose to start a regular cosine curve with an amplitude of 2 at $\frac{\pi}{2}$ and sketch one complete cycle, ending at $\frac{5\pi}{2}$.

13.

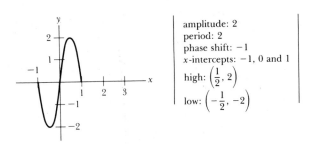

amplitude: 2
period: 2
phase shift: −1
x-intercepts: −1, 0 and 1

high: $\left(\frac{1}{2}, 2\right)$

low: $\left(-\frac{1}{2}, -2\right)$

15.

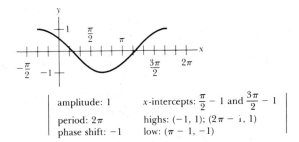

amplitude: 1   x-intercepts: $\frac{\pi}{2} - 1$ and $\frac{3\pi}{2} - 1$

period: 2π highs: $(-1, 1)$; $(2\pi - 1, 1)$

phase shift: −1   low: $(\pi - 1, -1)$

Problems which have periods or phase shifts not expressed in terms of π, as is the case here, sometimes present extra difficulties for students. Here $-\frac{C}{B} = -\frac{1}{1} = -1$, so the phase shift is −1 units. Recall that $\pi \approx 3.14$, so $\frac{\pi}{3} \approx 1$ for purposes of graphing the phase shift. For the $\cos\theta$, the maximum value occurs at $\theta = 0$ and $\theta = 2\pi$, or in this case $\theta = -1$ and $\theta = 2\pi - 1$. Since the amplitude is 1 the maximum is 1 in both cases. The minimum value for the cosine can be found halfway between these ends, at $\pi - 1$. It will be −1.

17.

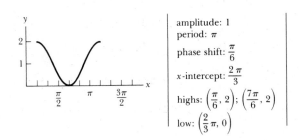

amplitude: 1
period: π

phase shift: $\frac{\pi}{6}$

x-intercept: $\frac{2\pi}{3}$

highs: $\left(\frac{\pi}{6}, 2\right)$; $\left(\frac{7\pi}{6}, 2\right)$

low: $\left(\frac{2}{3}\pi, 0\right)$

19.

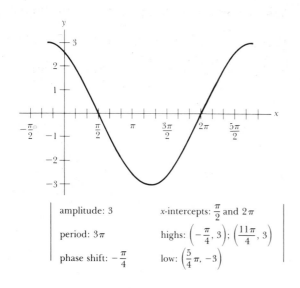

amplitude: 3 x-intercepts: $\frac{\pi}{2}$ and 2π

period: 3π highs: $\left(-\frac{\pi}{4}, 3\right)$; $\left(\frac{11\pi}{4}, 3\right)$

phase shift: $-\frac{\pi}{4}$ low: $\left(\frac{5}{4}\pi, -3\right)$

Try the following steps as an exercise when you graph a rather complex trigonometric function such as this.

Start with $y = \cos x$. Next, on the same set of axes, sketch the function with its new period. In this case, it is stretched out from 0 to 3π since $\frac{2\pi}{\frac{2}{3}} = 3\pi$. Now shift the previous curve by the phase shift, here $\frac{\pi}{4}$ to the left. Finally graph the last curve with the appropriate amplitude, here 3. You can try using different colors for each curve. This process will help you see how the various factors effect the final outcome when you are graphing.

21.

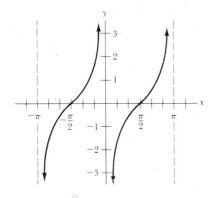

This is just $y = \tan x$ shifted $\frac{\pi}{2}$ units to the right.

23.

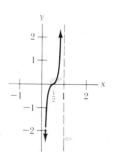

25.

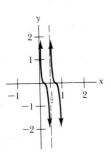

The interesting thing here is the period. Normally π for the tan and cot function, it is now $\frac{\pi}{2\pi}$ or $\frac{1}{2}$ in this problem.

27.

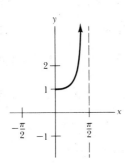

29.

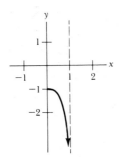

There is no phase shift here so the negative sign starts us off in the opposite direction from the standard sec graph. The period is $\frac{2\pi}{\pi}$ or 4. From 0 to 1 we see $\frac{1}{4}$ of one complete cycle.

31.

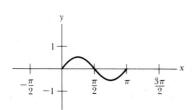

33.

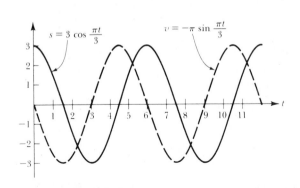

(a) Clearly the amplitude is 3.
    The period is $\dfrac{2\pi}{\frac{\pi}{3}} = 6$. For
    $0 \leq t \leq 12$, we get two
    complete cycles.

(b) The weight is furthest from
    the origin when $|s|$ is a
    maximum. Here it happens
    when $t = 0,3,6,9,12$ sec.

(c) The graph again shows us.

(d) The amplitude here is π, slightly more than 3. The graph here does
    not clearly show this.

39. (a) amplitude: 2, period: π

    (b) -2

EXERCISE SET 7.6

1. To find out let's substitute $\frac{\pi}{2}$ for θ in the given equation.

$$2 \cos^2 \theta - 3 \cos \theta = 0$$
$$2 \cos^2 \frac{\pi}{2} - 3 \cos \frac{\pi}{2} = 0$$
$$2(0)^2 - 3(0) = 0, \quad \text{yes.}$$

3. no

5. no

7. $\cos \theta = -1$

   Recalling the graph of $\cos \theta$ we see that $\cos \theta = -1$ for $\theta = \pi$. Since
   we want all solutions we take $\theta = \pi + 2\pi k$.

9. $x = \frac{\pi}{6} + 2\pi k; \ x = \frac{5}{6}\pi + 2\pi k; \ x = \frac{\pi}{2} + 2\pi k$

11. $\sin^2 x - \sin x - 6 = 0$ Let's factor.

$(\sin x - 3)(\sin x + 2) = 0$

Solving by setting each factor equal to zero, we have

$$\sin x - 3 = 0 \quad \text{or} \quad \sin x = 3$$

and

$$\sin x + 2 = 0 \quad \text{or} \quad \sin x = -2.$$

But, since the range of $\sin x$ is from -1 to $+1$, both solutions are impossible. There is no solution.

13. $\theta = \pi + 2\pi k$

15.
$$2 \cot^2 x + \csc^2 x - 2 = 0$$
$$2 \cot^2 x + (1 + \cot^2 x) - 2 = 0$$
$$3 \cot^2 x - 1 = 0$$
$$3 \cot^2 x = 1$$
$$\cot^2 x = \frac{1}{3}$$
$$\cot x = \pm \frac{1}{\sqrt{3}}$$

$\cot x = \dfrac{1}{\sqrt{3}}$ for $x = \frac{\pi}{3}$ and for every multiple of π added to $\frac{\pi}{3}$. The negative root is for $x = \frac{2}{3}\pi$ and also for $\frac{2}{3}\pi + k\pi$. We add multiples of π instead of 2π to tangents and cotangents because that is the period of these functions.

17. $\alpha = \frac{\pi}{6} + 2\pi k$

19. Tan $2\theta = -1$

The tangent is equal to -1 for angles of $135°$ and $315°$ so we take 2θ equal to these angles. But the simplest way to include all values of θ is to consider values of 2θ up to $720°$. The work looks like this.

19. (cont) $\tan 2\theta = -1$

$$2\theta = 135°, 315°, 495°, 675°$$

Now dividing by 2 we get

$$\theta = 67.5°, 157.5°, 247.5°, 337.5°$$

for the solutions from 0° to 360°. In the same way, for a problem

involving 3θ we must consider 3θ from 0° to $3 \cdot 360°$ to get θ from

0° to 360°.

21. $\sin \dfrac{\theta}{2} = \dfrac{1}{2}$

$$\dfrac{\theta}{2} = 30°, 150° \quad \text{and multiplying by 2}$$

$$\theta = 60°, 300°$$

23. For most problems involving more complicated sin and cos functions, it is

usually easiest to write the equation in terms of only sin or cos.

$$2 \sin^2 \theta - \cos 2\theta = 0$$

$$2 \sin^2 \theta - (1 - 2 \sin^2 \theta) = 0$$

$$4 \sin^2 \theta - 1 = 0$$

$$\sin^2 \theta = \dfrac{1}{4}$$

$$\sin \theta = \pm \dfrac{1}{2}$$

$$\theta = 30°, 150°, 210°, 330°$$

25. $\sin 2\theta = -2 \cos \theta$

$$2 \sin \theta \cos \theta = -2 \cos \theta$$

$$2 \sin \theta \cos \theta + 2 \cos \theta = 0$$

$$2 \cos \theta (\sin \theta + 1) = 0$$

$2 \cos \theta = 0$ $\sin \theta + 1 = 0$

$\cos \theta = 0$ $\sin \theta = -1$

$\theta = 90°, 270°$ $\theta = 270°$

25. (cont)

The solutions are therefore 90° and 270°.

27. no solution. How can $\cos \theta = \frac{5}{3}$?

29. $2 \sin^2 \theta + \sin \theta - 1 = 0$

$(2 \sin \theta - 1)(\sin \theta + 1) = 0$

$2 \sin \theta = 1$ $\sin \theta = -1$

$\sin \theta = \frac{1}{2}$ $\theta = 270°$

$\theta = 30°, 150°$

31. no solution

33. $2 \sin x = 1 - \cos x$

$2 \sin x + \cos x = 1$ now square

$4 \sin^2 x + 4 \sin x \cos x + \cos^2 x = 1$ regroup

$3 \sin^2 x + 4 \sin x \cos x + \sin^2 x + \cos^2 x = 1$

or $3 \sin^2 x + 4 \sin x \cos x = 0$

factoring gives $\sin x(3 \sin x + 4 \cos x) = 0$

$\sin x = 0$ $3 \sin x = -4 \cos x$

$x = 0°$ $\tan x = -\frac{4}{3}$ Divide by $\cos x$.

(360° if we include $x = 126.9°$ and $306.9°$

the right endpoint.)

Be sure and check: $2 \sin 0° = 1 - \cos 0°$

$2 \cdot 0 = 1 - 1$ ✓

126.9° also checks using a calculator but 306.9° doesn't.

35. This requires some insight, luck, or having seen it before. The left side

is the identity for the $\sin(3x + x)$ so we can change the equation to

the much simpler

35. (cont)

$$\sin(3x + x) = \frac{\sqrt{3}}{2}$$

$$\sin 4x = \frac{\sqrt{3}}{2}$$

$$4x = \frac{\pi}{3} , \frac{2}{3}\pi, \frac{7}{3}\pi, \frac{8}{3}\pi, \frac{13}{3}\pi, \frac{14}{3}\pi, \frac{19}{3}\pi, \frac{20}{3}\pi$$

We went from 0 to 8π because of the 4x. Now divide by 4, and we have

$$x = \frac{\pi}{12} , \frac{\pi}{6} , \frac{7}{12}\pi, \frac{2}{3}\pi, \frac{13}{12}\pi, \frac{7}{6}\pi, \frac{19}{12}\pi, \frac{5}{3}\pi,$$

all from 0 to 2π.

37. sin 5x = sin 3x

or sin 5x - sin 3x = 0. Following the hint, we look at formula b. The left side can be written as

$$2 \cos \frac{5x + 3x}{2} \sin \frac{5x - 3x}{2}$$

so we get

$$2 \cos 4x \sin x = 0.$$

which will be true if

$$\cos 4x = 0 \quad \text{or} \quad \sin x = 0.$$

cos 4x = 0   so

$$4x = \frac{\pi}{2} , \frac{3}{2}\pi, \frac{5}{2}\pi, \frac{7}{2}\pi, \frac{9}{2}\pi, \frac{11}{2}\pi, \frac{13}{2}\pi, \frac{15}{2}\pi$$

and

$$x = \frac{\pi}{8} , \frac{3}{8}\pi, \frac{5}{8}\pi, \frac{7}{8}\pi, \frac{9}{8}\pi, \frac{11}{8}\pi, \frac{13}{8}\pi, \frac{15}{8}\pi$$

sin x = 0   so   x = 0,π,2π for the final three solutions.

39. $x = \frac{\pi}{10} , \frac{\pi}{2} , \frac{9}{10}\pi, \frac{13}{10}\pi, \frac{17}{10}\pi$

41. $x = \frac{\pi}{3} , \frac{4}{3}\pi$

43.

$$4 \sin \theta - 3 \cos \theta = 2$$

$$4 \sin \theta = 3 \cos \theta + 2$$

$$16 \sin^2 \theta = 9 \cos^2 \theta + 12 \cos \theta + 4$$

$$16(1 - \cos^2 \theta) = 9 \cos^2 \theta + 12 \cos \theta + 4$$

$$16 - 16 \cos^2 \theta = 9 \cos^2 \theta + 12 \cos \theta + 4$$

$$0 = 25 \cos^2 \theta + 12 \cos \theta - 12$$

This is a quadratic in $\cos \theta$, and since it won't factor (you try) we must use the quadratic formula.

$$\cos \theta = \frac{-12 \pm \sqrt{(12)^2 - 4(25)(-12)}}{2(25)}$$

$$= \frac{-12 \pm \sqrt{1344}}{50}$$

$$= \frac{-12 \pm 8\sqrt{21}}{50}$$

$$= \frac{-6 \pm 4\sqrt{21}}{25}$$

so $\cos \theta = .4932$ and $-.9732$ and $\theta = 60.45°$ and the second solution, which incidentally won't check, is outside $0° < \theta < 90°$. We have $\theta = 60.45°$ as required.

EXERCISE SET 7.7

1. $\sin^{-1} \frac{\sqrt{3}}{2}$ is the number in the interval $\left[-\frac{\pi}{2}, \frac{\pi}{2}\right]$ whose sin is $\frac{\sqrt{3}}{2}$. That number is $\frac{\pi}{3}$.

3. $\frac{\pi}{3}$

5. $\arctan\left(-\frac{1}{\sqrt{3}}\right)$ is, by definition, the number whose tangent is $-\frac{1}{\sqrt{3}}$. It must be $-\frac{\pi}{6}$.

7. $\frac{\pi}{4}$

9. $\cos^{-1} 2\pi$ represents the number whose cosine is 2π,   or about   6.14.

    Since the cosine ranges from   -1   to   1,   there is no such number.

11. $\frac{1}{4}$

13. The definition on page 419 tells us that $\cos(\cos^{-1} x) = x$ for $-1 \le x \le 1$.

    Therefore $\cos(\cos^{-1} \frac{3}{4})$ must be $\frac{3}{4}$.   The cosine of the number (or angle)

    whose cosine is $\frac{3}{4}$,   must be $\frac{3}{4}$.   What year was the war of 1812?

15. $-\frac{\pi}{7}$

17. Again, by definition $\arcsin(\sin \frac{\pi}{2})$ is $\frac{\pi}{2}$.

19. 0,   since $\cos 2\pi = 1$ and $\arccos(1) = 0$.

21. A sketch will be useful for problems like 21-30.   In this case, draw the

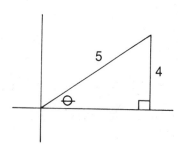

acute angle whose sin is $\frac{4}{5}$.   Pythagoras

tells us that the missing side is   3,   so the

tangent of the angle is $\frac{4}{3}$.

$$\tan(\sin^{-1} \frac{4}{5}) = \frac{4}{3}.$$

23. $\frac{\sqrt{2}}{2}$

25.

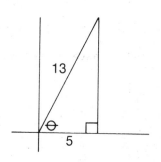

The missing side is   12,   and the tan of

angle $\theta = \frac{12}{5}$.

27. $\frac{1}{2}$

29.

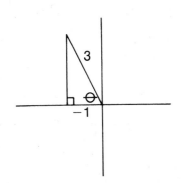

The sin θ is $\frac{2\sqrt{2}}{3}$.

31. (a) .84

(b) .84

(c) 1.26

(d) .90

33. $\sec[\cos^{-1}\frac{\sqrt{2}}{2} + \sin^{-1}(-1)]$

$\cos^{-1}\frac{\sqrt{2}}{2} = \frac{\pi}{4}$ and $\sin^{-1}(-1) = -\frac{\pi}{2}$, so their sum is $-\frac{\pi}{4}$. Therefore, we want to find $\sec[-\frac{\pi}{4}]$. That is the reciprocal of the $\cos(-\frac{\pi}{4})$. Since the latter is $\frac{\sqrt{2}}{2}$, $\sec(-\frac{\pi}{4})$ is $\sqrt{2}$ as required.

37. $\cos(2\sin^{-1}\frac{5}{13})$. Remember, $\sin^{-1}\frac{5}{13}$ is an angle so this has the form

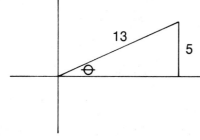

$\cos 2\theta$ which is $\cos^2\theta - \sin^2\theta$. Let's look at a picture of this θ. The missing side must be 12 and we have values for both sin θ and cos θ.

$$\cos 2\theta = \cos^2\theta - \sin^2\theta$$
$$= (\frac{12}{13})^2 - (\frac{5}{13})^2$$
$$= \frac{144}{169} - \frac{25}{169}$$
$$= \frac{119}{169}$$

So $\cos(2\sin^{-1}\frac{5}{13}) = \frac{119}{169}$ as required.

39. $\sin(\sin^{-1}\frac{1}{3} + \sin^{-1}\frac{1}{4})$ has the form $\sin(a + b)$ which is $\sin a \cos b +$
     $\cos a \sin b$. Again we need sketches of a and b so we can read values
     for their sines and cosines.

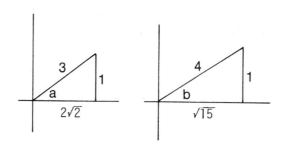

Substituting we get

$$\sin a \cdot \cos b + \cos a \cdot \sin b = \frac{1}{3} \cdot \frac{\sqrt{15}}{4} + \frac{2\sqrt{2}}{3} \cdot \frac{1}{4}$$

$$= \frac{\sqrt{15} + 2\sqrt{2}}{12} \quad \text{as required.}$$

47. We can picture these two angles. If we let $x = \arcsin\frac{4}{5}$ and
     $y = \arctan\frac{3}{4}$ we have,

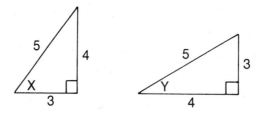

A careful look at the triangles involved shows that these are complementary
angles and their sum must be 90° or $\frac{\pi}{2}$ radians.

As an alternative let's evaluate the $\sin[\arcsin\frac{4}{5} + \arctan\frac{3}{4}]$ as
$\sin[x + y]$. It equals $\sin x \cos y + \cos x \sin y$ or $\frac{4}{5} \cdot \frac{4}{5} + \frac{3}{5} \cdot \frac{3}{5}$ which
gives $\frac{25}{25}$ or 1, and the sine is 1 for $\frac{\pi}{2}$. This confirms the other
result.

Chapter 8 Systems of Equations

Exercise Set 8.1

1. a, c, d

3. yes

    We simply test (5,1) in the two equations and see if it produces true
    statements.

    $$2(5) - 8(1) = 2$$
    $$10 - 8 = 2 \checkmark$$

    and

    $$3(5) + 7(1) = 22$$
    $$15 + 7 = 22 \checkmark$$

    (5,1) is a solution.

5. no

7. yes

9. To solve any system by substitution we need to solve one of the equations
    for one variable. Experience will soon show you the easiest way. Here, we

9. (cont)

will solve equation two for x.

$$x = -4 - 4y$$

and now substitute that value of x in equation one.

$$3(-4 - 4y) - 2y = -19$$

Now solve for y.

$$-12 - 12y - 2y = -19$$
$$-14y = -7$$
$$y = \frac{1}{2}$$

Now find x from equation two.

$$x = -4 - 4y$$
$$= -4 - 4(\frac{1}{2})$$
$$= -4 - 2$$
$$= -6$$

It is important to note that if we check, we must use equation one not the equation we just finished using.

$$\text{Does } \quad 3(-6) - 2(\frac{1}{2}) \quad \text{equal } \quad -19?$$
$$-18 - 1$$
$$-19 \quad \text{yes!}$$

We have a unique solution, $(6, \frac{1}{2})$. The system is independent.

11. 4x + 2y = 3

10x + 4y = 1

Neither equation is easily solved for a variable. Either will require a

11. (cont)

fraction. Let's solve the first equation for y

$$4x + 2y = 3$$

$$2y = 3 - 4x$$

$$y = \frac{3 - 4x}{2}$$

Now substitute.

$$10x + 4\left(\frac{3 - 4x}{2}\right) = 1$$

Multiplying by 2 we have

$$20x + 4(3 - 4x) = 2$$

$$20x + 12 - 16x = 2$$

$$4x = -10$$

$$x = -\frac{5}{2}$$

so

$$y = \frac{3 - 4(-\frac{5}{2})}{2}$$

$$= \frac{3 + 10}{2}$$

$$= \frac{13}{2}$$

The solution is $(-\frac{5}{2}, \frac{13}{2})$ and the system is independent.

13. $-7x + 2x = 0$

so $y = \frac{7x}{2}$

and substituting we get

$$13x - 8\left(\frac{7x}{2}\right) = -3$$

$$13x - 28x = -3$$

$$-15x = -3$$

$$x = \frac{1}{5}$$

and

13. (cont)
$$y = \frac{7\left(\frac{1}{5}\right)}{2} = \frac{7}{10}$$

Again, they are independent.

15. $\left(-\frac{60}{13}, \frac{60}{13}\right)$; independent

17. From equation 1
$$\sqrt{2}\, x = \sqrt{3} + \sqrt{3}\, y$$

$$x = \frac{\sqrt{3} + \sqrt{3}\, y}{\sqrt{2}}$$

When we substitute into equation 2 we get

$$\sqrt{3}\left(\frac{\sqrt{3} + \sqrt{3}\, y}{\sqrt{2}}\right) - \sqrt{8}\, y = \sqrt{2}$$

We need to distribute the $\sqrt{3}$ over the first term and multiply all three terms by the common denominator, $\sqrt{2}$.

$$\left(\frac{3 + 3y}{\sqrt{2}}\right) - \sqrt{8}\, y = \sqrt{2}$$

$$3 + 3y - 4y = 2$$

$$-y = -1$$

$$y = 1$$

and

$$x = \frac{\sqrt{3} + \sqrt{3}(1)}{\sqrt{2}}$$

$$= \frac{2\sqrt{3}}{\sqrt{2}}$$

$$= \sqrt{6}$$

The solution is $(\sqrt{6}, 1)$.

19.
$$5x + 6y = 4$$

$$2x - 3y = -3 \quad \text{Multiply by } 2 \text{ and add.}$$

$$5x + 6y = 4$$

$$4x - 6y = -6$$

$$9x \qquad = -2$$

$$x \qquad = -\frac{2}{9}$$

19.   (cont)

Substituting into either equation will give us a value for y.

$$5(-\frac{2}{9}) + 6y = 4$$

$$-\frac{10}{9} + 6y = 4$$

$$6y = \frac{46}{9}$$

$$y = \frac{23}{27}$$

$(-\frac{2}{9}, \frac{23}{27})$ is the solution.

21. $(-\frac{283}{242}, \frac{3}{121})$

23.   Equations of this form are usually most easily solved by multiplying each

equation by its LCD to eliminate fractions.

Equation 1 can be simplified by multiplying through by 12, and equation

2 by 20. We get

$$3x - 4y = 48$$

$$20x - 10y = 7$$

Let's eliminate y. Multiply by 5 in the first equation and -2 in the

second.

$$15x - 20y = 240$$

$$-40x + 20y = -14 \quad \text{now add}$$

$$-25x = 226$$

$$x = -\frac{226}{25}$$

and

$$3(-\frac{226}{25}) - 4y = 48$$

$$-678 - 100y = 1200$$

$$-100y = 1878$$

$$y = -\frac{939}{50} \quad \text{in lowest terms.}$$

$(-\frac{226}{25}, -\frac{939}{50})$ is our solution.

25. $(\frac{5}{8}, 0)$

27. Let's multiply equation two by $-\sqrt{3}$ so that the x coefficients will be equal.

$$\sqrt{6}\,x - \sqrt{3}\,y = 3\sqrt{2} - \sqrt{3}$$

$$-\sqrt{6}\,x + \sqrt{15}\,y = -3\sqrt{2} - \sqrt{15} \quad \text{now add}$$

$$(\sqrt{15} - \sqrt{3})y = -(\sqrt{15} + \sqrt{3})$$

$$y = -\left[\frac{\sqrt{15} + \sqrt{3}}{\sqrt{15} - \sqrt{3}}\right]$$

$$\text{or} \qquad y = -\frac{(\sqrt{3})(\sqrt{5} + 1)}{(\sqrt{3})(\sqrt{5} - 1)}$$

which reduces to $y = -\dfrac{(\sqrt{5} + 1)}{(\sqrt{5} - 1)}$. If we rationalize the denominator, we

have $\dfrac{\sqrt{5} + 1}{\sqrt{5} - 1} \cdot \dfrac{\sqrt{5} + 1}{\sqrt{5} + 1} = \dfrac{5 + 2\sqrt{5} + 1}{5 - 1} = \dfrac{6 + 2\sqrt{5}}{4}$ or finally $y = \dfrac{-3 - \sqrt{5}}{2}$.

Now substitute to find x.

$$\sqrt{2}\,x - \sqrt{5}\left(\frac{-3 - \sqrt{5}}{2}\right) = \sqrt{6} + \sqrt{5}$$

Multiplying by 2

$$2\sqrt{2}\,x + 3\sqrt{5} + 5 = 2\sqrt{6} + 2\sqrt{5}$$

$$2\sqrt{2}\,x = 2\sqrt{6} - \sqrt{5} - 5$$

or

$$x = \frac{2\sqrt{6} - \sqrt{5} - 5}{2\sqrt{2}}$$

We rationalize the denominator to get

$$x = \frac{2\sqrt{12} - \sqrt{10} - 5\sqrt{2}}{4}$$

finally

$$x = \frac{4\sqrt{3} - \sqrt{10} - 5\sqrt{2}}{4}$$

$\left(\dfrac{4\sqrt{3} - \sqrt{10} - 5\sqrt{2}}{4}, \dfrac{-3 - \sqrt{5}}{2}\right)$ is the solution.

29. The given points must satisfy the equations, so we get

$$4 = 0^2 + b \cdot 0 + c \quad \text{or} \quad 4 = c$$

and

$$14 = 2^2 + b \cdot 2 + c \quad \text{or} \quad 10 = 2b + c$$

This system, $c = 4$ and $2b + c = 10$ is easily solved by substitution.

$$2b + c = 10$$
$$2b + 4 = 10$$
$$2b = 6$$
$$b = 3$$

so the equation of the parabola is $y^2 = x^2 + 3x + 4$ as required.

31. Again, the points satisfy the equation.

$$Ax + By = 2 \quad \text{becomes first}$$
$$A(-4) + B(5) = 2 \quad \text{and then}$$
$$A(7) + B(-9) = 2$$

So we have

$$-4A + 5B = 2$$
$$7A - 9B = 2 \quad \text{Let's eliminate } A.$$

$$-28A + 35B = 14$$
$$28A - 36B = 8$$
$$-B = 22$$
$$B = -22$$

and

$$7A - 9(-22) = 2$$
$$7A + 198 = 2$$
$$7A = -196$$
$$A = -28 \quad \text{as required.}$$

33. $A = \frac{49}{20}$ sq units

35. If we follow example 7 in this section, we let x = the amount of 10%

solution and y the amount of the 35% solution. Then x + y = 200 cc.

Also we know that the amount of acid in each separate solution, 10% of x

and 35% of y must equal the acid in the final solution, 25% of x + y.

This second equation is usually in need of simplifying.

$$.10x + .35y = .25(x + y)$$

$$10x + 35y = 25(x + y)$$

$$2x + 7y = 5x + 5y$$

$$-3x + 2y = 0$$

This system is now solved by either method.

$$x + y = 200$$

$$-3x + 2y = 0$$

$$3x + 3y = 600$$

$$-3x + 2y = 0$$

$$5y = 600$$

$$y = 120$$

so   x = 80   and we need 80 cc   of the 10% solution and 120 cc of the 35%

solution.

Take a minute to consider what is a simpler solution. Using x + y = 200,

substitute in the larger equation

$$10x + 35y = 25(x + y)   \text{becomes}$$

$$10x + 35(200 - x) = 25(200)$$

or

35. (cont) $10x + 70000 - 35x = 5000$

$-25x = -2000$

$x = 80$ so $y = 120$

we get the same results with less work.

37. An equal amount of each type.

39. Eliminating fractions we get

$$bx + ay = ab \quad \text{and}$$

$$ax + by = ab$$

so

$$abx + a^2y = a^2b$$

$$-abx - b^2y = -ab^2 \quad \text{adding gives}$$

$$(a^2 - b^2)y = a^2b - ab^2$$

$$y = \frac{ab(a - b)}{(a^2 - b^2)}$$

If we factor and reduce, we have $y = \frac{ab}{(a + b)}$.   Now substitute to get x.

$$\frac{x}{a} + \frac{\frac{ab}{a + b}}{b} = 1$$

$$\frac{x}{a} + \frac{a}{a + b} = 1$$

$$(a + b)x + a^2 = a(a + b)$$

$$(a + b)x = a^2 + ab - a^2$$

$$x = \frac{ab}{a + b}$$

our result, $\left(\dfrac{ab}{a + b} , \dfrac{ab}{a + b} \right)$.

Try the check in equation 2.

$$\frac{\dfrac{ab}{a + b}}{b} + \frac{\dfrac{ab}{a + b}}{a} = 1$$

$$\frac{ab}{a + b} \cdot \frac{1}{b} + \frac{ab}{a + b} \cdot \frac{1}{a} = 1$$

$$\frac{a}{a + b} + \frac{b}{a + b} = 1$$

$$\frac{a + b}{a + b} = 1 \quad \text{Hey, it works!}$$

41. $\left(\dfrac{a + b}{ab} , - \dfrac{1}{ab} \right)$

43. This type system looks easier if we make a simple substitution. Let $\dfrac{1}{x} = a$ and $\dfrac{1}{y} = b$. Then we get

$$5a - 5b = \frac{1}{3}$$

$$2a - 3b = 4$$

We can either eliminate the $\dfrac{1}{3}$ by multiplying by 3 or just include the fraction in the problem. Let's get rid of a.

$$-10a + 10b = -\frac{2}{3}$$

$$10a - 15b = 20$$

$$-5b = 20 - \frac{2}{3}$$

$$-5b = \frac{58}{3}$$

$$b = -\frac{58}{15}$$

But remember, $\dfrac{1}{y} = b$ so $y = -\dfrac{15}{58}$. Substituting back gives us $x = -\dfrac{5}{19}$.

45. First let's clear of fractions and put into a standard form.

$$\frac{2w - 1}{3} + \frac{z + 2}{4} = 4 \quad \text{multiplying by 12 we get}$$

$$4(2w - 1) + 3(z + 2) = 12 \cdot 4$$

$$8w - 4 + 3z + 6 = 48$$

$$8w + 3z = 46$$

45. (cont)

The second equation will be $w + 2z = 9$.

$$8w + 3z = 46$$
$$w + 2z = 9$$

or

$$8w + 3z = 46$$
$$-8w - 16z = -72$$
$$-13z = -26$$
$$z = 2$$

and $w = 9 - 2(2) = 5$

$w = 5$ and $z = 2$ is the solution.

47. $u = -\dfrac{1}{11}$; $v = \dfrac{1}{9}$

49. $\left(\dfrac{5}{2}, \dfrac{1}{2}\right)$

51. If we take tu as our number, then it is important to distinguish between
its value, $10t + u$, and the sum of its digits $t + u$. Here we are told
that $t + u = 14$ and that $2t = u + 1$. We solve this system

$$t + u = 14$$
$$2t - u = 1$$

$$3t = 15$$
$$t = 5$$

so $u = 9$ and our original two digit number was 59.

53. 5 in. × 12 in.

55. (60,40)

57. (0,a)

59. $\left(\dfrac{1}{b}, \dfrac{1}{a}\right)$

61. $(-ab, a + b)$

EXERCISE SET 8.2

1.   (a)   Follow the rule on page 441 we have

$$\begin{vmatrix} 2 & -17 \\ 1 & 6 \end{vmatrix} = (2)(6) - (1)(-17) = 29$$

(b)
$$\begin{vmatrix} 1 & 6 \\ 2 & -17 \end{vmatrix} = (1)(-17) - (2)(6) = -29$$

3.   (a)   0

(b)   0

5.
$$\begin{vmatrix} \sqrt{2} - 1 & \sqrt{2} \\ \sqrt{2} & \sqrt{2} + 1 \end{vmatrix} = (\sqrt{2} - 1)(\sqrt{2} + 1) - (\sqrt{2})(\sqrt{2}) = -1$$

7.
$$D = \begin{vmatrix} 7 & -8 \\ 4 & 9 \end{vmatrix} = 63 - (-32) = 95$$

$$D_x = \begin{vmatrix} -1 & -8 \\ 1 & 9 \end{vmatrix} = -9 - (-8) = -1$$

$$D_y = \begin{vmatrix} 7 & -1 \\ 4 & 1 \end{vmatrix} = 7 - (-4) = 11$$

9. $D = -49$; $D_x = -63$; $D_y = -57$

11.   We first calculate D, D_x, D_y.

$$D = \begin{vmatrix} 4 & 5 \\ 3 & 8 \end{vmatrix} = 32 - 15 = 17$$

$$D_x = \begin{vmatrix} 9 & 5 \\ 2 & 8 \end{vmatrix} = 72 - 10 = 62$$

$$D_y = \begin{vmatrix} 4 & 9 \\ 3 & 2 \end{vmatrix} = 8 - 27 = -19$$

11. (cont)

so $x = \dfrac{D_x}{D} = \dfrac{62}{17}$ and $y = \dfrac{D_y}{D} = \dfrac{-19}{17}$. The solution is the pair $(\dfrac{62}{17}, \dfrac{-19}{17})$.

13.

$$D = \begin{vmatrix} \frac{1}{2} & \frac{1}{3} \\ \frac{1}{3} & \frac{1}{2} \end{vmatrix} = \frac{1}{4} - \frac{1}{9} = \frac{5}{36}$$

$$D_x = \begin{vmatrix} 6 & \frac{1}{3} \\ \frac{13}{2} & \frac{1}{2} \end{vmatrix} = 3 - \frac{13}{6} = \frac{5}{6}$$

$$D_y = \begin{vmatrix} \frac{1}{2} & 6 \\ \frac{1}{3} & \frac{13}{2} \end{vmatrix} = \frac{13}{4} - 2 = \frac{5}{4}$$

We have $x = \dfrac{D_x}{D} = \dfrac{\frac{5}{6}}{\frac{5}{36}} = \dfrac{5}{6} \cdot \dfrac{36}{5} = 6$ and $y = \dfrac{D_y}{D} = \dfrac{\frac{5}{4}}{\frac{5}{36}} = 9.$

(6,9) is our solution.

15. (a) Here we have

$$D = \begin{vmatrix} 6 & -8 \\ 9 & -12 \end{vmatrix} = -72 - (-72) = 0.$$

A close look shows that these equations are dependent. The ratios of the coefficients are equal.

$$\frac{6}{9} = \frac{-8}{-12} = \frac{9}{\frac{27}{2}}$$

Solving the first equation for y gives $y = \dfrac{6x - 9}{8}$, so any point of the form $(x, \dfrac{6x - 9}{8})$ will work.

(b) Here the lines are inconsistent, they are parallel. There is no solution.

17.
$$D = \begin{vmatrix} 4 & -3 \\ 2 & 7 \end{vmatrix} = 28 + 6 = 34$$

$$D_x = \begin{vmatrix} \sqrt{5} - 1 & -3 \\ 9\sqrt{5} - 5 & 7 \end{vmatrix} = 7\sqrt{5} - 7 + 27\sqrt{5} - 15 = 34\sqrt{5} - 22$$

$$D_y = \begin{vmatrix} 4 & \sqrt{5} - 1 \\ 2 & 9\sqrt{5} - 5 \end{vmatrix} = 36\sqrt{5} - 20 - 2\sqrt{5} + 2 = 34\sqrt{5} - 18$$

$\left(\dfrac{17\sqrt{5} - 11}{17} , \dfrac{17\sqrt{5} - 9}{17} \right)$ is the reduced solution.

19. $\left(-\dfrac{585}{124} , -\dfrac{1130}{31} \right)$

21. We will just follow the same pattern using a's and b's as numerical coefficients.

$$D = \begin{vmatrix} a & b \\ b & a \end{vmatrix} = a^2 - b^2$$

$$D_x = \begin{vmatrix} a^2 & b \\ b^2 & a \end{vmatrix} = a^3 - b^3$$

$$D_y = \begin{vmatrix} a & a^2 \\ b & b^2 \end{vmatrix} = ab^2 - a^2b$$

$$x = \frac{a^3 - b^3}{a^2 - b^2} = \frac{(a - b)(a^2 + ab + b^2)}{(a + b)(a - b)} = \frac{a^2 + ab + b^2}{a + b} \;\cdot$$

$$y = \frac{ab^2 - a^2b}{a^2 - b^2} = \frac{ab(b - a)}{(a + b)(a - b)} = \frac{-ab}{a + b} \;\cdot$$

Remember, $\dfrac{b - a}{a - b} = \dfrac{-a + b}{a - b} = \dfrac{-(a - b)}{(a - b)} = -1.$

23. $(2a, 2b)$

25. $(-ab(a^2 + ab + b^2), b^2(b + a)(b^2 + a^2))$

33. Evaluating the determinant we get

$$(a - x)(b - x) - \sqrt{ab} \cdot \sqrt{ab} = 0$$

$$ab - bx - ax + x^2 - ab = 0 \quad \text{or}$$

$$x^2 - ax - bx = 0 \quad \text{and}$$

$$x(x - a - b) = 0$$

From which we get $x = 0$ and $x = a + b$ as roots.

37. Sharpen the pencils because this is a long algebraic exercise.

$$D = \begin{vmatrix} \dfrac{1}{a^2 - b^2} & \dfrac{-1}{a^2 + ab + b^2} \\[3mm] \dfrac{1}{a^2 + b^2} & \dfrac{1}{a^2 - ab + b^2} \end{vmatrix}$$

$$= \frac{1}{(a^2 - b^2)(a^2 - ab + b^2)} + \frac{1}{(a^2 + b^2)(a^2 + ab + b^2)}$$

$$= \frac{(a^2 + b^2)(a^2 + ab + b^2) + (a^2 - b^2)(a^2 - ab + b^2)}{(a^2 - b^2)(a^2 + b^2)(a^2 - ab + b^2)(a^2 + ab + b^2)}$$

$$= \frac{2a(a^3 + ab^2 + b^3)}{(a^2 - b^2)(a^2 + b^2)(a^2 - ab + b^2)(a^2 + ab + b^2)}$$

$$D_x = \begin{vmatrix} ab & \dfrac{-1}{a^2 + ab + b^2} \\[3mm] a(a + b) & \dfrac{1}{a^2 - ab + b^2} \end{vmatrix}$$

$$= \frac{ab}{a^2 - ab + b^2} + \frac{a(a + b)}{a^2 + ab + b^2}$$

$$= \frac{ab(a^2 + ab + b^2) + a(a + b)(a^2 - ab + b^2)}{(a^2 - ab + b^2)(a^2 + ab + b^2)} .$$

$$= \frac{a(a^3 + a^2b + ab^2 + 2b^3)}{(a^2 - ab + b^2)(a^2 + ab + b^2)}$$

And, in a similar fashion, we find

37. (cont)
$$D_y = \frac{a(a^2 - ab + 2b^2)}{(a - b)(a^2 + b^2)}$$

Now, $x = \dfrac{D_x}{D}$. When we invert and multiply, this complex fraction becomes

$$x = \frac{a(a^3 + a^2b + ab^2 + 2b^3)}{(a^2 - ab + b^2)(a^2 + ab + b^2)} \cdot \frac{(a^2 - b^2)(a^2 + b^2)(a^2 - ab + b^2)(a^2 + ab + b^2)}{2a(a^3 + ab^2 + b^3)}$$

$$= \frac{(a^2 + b^2)(a^2 - b^2)(a^3 + a^2b + ab^2 + 2b^3)}{2(a^3 + ab^2 + b^3)} \; . \quad \text{Do you believe that!}$$

The value for y is obtained in a similar fashion.

$$y = \frac{(a^3 + ab^2 + 2b^3)(a^2 + ab + b^2)(a^2 - ab + b^2)}{2(a^3 + ab^2 + b^3)}$$

I even checked these roots in equation one and it simplifies to ab.

39. $((a^2 + b^2)(a^2 - b^2), (a^2 + ab + b^2)(a^2 - ab + b^2))$

EXERCISE SET 8.3

1. Given $2x + y + z = -9$

$$3y - 2z = -4$$

$$8z = -8$$

we start with the third equation, solve for z and substitute back up the line. First $z = -1$, so

$$3y - 2(-1) = -4$$

$$\text{or} \qquad y = -2$$

and then in the first equation

$$2x + (-2) + (-1) = -9$$

$$x = -3$$

$(-3, -2, -1)$ is our solution.

3. $\left(-\dfrac{1}{60}, -\dfrac{2}{15}, \dfrac{3}{5}\right)$

5.
$$-4x + 5y \qquad = 0$$
$$3y + 2z = 1$$
$$3z = -1$$

Working backwards we have $z = -\dfrac{1}{3}$, then

$$3y + 2\left(-\dfrac{1}{3}\right) = 1$$
$$\text{or} \qquad y = \dfrac{5}{9}$$

and then $-4x + 5\left(\dfrac{5}{9}\right) = 0$, from which we find $x = \dfrac{25}{36}$.

7.
$$-x + 8y + 3z = 0$$
$$2z = 0$$

We see that $z = 0$, so the first equation becomes

$$-x + 8y = 0$$
$$\text{or} \qquad y = \dfrac{1}{8}x.$$

Any triple of the form $\left(x, \dfrac{1}{8}x, 0\right)$ will be a solution.

9.
$$2x + 3y + z + w = -6$$
$$y + 3z - 4w = 23$$
$$6z - 5w = 31$$
$$-2w = 10$$

First $w = -5$, then

$$6z - 5(-5) = 31$$
$$6z = 6$$
$$z = 1.$$

Next,

9. (cont)
$$y + 3(1) - 4(-5) = 23$$
$$y = 0.$$

Finally

$$2x + 3(0) + 1 + (-5) = -6$$
$$x = -1.$$

$(-1,0,1,-5)$ is the solution.

11. We must arrange this according to echelon form. First add negative two times the first equation to the second one, and -3 times it to the third.

$$x + y + z = 12$$
$$-3y - 3z = -25$$
$$-y - 2z = -14.$$

We want to eliminate the y term from the third equation so let's inter-change the 2nd and 3rd equations

$$x + y + z = 12$$
$$-y - 2z = -14$$
$$-3y - 3z = -25$$

and add -3 times the 2nd to the third.

$$x + y + z = 12$$
$$-y - 2z = -14$$
$$3z = 17$$

We are now in echelon form and solve as we have previously.

$$z = \frac{17}{3},$$
$$-y - 2(\frac{17}{3}) = -14$$
$$-y - \frac{34}{3} = -\frac{42}{3}$$
$$y = \frac{8}{3}$$

11. (cont)

and finally x must be $\frac{11}{3}$.

$(\frac{11}{3}, \frac{8}{3}, \frac{17}{3})$ is our solution.

13. (1,0,1)

15. There is no single "right" way to put a system into echelon form. We simply practice using the rules on page 452. In problem 15, let's subtract equation 2 from 3 and put that new result first.

$$x + 3y + 2z = 13$$
$$3x + 3y - 2z = 13$$
$$6x + 2y - 5z = 13$$

Now we eliminate x in the 2nd two equations by adding -3 times the first to the 2nd and -2 times the second to the third.

$$x + 3y + 2z = 13$$
$$-6y - 8z = -26$$
$$-4y - z = -13$$

Divide the 2nd equation by 2

$$x + 3y + 2z = 13$$
$$-3y - 4z = -13$$
$$-4y - z = -13$$

Now we can subtract the 2nd equation from the first to get

$$x + 3y + 2z = 13$$
$$-y + 3z = 0$$
$$-3y - 4z = -13$$

Now finally to eliminate y in the 3rd equation, we will add -3 times the 2nd equation to it.

15. (cont)
$$x + 3y + 2z = 13$$
$$-y + 3z = 0$$
$$-13z = -13$$

And, we solve to get first $z = 1$, then $y = 3$ and finally $x = 2$.

17. (1,1,-1)

19. We will write the equations in this order

$$x + 3y - 2z = 2$$
$$2x - y + z = -1$$
$$3x - 2y + 3z = 1$$

Let's take 2 from 3 in the interest of small coefficients.

$$x + 3y - 2z = 2$$
$$2x - y + z = -1$$
$$x - y + 2z - 2$$

Now eliminate x in 2 and 3.   Here I have added -2 times 3 to 2 and -1 times 1 to 3.

$$x + 3y - 2z = 2$$
$$y - 3z = -5$$
$$-4y + 4z = 0$$

Finally, add 4 times equation 2 to equation 3 we get

$$x + 3y - 2z = 2$$
$$y - 3z = -5$$
$$-8z = -20$$

So $z - \dfrac{5}{2}$,   next $y = \dfrac{5}{2}$ and $x = -\dfrac{1}{2}$.

21. dependent

23. Use equation 1 to get rid of x in the other 3.

$$x + y + z + w = 4$$

$$-3y - 2z - 2w = -1$$

$$-3y - z - 3w = -6$$

$$-2y + z - 3w = -11$$

Subtract 3 from 4 and reorder

$$x + y + z + w = 4$$

$$y + 2z = -5$$

$$-3y - 2z - 2w = -1$$

$$-3y - z - 3w = -6$$

Use 2 to eliminate y in 3 and 4.

$$x + y + z + w = 4$$

$$y + 2z = -5$$

$$4z - 2w = -16$$

$$5z - 3w = -21$$

Subtract 3 from 4, reorder, divide 3 by 2.

$$x + y + z + w = 4$$

$$y + 2z = -5$$

$$z - w = -5$$

$$2z - w = -8$$

Subtract twice 3 from 4.

$$x + y + z + w = 4$$

$$y + 2z = -5$$

$$z - w = -5$$

$$w = 2$$

23. (cont)

Now working backward we get (4,1,-3,2) as our solution.

25. $$x +\ y + z = 1$$

$$ax +\ y + z = a$$

$$x + ay + z = a$$

becomes

$$x +\qquad y +\qquad z = 1$$

$$(1 - a)y + (1 - a)z = 0$$

$$(a - 1)y \qquad\qquad = a - 1$$

When we use equation 1 to eliminate x in the second two equations. The

last equation gives

$$(a - 1)y = a - 1$$

$$\text{or} \quad y = 1$$

Substituting in equation 2 we find

$$(1 - a)(1) + (1 - a)z = 0$$

$$(1 - a)z = -(1 - a)$$

$$z = -1.$$

And finally in the first equation

$$x + y + z = 1$$

$$x + 1 - 1 = 1$$

$$x = 1.$$

So (1,1,-1) is the required solution.

27. $\left(\dfrac{b + c}{2},\ \dfrac{a - c}{2},\ \dfrac{a - b}{2} \right)$

29. The sample partial fraction problems in the text have told us to add the right hand fractions by using a common denominator. We then equate coefficients of similar terms. Let's try it.

$$\frac{A}{(x - 2)} + \frac{B}{(x + 2)} + \frac{C}{(x + 2)^2} \quad \text{becomes}$$

$$\frac{A(x + 2)^2 + B(x - 2)(x + 2) + C(x - 2)}{(x - 2)(x + 2)^2} \quad \text{or}$$

$$\frac{Ax^2 + 4Ax + 4A + Bx^2 - 4B + Cx - 2C}{(x - 2)(x + 2)^2} \quad \text{or finally}$$

$$\frac{(A + B)x^2 + (4A + C)x + (4A - 4B - 2C)}{(x - 2)(x + 2)^2} \ .$$

Now, this must be identical to $\dfrac{1}{(x - 2)(x + 2)^2}$ on the left side. Equating coefficients gives us the following system

$$A + B = 0$$

$$4A + C = 0$$

$$4A - 4B - 2C = 1$$

We solve this system by any techinque which appeals to us. Here, let's find B and C in terms of A.

$$A + B = 0 \quad \text{says} \quad B = -A$$

$$4A + C = 0 \quad \text{means} \quad C = -4A$$

Substituting in the 3rd equation, we have

$$4A - 4(-A) - 2(-4A) = 1$$

$$4A + 4A + 8A = 1$$

$$\text{or} \qquad\qquad A = \frac{1}{16}$$

Therefore $B = -\dfrac{1}{16}$ and $C = -\dfrac{1}{4}$, as required.

31. $A = \dfrac{3}{64}$; $B = -\dfrac{3}{64}$; $C = -\dfrac{3}{8}$

33. $A = \dfrac{1}{3}$; $B = \dfrac{1}{3}$; $C = -\dfrac{1}{3}$; $D = \dfrac{1}{3}$

35.
$$\frac{A}{x} + \frac{B}{1 - x}$$

is

$$\frac{A(1 - x) + Bx}{x(1 - x)} \quad \text{or}$$

$$\frac{A - Ax + Bx}{x(1 - x)} \quad \text{and finally}$$

$$\frac{(-A + B)x + A}{x(1 - x)}$$

That means

$$-A + B = 0 \quad \text{or} \quad A = B,$$

and
$$A = 4.$$

Our partial fraction would be

$$\frac{4}{x} + \frac{4}{1 - x} = \frac{4}{x(1 - x)}$$

for all x.   Try it!

39. From the figure in the text, we obtain the system of three equations

$$\begin{cases} r_1 + r_2 = a \\ r_2 + r_3 = b \\ r_1 + r_3 = c \end{cases}$$

This system can be solved by repeated substitution, or by using the
following technique. Add the three equations and then divide by 2 to
obtain $r_1 + r_2 + r_3 = \dfrac{a + b + c}{2}$. Now replace $r_2 + r_3$ in this last
equation by b. The result is $r_1 = \dfrac{a + b + c}{2} - b$. Thus $r_1 = \dfrac{a - b + c}{2}$.
Similarly, we find that $r_2 = \dfrac{a + b - c}{2}$ and $r_3 = \dfrac{b + c - a}{2}$.

41. Using the given points in the equation yields the following system

$$a - b + c = -2$$
$$a + b + c = -10$$
$$4a + 2b + c = -17$$

Subtracting equation 1 from 2 gives

$$0 + 2b + 0 = -8$$

or
$$b = -4$$

We can now write equations 1 or 2 as $a + c = -6$ and equation 3 as

$4a + c = -9$. Subtracting 1 from 2 yields $3a = -3$ or $a = -1$. c must

be -5, and the equation is $y = -x^2 - 4x - 5$ as required.

43. Any circle has the form $(x - h)^2 + (y - k)^2 = r^2$ where (h,k) are the

coordinates of the center and r is the radius. Substituting the three

points gives

$$h^2 + k^2 = r^2$$
$$(8 - h)^2 + (-4 - k)^2 = r^2$$
$$(7 - h)^2 + (-1 - k)^2 = r^2$$

or

$$h^2 + k^2 = r^2$$
$$64 - 16h + h^2 + 16 + 8k + k^2 = r^2$$
$$49 - 14h + h^2 + 1 + 2k + k^2 = r^2$$

Note that each of the last two equations has an $h^2 + k^2$ term on the left

and an r^2 term on the right. Since the first equation tells us that these

two quantities are equal, the system simplifies to

$$-16h + 8k = -80$$
$$-14h + 2k = -50$$

or

43. (cont) $-2h + k = -10$

                                    $-7h + k = -25.$

From which we get

$$-5h = -15$$

$$h = 3$$

and $-2(3) + k = -10$

or $k = -4$

The desired equation is therefore

$$(x - 3)^2 + (y + 4)^2 = 25,$$

a circle with center at $(3,-4)$ and a radius of 5.

45. $a = 3,2,-1$

47. $(\dfrac{a(b + c - a)}{2} , \dfrac{b(a + c - b)}{2} , \dfrac{c(a + b - c)}{2})$

49. (p,q,r)

51. $(\dfrac{a + b + c + d}{2} , \dfrac{a + b - c - d}{2} , \dfrac{a - b + c - d}{2} , \dfrac{a - b - c + d}{2})$

53. (a) We will eliminate x twice to give us a 2×2 system

        eq. 1 $\lambda x + y + z = a$
        eq. 2 $\times \lambda$ $\lambda x + \lambda^2 y + \lambda z = \lambda b$

                    $(1 - \lambda^2)y + (1 - \lambda)z = a - \lambda b$

        eq. 2 $x + \lambda y + z = b$
                               $x + y + \lambda z = c$

                    $(\lambda - 1)y + (1 - \lambda)z = b - c$

Now we have

53. (cont) $(1 - \lambda^2)y + (1 - \lambda)z = a - \lambda b$

$(\lambda - 1)y + (1 - \lambda)z = b - c$

subtracting $[(1 - \lambda^2) - (\lambda - 1)]y = (a - \lambda b) - (b - c)$

$$y = \frac{a - \lambda b - b + c}{1 - \lambda^2 - \lambda + 1} ,$$

or when we multiply top and bottom by -1 and factor

$$y = \frac{b(\lambda + 1) - a - c}{(\lambda - 1)(\lambda + 2)}$$

In a similar fashion we find that

$$x = \frac{a(\lambda + 1) - b - c}{(\lambda - 1)(\lambda + 2)} \quad \text{and} \quad z = \frac{c(\lambda + 1) - a - b}{(\lambda - 1)(\lambda + 2)}$$

(b) a, b, and c must satisfy the equation $a + b + c = 0$. In this case
we have infinitely many solutions $(\frac{3z + 2c + b}{3} , \frac{3z + c - b}{3} , z)$,
where z can be any real number.

(c) a, b, and c must all be equal. In this case the solutions are
$(a - z - y, y, z)$, where y and z can be any real numbers.

55. $$\frac{A}{x - a} + \frac{B}{x - b} = \frac{A(x - b) + B(x - a)}{(x - a)(x - b)}$$

$$= \frac{Ax - Ab + Bx - aB}{(x - a)(x - b)}$$

$$= \frac{(A + B)x + (-Ab - aB)}{(x - a)(x - b)}$$

We conclude that $A + B = D$

and $-Ab - aB = Q$

Substituting from one into two

$$-(p - B)b - aB = Q$$

$$-bp + bB - aB = Q$$

$$(b - a)B = Q + bp$$

55. (cont) $$B = \frac{Q + bp}{b - a}$$

and substituting back $$A = \frac{Q + ap}{a - b} \;.$$

59. $$\frac{A}{(x - a)} + \frac{B}{(x - a)^2} = \frac{A(x - a) + B}{(x - a)^2}$$

$$= \frac{Ax - aA + B}{(x - a)^2}$$

So $A = p$ and $-aA + B = q$ or $B = q + ap.$

61. $$A = \frac{a^2}{(a - b)(a - c)} \;;\; B = \frac{b^2}{(b - a)(b - c)} \;;\; C = \frac{c^2}{(c - a)(c - b)}$$

EXERCISE SET 8.4

1. (a) 2 by 3 or 2 × 3.

(b) 3 by 2 or 3 × 2.

3. 5 × 4

5. coefficient matrix: $\begin{pmatrix} 5 & -1 & 1 \\ 0 & 4 & 2 \\ 3 & 1 & 1 \end{pmatrix}$

augmented matrix: $\begin{pmatrix} 5 & -1 & 1 & \vdots & 0 \\ 0 & 4 & 2 & \vdots & 1 \\ 3 & 1 & 1 & \vdots & -1 \end{pmatrix}$

9. Written in matrix form the system becomes.

$$\begin{pmatrix} 1 & -1 & 2 & \vdots & 7 \\ 3 & 2 & -1 & \vdots & -10 \\ -1 & 3 & 1 & \vdots & -2 \end{pmatrix} \xrightarrow[R_3 + R_1]{R_2 - 3R_1} \begin{pmatrix} 1 & -1 & 2 & \vdots & 7 \\ & 5 & -7 & \vdots & -31 \\ & 2 & 3 & \vdots & 5 \end{pmatrix}$$

$$\xrightarrow[\longleftrightarrow]{R_2 - 2R_3} \begin{pmatrix} 1 & -1 & 2 & \vdots & 7 \\ & 1 & -13 & \vdots & -41 \\ & 2 & 3 & \vdots & 5 \end{pmatrix} \xrightarrow{R_3 - 2R_2} \begin{pmatrix} 1 & -1 & 2 & \vdots & 7 \\ & 1 & -13 & \vdots & -41 \\ & & 29 & \vdots & 87 \end{pmatrix}$$

9. (cont)

Now we are in echelon form.

$$29z = 87$$

$$z = 3$$

Then

$$y - -13(3) = -41$$

$$y = -2$$

and

$$x = -1$$

The solution is $(-1, -2, 3)$.

11. $(-5, 1, 3)$

13. Let's start with integral coefficients

$$3x - 2y + z = 60$$

$$4x + 3y - 6z = -120$$

$$x + y - z = -24$$

Our augmented matrix is

$$\begin{pmatrix} 3 & -2 & 1 & \vdots & 60 \\ 4 & 3 & -6 & \vdots & -120 \\ 1 & 1 & -1 & \vdots & -24 \end{pmatrix} \xrightarrow{R_1 \leftrightarrow R_3} \begin{pmatrix} 1 & 1 & -1 & \vdots & -24 \\ 4 & 3 & -6 & \vdots & -120 \\ 3 & -2 & 1 & \vdots & 60 \end{pmatrix}$$

$$\xrightarrow[R_3 - 3R_1]{R_2 - 4R_1} \begin{pmatrix} 1 & 1 & -1 & \vdots & -24 \\ & -1 & -2 & \vdots & -24 \\ & -5 & 4 & \vdots & 132 \end{pmatrix} \xrightarrow{R_3 - 5R_2} \begin{pmatrix} 1 & 1 & -1 & \vdots & -24 \\ & -1 & -2 & \vdots & -24 \\ & & 14 & \vdots & 252 \end{pmatrix}$$

So, $z = 18$, $y = -12$, and $x = 6$.

15. $(8, 9, -1)$

17. Note that the equations are not all independent. The third is the sum of the first two. Our choice is therefore to solve for x and y in terms of z. Looking at the system

17. (cont)
$$4x - 3y = 2 - 3z$$
$$5x + y = 1 + 4z \quad \text{we multiply by } 3.$$
$$4x - 3y = 2 - 3z$$
$$15x + 3y = 3 + 12z \quad \text{adding}$$
$$19x = 5 + 9z$$

and

$$x = \frac{9z + 5}{19}$$

we can substitute and find $y = \dfrac{31z - 6}{19}$. Any triple of the form

$(\dfrac{9z + 5}{19}, \dfrac{31z - 6}{19}, z)$ will work.

19. We start with

$$\begin{pmatrix} 1 & -1 & 1 & 1 & \vdots & 6 \\ 1 & 1 & -1 & 1 & \vdots & 4 \\ 1 & 1 & 1 & -1 & \vdots & -2 \\ -1 & 1 & 1 & 1 & \vdots & 0 \end{pmatrix} \xrightarrow[R_2 - R_1]{R_4 + R_1, \ R_3 - R_1} \begin{pmatrix} 1 & -1 & 1 & 1 & \vdots & 6 \\ & 2 & -2 & 0 & \vdots & -2 \\ & 2 & 0 & -2 & \vdots & -8 \\ & 2 & 2 & & \vdots & 6 \end{pmatrix}$$

$$\xrightarrow{R_3 - R_2} \begin{pmatrix} 1 & -1 & 1 & 1 & \vdots & 6 \\ & 2 & -2 & 0 & \vdots & -2 \\ & & 2 & -2 & \vdots & -6 \\ & & 2 & 2 & \vdots & 6 \end{pmatrix} \xrightarrow{R_4 - R_3} \begin{pmatrix} 1 & -1 & 1 & 1 & \vdots & 6 \\ & 2 & -2 & 0 & \vdots & -2 \\ & & 2 & -2 & \vdots & -6 \\ & & & 4 & \vdots & 12 \end{pmatrix}$$

And we get $(2, -1, 0, 3)$ as the solution.

21. no solution

23. A + B will be

$$\begin{pmatrix} 2 & 3 \\ -1 & 4 \end{pmatrix} + \begin{pmatrix} 1 & -1 \\ 3 & 0 \end{pmatrix} \quad \text{or} \quad \begin{pmatrix} 2 + 1 & 3 + (-1) \\ -1 + 3 & 4 + 0 \end{pmatrix},$$

which is $\begin{pmatrix} 3 & 2 \\ 2 & 4 \end{pmatrix}$ when simplified. We simply add corresponding terms.

25.

$$2A = \begin{pmatrix} 4 & 6 \\ -2 & 8 \end{pmatrix} \quad \text{and} \quad 2B = \begin{pmatrix} 2 & -2 \\ 6 & 0 \end{pmatrix}$$

so,

25. (cont)

$$2A + 2B = \begin{pmatrix} 6 & 4 \\ 4 & 8 \end{pmatrix}.$$

27. Since the number of columns in A equals the number of rows in B this multiplication is defined

$$AB = \begin{pmatrix} 2 & 3 \\ -1 & 4 \end{pmatrix}\begin{pmatrix} 1 & -1 \\ 3 & 0 \end{pmatrix} = \begin{pmatrix} 11 & -2 \\ 11 & 1 \end{pmatrix}.$$

If this is tricky for you, go back and carefully review the step by step process on page 472 until you see where each element of the answer comes from.

29. $\begin{pmatrix} 2 & 3 \\ -1 & 4 \end{pmatrix}$

31. not defined

33. 2F - 3G

$$2F = \begin{pmatrix} 10 & -2 \\ -8 & 0 \\ 4 & 6 \end{pmatrix} \text{ but } 3G \text{ is still } \begin{pmatrix} 0 & 0 \\ 0 & 0 \\ 0 & 0 \end{pmatrix},$$

and adding or subtracting multiples of G will have no effect on 2F.

35. $\begin{pmatrix} 2 & 4 & 11 \\ -12 & 16 & 19 \\ 14 & 12 & 43 \end{pmatrix}$

37. $\begin{pmatrix} -9 & 10 & 10 \\ 4 & -8 & -12 \\ 10 & 4 & 21 \end{pmatrix}$

39. not defined

41. $\begin{pmatrix} 0 & 0 & 0 \\ 0 & 0 & 0 \\ 0 & 0 & 0 \end{pmatrix}$

43. $\begin{pmatrix} 4 & 2 \\ 2 & 5 \end{pmatrix}$

45. not defined

47. $A^2 = \begin{pmatrix} 2 & 3 \\ -1 & 4 \end{pmatrix} \begin{pmatrix} 2 & 3 \\ -1 & 4 \end{pmatrix} = \begin{pmatrix} 1 & 18 \\ -6 & 13 \end{pmatrix}$

49. $\begin{pmatrix} -16 & 75 \\ -25 & 34 \end{pmatrix}$

51. Let's try the first of the two methods given in the book. We will solve for the matrix, X.

$$2X - A = 3B$$

$$2X = 3B + A$$

$$X = \frac{1}{2} [3B + A]$$

so

$$X = \frac{1}{2} \left[3 \begin{pmatrix} 0 & 1 & -1 \\ 5 & 3 & -2 \end{pmatrix} + \begin{pmatrix} 1 & 0 & 3 \\ -2 & 4 & 5 \end{pmatrix} \right]$$

$$= \frac{1}{2} \left[\begin{pmatrix} 0 & 3 & -3 \\ 15 & 9 & -6 \end{pmatrix} + \begin{pmatrix} 1 & 0 & 3 \\ -2 & 4 & 5 \end{pmatrix} \right]$$

$$= \frac{1}{2} \begin{pmatrix} 1 & 3 & 0 \\ 13 & 13 & -1 \end{pmatrix}$$

$$= \begin{pmatrix} \frac{1}{2} & \frac{3}{2} & 0 \\ \frac{13}{2} & \frac{13}{2} & -\frac{1}{2} \end{pmatrix}, \quad \text{as required.}$$

53. $\begin{pmatrix} \frac{11}{2} & \frac{3}{2} & \frac{7}{2} \\ -\frac{7}{2} & 6 & \frac{15}{2} \end{pmatrix}$

55. (a) and (b): $\begin{pmatrix} -13 & 1 & 40 \\ 43 & 17 & 0 \\ 89 & 61 & 60 \end{pmatrix}$; (c) and (d): $\begin{pmatrix} -52 & -82 & 61 \\ 87 & 141 & 0 \\ 216 & 318 & 165 \end{pmatrix}$

57. (a) $A^2 = \begin{pmatrix} 3 & 5 \\ 7 & 9 \end{pmatrix} \begin{pmatrix} 3 & 5 \\ 7 & 9 \end{pmatrix} = \begin{pmatrix} 44 & 60 \\ 84 & 116 \end{pmatrix}$

$B^2 = \begin{pmatrix} 2 & 4 \\ 6 & 8 \end{pmatrix} \begin{pmatrix} 2 & 4 \\ 6 & 8 \end{pmatrix} = \begin{pmatrix} 28 & 40 \\ 60 & 88 \end{pmatrix}$

So $A^2 - B^2 = \begin{pmatrix} 16 & 20 \\ 24 & 28 \end{pmatrix}$

57. (cont)

(b) $(A - B) = \begin{pmatrix} 1 & 1 \\ 1 & 1 \end{pmatrix}$ $(A + B) = \begin{pmatrix} 5 & 9 \\ 13 & 17 \end{pmatrix}$ and $(A - B)(A + B) =$

$\begin{pmatrix} 1 & 1 \\ 1 & 1 \end{pmatrix}\begin{pmatrix} 5 & 9 \\ 13 & 17 \end{pmatrix} = \begin{pmatrix} 18 & 26 \\ 18 & 26 \end{pmatrix}$.

(c) Here we want $(A + B)(A - B) = \begin{pmatrix} 5 & 9 \\ 13 & 17 \end{pmatrix}\begin{pmatrix} 1 & 1 \\ 1 & 1 \end{pmatrix} = \begin{pmatrix} 14 & 14 \\ 30 & 30 \end{pmatrix}$

(d) We first need AB and BA.

$$AB = \begin{pmatrix} 3 & 5 \\ 7 & 9 \end{pmatrix}\begin{pmatrix} 2 & 4 \\ 6 & 8 \end{pmatrix} = \begin{pmatrix} 36 & 52 \\ 68 & 100 \end{pmatrix}$$

$$BA = \begin{pmatrix} 2 & 4 \\ 6 & 8 \end{pmatrix}\begin{pmatrix} 3 & 5 \\ 7 & 9 \end{pmatrix} = \begin{pmatrix} 34 & 46 \\ 74 & 102 \end{pmatrix}$$

So, we write $A^2 + AB - BA - B^2$ as

$$\begin{pmatrix} 44 & 60 \\ 84 & 116 \end{pmatrix} + \begin{pmatrix} 36 & 52 \\ 68 & 100 \end{pmatrix} - \begin{pmatrix} 34 & 46 \\ 74 & 102 \end{pmatrix} - \begin{pmatrix} 28 & 40 \\ 60 & 88 \end{pmatrix}$$

and it equals $\begin{pmatrix} 18 & 26 \\ 18 & 26 \end{pmatrix}$. We made it!

59. (a) $\begin{pmatrix} x \\ -y \end{pmatrix}$; (b) $\begin{pmatrix} -x \\ y \end{pmatrix}$; (c) $\begin{pmatrix} -x \\ -y \end{pmatrix}$ reflection in y-axis followed by

reflection in x-axis (or vice versa).

61. This is simply an exercise in using this definition of a "trace".

(a) $A + B = \begin{pmatrix} 1 & 2 \\ 3 & 4 \end{pmatrix} + \begin{pmatrix} 5 & 6 \\ 7 & 8 \end{pmatrix} = \begin{pmatrix} 6 & 8 \\ 10 & 12 \end{pmatrix}$ and

tr$(A + B) = 6 + 12 = 18$.

But, tr $A = 5$ and tr $B = 13$ and the sum tr $A +$ tr $B = 18$ also.

(b) tr$(A + B) = a + e + d + h$

tr $A = a + d$

tr $B = e + h$

So tr $A +$ tr $B =$ tr$(A + B) = a + d + e + h$ as required.

65. $AI = \begin{pmatrix} a & b \\ c & d \end{pmatrix}\begin{pmatrix} 1 & 0 \\ 0 & 1 \end{pmatrix} = \begin{pmatrix} a & b \\ c & d \end{pmatrix}$

$IA = \begin{pmatrix} 1 & 0 \\ 0 & 1 \end{pmatrix}\begin{pmatrix} a & b \\ c & d \end{pmatrix} = \begin{pmatrix} a & b \\ c & d \end{pmatrix}$

and $A = \begin{pmatrix} a & b \\ c & d \end{pmatrix}$ as required.

EXERCISE SET 8.5

1. The minor will be $\begin{vmatrix} 5 & 1 \\ 10 & -10 \end{vmatrix} = (-50) - (10) = -60.$

3. 9

5. (a) We will have

$$-6\begin{vmatrix} -4 & 1 \\ 9 & -10 \end{vmatrix} + 3\begin{vmatrix} 5 & 1 \\ 10 & -10 \end{vmatrix} + 8\begin{vmatrix} 5 & -4 \\ 10 & 9 \end{vmatrix}$$

$$= -6(31) + 3(-60) + 8(85)$$

$$= 314$$

(b) Applying the rule for cofactors on page 477 we get

$$-6(31) - 3(-60) + 8(85) = 674.$$

(c) The answer in part (b) represents the value of the determinant.

7. (a) 0

(b) 0

(c) 0

(d) 0

9. $\begin{vmatrix} 5 & 10 & 15 \\ 1 & 2 & 3 \\ -9 & 11 & 7 \end{vmatrix}$ We could simply expand along a row or column, but let's try to simplify.

$= 5\begin{vmatrix} 1 & 2 & 3 \\ 1 & 2 & 3 \\ -9 & 11 & 7 \end{vmatrix}$ Now look what we're done by factoring 5 from the first row. If we subtract row 2 from 1 we get

9. (cont) $= 5 \begin{vmatrix} 0 & 0 & 0 \\ 1 & 2 & 3 \\ -9 & 11 & 7 \end{vmatrix}$ and expanding along row 1 gives a value of zero.

11. -3

13. 6848

15. 17120

17. Let's subtract row 2 from 1 and 3 from 2. (There are other options). We get

$$\begin{vmatrix} 0 & x-y & x^2-y^2 \\ 0 & y-z & y^2-z^2 \\ 1 & z & z^2 \end{vmatrix}$$

Now expand along column one since 2 zeros appear there.

$1 \begin{vmatrix} x-y & x^2-y^2 \\ y-z & y^2-z^2 \end{vmatrix}$ We can factor $(x-y)$ from row 1 and $(y-z)$ from row 2 to get

$$(x-y)(y-z) \begin{vmatrix} 1 & x+y \\ 1 & y+z \end{vmatrix} = (x-y)(y-z)[(y+z)-(x+y)]$$

$$= (x-y)(y-z)(z-x)$$

as required. Note that other orders are possible.

19. $\begin{vmatrix} 1 & 1 & 1 \\ 1 & 1+x & 1 \\ 1 & 1 & 1+y \end{vmatrix}$ Subtract row 1 from 2 and row 1 from 3.

$$\begin{vmatrix} 1 & 1 & 1 \\ 0 & x & 0 \\ 0 & 0 & y \end{vmatrix} = 1 \begin{vmatrix} x & 0 \\ 0 & y \end{vmatrix} = xy$$

21. Substituting the two points into the matrix form gives

$$\begin{vmatrix} x & y & 1 \\ 7 & -6 & 1 \\ 10 & 3 & 1 \end{vmatrix} = 0 \qquad \text{Subtract 2 from 1 and 3 from 2.}$$

$$\begin{vmatrix} x-7 & y+6 & 0 \\ -3 & -9 & 0 \\ 10 & 3 & 1 \end{vmatrix} = 0 \qquad \text{expand on the 1.}$$

$$1 \begin{vmatrix} x-7 & y+6 \\ -3 & -9 \end{vmatrix} = 0$$

$$-9(x - 7) - (-3)(y + 6) = 0$$

$$-9x + 63 + 3y + 18 = 0$$

$$3y = 9x - 81$$

$$y = 3x - 27$$

is the desired equation.

23. $y = \dfrac{\sqrt{3}}{3} x$

25. $\begin{vmatrix} 3 & -2 & 3 & 4 \\ 1 & 4 & -3 & 2 \\ 6 & 3 & -6 & -3 \\ -1 & 0 & 1 & 5 \end{vmatrix}$ We are looking for a way to get 3 zeros in a row or column so we can expand there. We have 1 zero so let's concentrate on it. If I add twice row 3 to row 1 and twice row 1 to 2 look at what happens.

$$= 3 \begin{vmatrix} 3 & -2 & 3 & 4 \\ 1 & 4 & -3 & 2 \\ 2 & 1 & -2 & -1 \\ -1 & 0 & 1 & 5 \end{vmatrix}$$

$$= 3 \begin{vmatrix} 7 & 0 & -1 & 2 \\ 7 & 0 & 3 & 10 \\ 2 & 1 & -2 & -5 \\ -1 & 0 & 1 & 5 \end{vmatrix} \qquad \text{Expand on the 1.}$$

25. (cont)

$$= 3(-1) \begin{vmatrix} 7 & -1 & 2 \\ 7 & 3 & 10 \\ -1 & 1 & 5 \end{vmatrix}$$ Subtract row 1 from 2 and add column 2 to column 1.

$$= 3(-1) \begin{vmatrix} 0 & -4 & -8 \\ 7 & 3 & 10 \\ -1 & 1 & 5 \end{vmatrix}$$ Factor row 1. Add 7 times now 3 to row 2.

$$= 3(-1)(4) \begin{vmatrix} 0 & -1 & -2 \\ 0 & 10 & 45 \\ -1 & 1 & 5 \end{vmatrix}$$ Now expand

$$= 3(-1)(4)(-1) \begin{vmatrix} -1 & -2 \\ 10 & 45 \end{vmatrix}$$

$$= 3(-1)(4)(-1)(-25) = -300$$

These methods are certainly not unique, and practice will improve your insights dramatically.

27. 7840

29. (a) $(0,0,0)$

    (b) -1

    (c) $(0,0,0)$

31. $$D = \begin{vmatrix} 3 & -1 & -4 \\ 1 & 2 & -3 \\ 2 & -1 & 2 \end{vmatrix}$$ Subtract row 1 from 3 and add twice row 1 to 2.

$$D = \begin{vmatrix} 3 & -1 & -4 \\ 7 & 0 & -11 \\ -1 & 0 & 6 \end{vmatrix} = -(-1) \begin{vmatrix} 7 & -11 \\ -1 & 6 \end{vmatrix} = 31$$

$$D_x = \begin{vmatrix} 3 & -1 & -4 \\ 9 & 2 & -3 \\ -8 & -1 & 2 \end{vmatrix}$$ Subtract row 3 from 1 and add twice row 3 to row 1.

$$D_x = \begin{vmatrix} 11 & 0 & -6 \\ -7 & 0 & 1 \\ -8 & -1 & 2 \end{vmatrix}$$ expand on -1.

31. (cont)

$$D_x = -(-1)\begin{vmatrix} 11 & -6 \\ -7 & 1 \end{vmatrix}$$

$$= 1(11 - 42) = -31$$

So $x = \dfrac{D_x}{D} = \dfrac{31}{-31} = -1.$

In a similar fashion we find D_y and D_z and have $(-1,2,-2)$ as the required solution.

33. $(1,-3,-2)$

35. $(2 - w, 2 + 2w, w)$

37. $D = \begin{vmatrix} 3 & 4 & 2 \\ 4 & 6 & 2 \\ 2 & 3 & 1 \end{vmatrix}$

Subtracting twice row 3 from row 2 gives

$D = \begin{vmatrix} 3 & 4 & 2 \\ 0 & 0 & 0 \\ 2 & 3 & 1 \end{vmatrix} = 0$ so Cramer's Rule is out.

The last two equations are inconsistant and any other method yields an impossible situation such as $0 = -3.$ Our conclusion is that there is no solution.

39. $D = \begin{vmatrix} 2 & -1 & -3 & 2 \\ 1 & -2 & 1 & -3 \\ 3 & -4 & 2 & -4 \\ 2 & 3 & -1 & -2 \end{vmatrix}$ Multiply row 2 by 2, 3, and 2. Then subtract these results from rows 1, 3, and 4 respectively. We then have

$D = \begin{vmatrix} 0 & 3 & -5 & 8 \\ 1 & -2 & 1 & -3 \\ 0 & 2 & -1 & 5 \\ 0 & 7 & -3 & 4 \end{vmatrix}$ expanding on the 1 we get

39. (cont)

$$D = (-1)\begin{vmatrix} 3 & -5 & 8 \\ 2 & -1 & 5 \\ 7 & -3 & 4 \end{vmatrix}$$ Now use the -1 in column 2 to change the 2 and

5 beside it into zeros.

$$D = (-1)\begin{vmatrix} -7 & -5 & -17 \\ 0 & -1 & 0 \\ 1 & -3 & -11 \end{vmatrix}$$ And expand again

$$D = (-1)(-1)\begin{vmatrix} -7 & -17 \\ 1 & -11 \end{vmatrix} = 77 + 17 = 94$$

Now for D_x.

$$D_x = \begin{vmatrix} -2 & -1 & -3 & 2 \\ 4 & -2 & 1 & -3 \\ 12 & -4 & 2 & -4 \\ -4 & 3 & -1 & -2 \end{vmatrix}$$ Factor 2 from column 1.

$$D_x = 2\begin{vmatrix} -1 & -1 & -3 & 2 \\ 2 & -2 & 1 & -3 \\ 6 & -4 & 2 & -4 \\ -2 & 3 & -1 & -2 \end{vmatrix}$$ Now factor a 2 from row 3.

$$D_x = 2(2)\begin{vmatrix} -1 & -1 & -3 & 2 \\ 2 & -2 & 1 & -3 \\ 3 & -2 & 1 & -2 \\ -2 & 3 & -1 & -2 \end{vmatrix}$$ Let's build some zeros in column 3 by

working with the -1.

$$D_x = 4\begin{vmatrix} 5 & -10 & 0 & 8 \\ 0 & 1 & 0 & -5 \\ 1 & 1 & 0 & -4 \\ -2 & 3 & -1 & -2 \end{vmatrix}$$ expand on that -1.

$$D_x = -(-1)(4)\begin{vmatrix} 5 & -10 & 8 \\ 0 & 1 & -5 \\ 1 & 1 & -4 \end{vmatrix}$$ 5 times column 2 added to 3 yields

39. (cont)

$$D_x = 4 \begin{vmatrix} 5 & -10 & -42 \\ 0 & 1 & 0 \\ 1 & 1 & 1 \end{vmatrix}$$ expand on the center element.

$$D_x = (1)(4) \begin{vmatrix} 5 & -42 \\ 1 & 1 \end{vmatrix} = 4(4 + 42) = 188$$

Finally $A = \dfrac{D_x}{D} = \dfrac{188}{94} = 2.$

I'll leave B, C and D to you. Our solution is (2,-1,3,1). Good luck.

41. $\begin{vmatrix} 1 & x & x^2 \\ 1 & 1 & 1 \\ 4 & 5 & 0 \end{vmatrix} = 0$ Subtracting row 2 from 1 and 4 times row 2 from row 3

gives

$$\begin{vmatrix} 0 & x-1 & x^2-1 \\ 1 & 1 & 1 \\ 0 & 1 & -4 \end{vmatrix} = 0$$ expand

$$(1) \begin{vmatrix} x-1 & x^2-1 \\ 1 & -4 \end{vmatrix} = 0$$ We could factor x - 1 from row 1, but let's

just evaluate.

$$-4(x - 1) - 1(x^2 - 1) = 0$$

$$-4x + 4 - x^2 + 1 = 0$$

$$-x^2 - 4x + 5 = 0$$

$$x^2 + 4x - 5 = 0$$

$$(x + 5)(x - 1) = 0$$

The solutions are then x = 1 or -5.

43. (a) $\begin{vmatrix} 0 & 1 & 1 \\ 1 & 0 & 1 \\ 1 & 1 & 0 \end{vmatrix}$ Many choices. Subtract column 2 from 3.

$$\begin{vmatrix} 0 & 1 & 0 \\ 1 & 0 & 1 \\ 1 & 1 & -1 \end{vmatrix}$$ Expand

43. (a) (cont)

$$(-1)\begin{vmatrix} 1 & 1 \\ 1 & -1 \end{vmatrix} \quad \text{which is} \quad (-1)[-1 \quad -1] \quad \text{or} \quad 2.$$

(b)
$$\begin{vmatrix} 0 & 1 & 1 & 1 \\ 1 & 0 & 1 & 1 \\ 1 & 1 & 0 & 1 \\ 1 & 1 & 1 & 0 \end{vmatrix} \quad \text{Let's take column 2 from 3 and 4.}$$

$$\begin{vmatrix} 0 & 1 & 0 & 0 \\ 1 & 0 & 1 & 1 \\ 1 & 1 & -1 & 0 \\ 1 & 1 & 0 & -1 \end{vmatrix} \quad \text{Expand}$$

$$(-1)\begin{vmatrix} 1 & 1 & 1 \\ 1 & -1 & 0 \\ 1 & 0 & -1 \end{vmatrix} \quad \text{Add columns 1 and 2.}$$

$$(-1)\begin{vmatrix} 2 & 1 & 1 \\ 0 & -1 & 0 \\ 1 & 0 & -1 \end{vmatrix} \quad \text{Expand}$$

$$(-1)(-1)\begin{vmatrix} 2 & 1 \\ 1 & -1 \end{vmatrix} = 1(-2 - 1) = -3$$

49.
$$\begin{vmatrix} a & a & x \\ c & c & c \\ b & x & b \end{vmatrix} = 0 \quad \text{Subtract column 1 from 2}$$

$$\begin{vmatrix} a & 0 & x \\ c & 0 & c \\ b & x-b & b \end{vmatrix} = 0 \quad \text{Expand}$$

$$-(x - b)\begin{vmatrix} a & x \\ c & c \end{vmatrix} = 0$$

$$-(x - b)(ac - cx) = 0$$

Factor the c.

49. (cont) $-c(x - b)(a - x) = 0$

c cannot be zero and our roots are $x = b$ or $x = a$ as required.

55. a^3

57. $-8abcd$

EXERCISE SET 8.6

1. $y = 3x$

   $y = x^2$

   Substituting we get

   $$x^2 = 3x$$

   $$x^2 - 3x = 0 \quad \text{now factor}$$

   $$x(x - 3) = 0$$

   From which we get $x = 0$ or 3. If $x = 0$, $y = 3 \cdot 0 = 0$ and if $x = 3$,
   $y = 9$. Our solutions are $(0,0)$ and $(3,0)$. Note that we have found
   the points of intersection of a line and a parabola.

3. Since $x^2 = 24y$, $x^2 + y^2 = 25$ becomes

   $$24y + y^2 = 25$$

   or $$y^2 + 24y - 25 = 0$$

   $$(y + 25)(y - 1) = 0$$

   $$y = -25 \quad \text{and} \quad y = 1$$

   When $y = 1$ we get $x^2 = 24$ or $x = \pm 2\sqrt{6}$ but $y = -25$ means $x^2 = -600$
   which is impossible. Our two solutions are $(2\sqrt{6},1)$ and $(-2\sqrt{6},1)$.

5. $xy = 1$ and $y = -x^2$

   Try to graph or at least visualize when it is possible. $xy = 1$ is the
   rectangular hyperbola shown on page 490 and $y = -x^2$ is a parabola opening
   down from the origin. Clearly they have only one point of intersection, and

5. (cont)

it is in the third quadrant. Let's see.

$$x(-x^2) = 1$$
$$-x^3 = 1$$
$$x^3 = -1$$
$$x = \sqrt[3]{-1} \text{ which is } -1.$$

If $x = -1$ so does y. The only solution is the point $(-1,-1)$.

7. $2x^2 + y^2 = 17$

$x^2 + 2y^2 = 22$

$-4x^2 - 2y^2 = -34$

$x^2 + 2y^2 = 22$ add

$-3x^2 \qquad = -12$

$x^2 \qquad = 4$

$x \qquad = \pm 2$

When $x = \pm 2$, $x^2 = 4$ and

$2x^2 + y^2 = 17$ becomes

$8 + y^2 = 17$

$y^2 = 9$

$y = \pm 3.$

Our four possible solutions are $(2,3)$, $(2,-3)$, $(-2,3)$ and $(-2,-3)$.

9. $y = 1 - x^2$

$y = x^2 - 1$

$1 - x^2 = x^2 - 1$

$2 = 2x^2$

$1 = x^2$

$x = \pm 1$ which gives $y = 0$

9. (cont)

Our solutions, (1,0) (-1,0). Can you see the graphs?

11. $xy = 4$

$y = 4x + 1$

$x(4x + 1) = 4$

$4x^2 + x = 4$

$4x^2 + x - 4 = 0$

We can't factor, so let's try the formula.

$$x = \frac{-1 \pm \sqrt{1^2 - 4(4)(-4)}}{2(4)}$$

$$x = \frac{-1 \pm \sqrt{65}}{8}$$

For the positive root

$$y = 4\left(\frac{-1 + \sqrt{65}}{8}\right) + 1$$

$$y = \frac{1 + \sqrt{65}}{2} .$$

The two solutions are

$$\left(\frac{-1 + \sqrt{65}}{8} , \frac{1 + \sqrt{65}}{2}\right) \text{ and } \left(\frac{-1 - \sqrt{65}}{8} , \frac{1 - \sqrt{65}}{2}\right)$$

13. Following example 5 in the text we let $\frac{1}{x^2} = a$ and $\frac{1}{y^2} = b$. Then the equations become

$$a - 3b = 14$$

$$2a + b = 35$$

$$-2a + 6b = -28$$

$$2a + b = 35$$

$$7b = 7$$

$$b = 1 \text{ and}$$

13. (cont) $a - 3(1) = 14$

$a = 17$

Now, substituting back we get

$$\frac{1}{x^2} = 17 \qquad \text{and} \quad \frac{1}{y^2} = 1$$

$$\text{or} \qquad x^2 = \frac{1}{17} \qquad\qquad y^2 = 1$$

$$x = \pm \frac{\sqrt{17}}{17} \qquad\qquad y = \pm 1$$

Our solutions, $\left(\frac{\sqrt{17}}{17}, 1\right)$, $\left(\frac{\sqrt{17}}{17}, -1\right)$, $\left(\frac{-\sqrt{17}}{17}, 1\right)$, and $\left(\frac{-\sqrt{17}}{17}, -1\right)$

15. $(1, 0)$, $(4, -\sqrt{3})$

17. We are asked to use the substitution $y = mx$ here.

$$3x(mx) - 4x^2 = 2$$

$$3(mx)^2 - 5x^2 = 7$$

$$x^2(3m - 4) = 2$$

$$x^2(3m^2 - 5) = 7 \quad \text{Dividing we get}$$

$$\frac{3m - 4}{3m^2 - 5} = \frac{2}{7}$$

$$7(3m - 4) = 2(3m^2 - 5)$$

$$21m - 28 = 6m^2 - 10$$

$$0 = 6m^2 - 21m + 18$$

$$0 = 2m^2 - 7m + 6$$

$$0 = (2m - 3)(m - 2)$$

and we find $m = \frac{3}{2}$ and 2.

For $m = \frac{3}{2}$, $x^2(3 \cdot \frac{3}{2} - 4) = 2$

17. (cont)

$$\frac{x^2}{2} = 2$$

$$x^2 = 4$$

$$x = \pm 2$$

When m = 2

$$x^2(3 \cdot 2 - 4) = 2$$

$$2x^2 = 2$$

$$x^2 = 1$$

$$x = \pm 1$$

Now for y. Since y = mx

$$y = \frac{3}{2} (\pm 2) = \pm 3$$

and $$y = 2(\pm 1) = \pm 2$$

The results: (2,3), (-2,-3), (1,2), and (-1,-2).

19. (2,-1), (-2,1)

21. Again, let y = mx.

$$m^2 x^2 + x(mx) = 84$$

$$x^2 + x(mx) = 60$$

$$x^2(m^2 + m) = 84$$

$$x^2(1 + m) = 60$$

Dividing

$$\frac{m^2 + m}{1 + m} = \frac{84}{60} = \frac{7}{5}$$

$$5m^2 + 5m = 7 + 7m$$

$$5m^2 - 2m - 7 = 0$$

$$(5m - 7)(m + 1)$$

$$m = \frac{7}{5} \text{ and } m = -1$$

Now to find x.

21. (cont) $x^2[(\frac{7}{5})^2 + \frac{7}{5}] = 84$ and $x^2[1 + (-1)] = 60$

$$\frac{84}{25} x^2 = 84 \qquad\qquad 0 \cdot x^2 = 60$$

$$x^2 = 25$$

$$x = \pm 5$$

Solutions: (5,7) (-5,-7)

Note that there is no x value which will satisfy the second equation.

25. $ax + by = 2$

$$abxy = 1$$

Solving the first equation for y we have

$$by = 2 - ax$$

$$y = \frac{2 - ax}{b}\ .$$

Now substituting in two we get

$$abx\left(\frac{2 - ax}{b}\right) = 1$$

$$ax(2 - ax) = 1$$

$$2ax - a^2x^2 = 1$$

$$a^2x^2 - 2ax + 1 = 0$$

$$(ax - 1)(ax - 1) = 0$$

and $x = \frac{1}{a}$. So $y = \frac{1}{b}$.

The solution: $(\frac{1}{a}, \frac{1}{b})$

27. Since $y = 23 - x$, we substitute and find

$$x^3 + (23 - x)^3 = 3473$$

Expanding gives

27.   (cont) $x^3 + 12167 - 1587x + 69x^2 - x^3 = 3473$

   or $69x^2 - 1587x + 8694 = 0$

   or $x^2 - 23x + 126 = 0$

The factors are $(x - 9)$ and $(x - 14)$ so $x = 9$ and 14 are roots.

The two complete solutions: $(9,14)$ $(14,9)$.

31.   If we follow the lead offered we have

$$(\sqrt{u + v} + \sqrt{u - v})^2 = 4^2$$

   or $(\sqrt{u + v})^2 + 2\sqrt{u + v}\,\sqrt{u - v} + (\sqrt{u - v})^2 = 16$

$$u + v + 2\sqrt{u^2 - v^2} + u - v = 16.$$

But, since $u^2 - v^2 = 9$ from the 1st equation

$$2u + 2\sqrt{9} = 16$$

$$2u + 6 = 16$$

$$2u = 10$$

$$u = 5$$

When $u = 5$

$$5^2 - v^2 = 9$$

$$v^2 = 16$$

$$v = \pm 4$$

The solutions: $(5,4)$ $(5,-4)$.   Note that $u \neq -5$ in equation 2.

33. $x = \dfrac{p^2}{\sqrt{p^2 + q^2 + r^2}}$; $y = \dfrac{q^2}{\sqrt{p^2 + q^2 + r^2}}$; $z = \dfrac{r^2}{\sqrt{p^2 + q^2 + r^2}}$

35. $A = \frac{1}{2} b \cdot h$ where b and h are the missing legs.   We have

$$180 = \frac{1}{2} b \cdot h \text{ or } bh = 360$$

35. (cont)

Also from the Pythagorean Theorem $b^2 + h^2 = 41^2$. Let's substitute

$$(\frac{360}{h})^2 + h^2 = 41^2$$

$$\frac{129600}{h^2} + h^2 = 1681$$

$$129600 + h^4 = 1681h^2$$

Which is $h^4 - 1681h^2 + 129600 = 0$. If we factor this, looking at it as a quadratic in h^2 we get

$$(h^2 - 1600)(h^2 - 81) = 0$$

so $h^2 = 1600$ and $h^2 = 81$

or $h = \pm 40$ and $h = \pm 9$

Since these must be length of sides, we can neglect the negative possibilities.
The legs are 9 and 40 cm.

37. $L \cdot W = 60$

$2L + 2W = 46$ or $L + W = 23$

Substituting: $(23 - W) \cdot W = 60$

$$23W - W^2 = 60$$

$$W^2 - 23W + 60 = 0$$

$$(W - 20)(W - 3) = 0$$

$$W = 20 \qquad W = 3$$

The rectangle must be 3 by 20 cm.

39. legs 5 and 12; hypotenuse 13

EXERCISE SET 8.7

1. (a) Since substituting the pair (1,2) into $4x - 6y + 3 \geq 0$ gives

$$4(1) - 6(2) + 3 \geq 0$$
$$4 - 12 + 3 \geq 0$$
$$-5 \geq 0$$

our answer is no.

(b) $4(0) - 6(\frac{1}{2}) + 3 \geq 0$
$$0 - 3 + 3 \geq 0$$
$$0 \geq 0 \quad \text{yes.}$$

5.

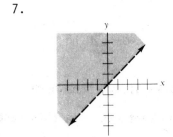

Using intercepts or putting $2x - 3y \geq 6$ into $y = mx + b$ form, we have this graph. We test and obvious point, say the origin here, to find the shaded side. $2(0) - 3(0) \geq 6$ is false, so we shade the lower portion. The line is included.

7.   9.   11.

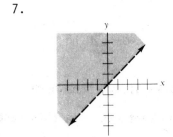   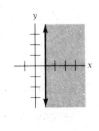   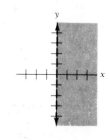

13.

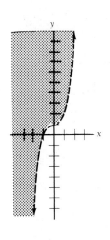

15.

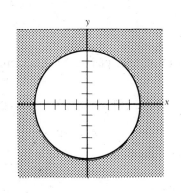

We know $x^2 + y^2 = 25$ as a circle, so if $x^2 + y^2$ must be ≥ 25 we shade the area outside the circle.

17.

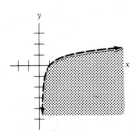

19.

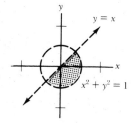

21.

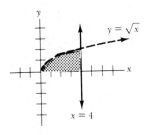

23.

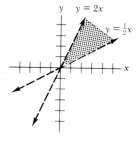

25.

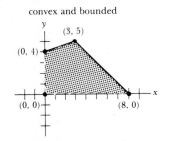

convex and bounded

We simply graph each inequality, and where necessary solve to find vertices. In this case

$$-x + 3y = 12$$
$$x + y = 8$$
$$4y = 20$$
$$y = 5 \quad \text{and} \quad x = 3.$$

27.

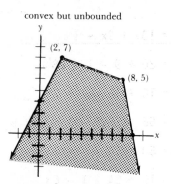

convex but unbounded

Number 27 and 29 are unbounded because no circle, no matter how large, could contain them. They have an open side.

29.

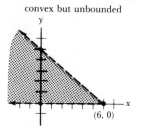

convex but unbounded

31.

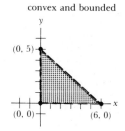

convex and bounded

33.

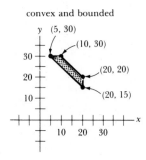

convex and bounded

35.

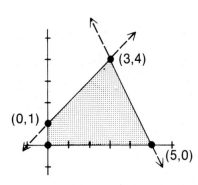

Vertex	C = 3y - x
(0,0)	C = 3·0 - 0 = 0
(5,0)	C = 3·0 - 5 = -5
(3,4)	C = 3·4 - 3 = 9
(0,1)	C = 3·1 - 0 = 3

Our conclusion: C is a max of 9 at (3,4) and a min of -5 at (5,0).

37. max = 4 at (1,2); min = -4 at (-1,-2)

39.

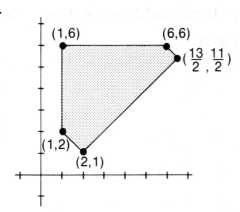

Vertex	C = 10y + 9x - 1
(1,2)	C = 20 + 9 - 1 = 28
(2,1)	C = 10 + 18 - 1 = 27
$(\frac{13}{2}, \frac{11}{2})$	C = 55 + 58.5 = 1 = 112.5
(6,6)	C = 60 + 54 - 1 = 113
(1,6)	C = 10 + 54 - 1 = 63

max C of 113 at (6,6)

min C of 27 at (2,1)

41. max = 188 at (6,7); min = 100 at (0,0)

43.

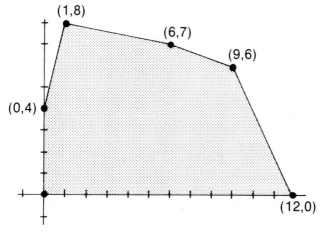

Vertex	(a) C = 19x + 100y	(b) C = 21x + 100y
(0,0)	C = 0 + 0 = 0	C = 0 + 0 = 0
(12,0)	C = 228 + 0 = 228	C = 252 + 0 = 252
(9,6)	C = 171 + 600 = 771	C = 189 + 600 = 789
(6,7)	C = 114 + 700 = 814	C = 126 + 700 = 826
(1,8)	C = 19 + 800 = 819	C = 21 + 800 = 821
(0,4)	C = 0 + 400 = 400	C = 0 + 400 = 400

43. (cont)

The results of a small change in the objective function are clear.

45. (a) max = 12 at (9,3)

(b) (0,-100)

(c) (0,-1000)

(d) $(0,-10^6)$

47. We will follow example 4 in the text by first organizing the data in tables.

Shipping	Costs
W_1 to R_1	8
W_1 to R_2	12
W_2 to R_1	13
W_2 to R_2	7

Supply and Demand	
W_1 has 100	W_2 has 120
R_1 wants 55	R_2 wants 75

Let's let $x = W_1$ to R_1 then

$$55 - x = W_2 \text{ to } R_1.$$

If $y = W_1$ to R_2 then $75 - y = W_2$ to R_2.

The cost function will then be

$$C = 8 \cdot x + 13(55 - x) + 12 \cdot y + 7(75 - y)$$

$$= 8x + 715 - 13x + 12y + 525 - 7y$$

$$= -5x + 5y + 1240$$

The constraints:

(1) $x \geq 0$ 　　　　　(5) $x + y \leq 100$

(2) $y \geq 0$ 　　　　　(6) $(55 - x) + (75 - y) \leq 120$

(3) $x \leq 55$ or $-x - y \leq -10$

(4) $y \leq 75$ or $x + y \geq 10$

Next we graph these six constraints to find vertices.

47.

Vertices	C = 5y - 5x + 1240
(0,10)	C = 1290
(10,0)	C = 1190
(55,0)	C = 965
(55,45)	C = 1190
(25,75)	C = 1490
(0,75)	C = 1615

The least expensive solution is at the vertex (55,0).

If $x = 55$ we send 55 from TV's from W_1 to R_1 and 75 from W_2 to R_2. The total cost will be $965.

49. 800 units of A and 350 units of B for a profit of $760

51. 100 acres of cherry tomatoes and 500 acres of regular tomatoes for a profit of $11,500

53. Using the suggested notation we find these constraints

$$x \geq 1000$$

$$y \geq 1000$$

$$10000 - x - y \geq 1000 \quad \text{or} \quad x + y \leq 9000$$

also $$x + y \geq 5000$$

and $$y \leq 5x.$$

Our profit will be $.04x + .05y + .06(10,000 - x - y)$ or $P = 600 - .02x - .01y$. This is the objective function

53. (cont)

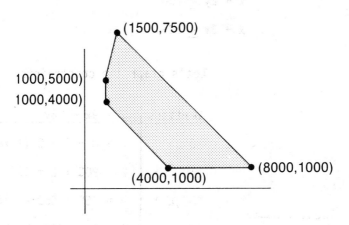

Vertices	P = 600 - .02x - .01y
(4000,1000)	P = 600 - 80 - 10 = 510
(8000,1000)	P = 600 - 160 - 10 = 430
(1500,7500)	P = 600 - 30 - 75 = 495
(1000,5000)	P = 600 - 20 - 50 = 530
(1000,4000)	P = 600 - 20 - 40 = 540

We invest $1000 in A, $4000 in B and $5000 in C for a maximum profit
of $540.

55. invest $1500 in A, $7500 in B, and $1000 in C for a profit of $645

57. Let x = small motors and y = large ones. Since profit = revenue minus
cost,

$$P = (40x + 104y) - [(15 + 16)x + (30 + 48)y]$$

so

$$P = 9x + 26y.$$

This is our objective function. Clearly $x \geq 0$ and $y \geq 0$. Also we
get $1500 max each day for material. Hence, $15x + 30y \leq 1500$.
Also $2000 at most for a day's labor means $16x + 48y \leq 2000$. These
last two constraints simplify to

57. (cont) $x + 2y \le 100$

                                         $x + 3y \le 125.$

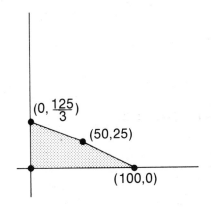

Let's graph the constraints

Vertices	P = 9x + 26y
(0,0)	$P = 0 + 0 = 0$ (take the day off)
(100,0)	$P = 900 + 0 = 900$
(50,25)	$P = 450 + 650 = 110$
$(0, \frac{125}{3})$	$P = 0 + 1083 \frac{1}{3} = 1083 \frac{1}{3}$

Conclusion: make 50 small and 25 large motors for an $1100 profit.

59. the minimum budget is $54,000; show 12 daytime and 5 evening television

     commercials

Chapter 9   Analytic Geometry

1. The distance formula is $d = \sqrt{(x_2 - x_1)^2 + (y_2 - y_1)^2}$

$$d = \sqrt{[3 - (-5)]^2 + [-1 - (-6)]^2}$$

$$= \sqrt{8^2 + 5^2}$$

$$= \sqrt{89}$$

3. If it is perpendicular to $4x - 5y - 20 = 0$ then its slope is the negative reciprocal. We will solve for y.

$$-5y = -4x + 20$$

$$y = \frac{4}{5} x - 4$$

Our desired slope is therefore $-\frac{5}{4}$.
The line $x - y + 1 = 0$ or $y = x + 1$ has a y-intercept of 1.
Substituting these two facts into $y = mx + b$ gives

$$y = -\frac{5}{4} x + 1$$

$$\text{or} \quad 4y = -5x + 4$$

$$\text{or} \quad 5x + 4y - 4 = 0 \quad \text{as required.}$$

5. We need to find both the slope of this segment and the coordinates of its
    mid-point and then use the point-slope equation:

$$m = \frac{y_2 - y_1}{x_2 - x_1} = \frac{7 - 1}{6 - 2} = \frac{6}{4} = \frac{3}{2}$$

We must remember to use the negative reciprocal however.

$$x_m = \frac{2 + 6}{2} = 4$$

$$y_m = \frac{1 + 7}{2} = 4$$

Now we use

$$y - y_1 = m(x - x_1)$$

$$y - 4 = -\frac{2}{3}(x - 4)$$

$$3y - 12 = -2x + 8$$

$$\text{or} \quad 2x + 3y - 20 = 0$$

7. A graph can sometimes help, but only when the intercepts are simple numbers.
    Using the equation of a circle we found in Chapter 1 we get

$$(x - h)^2 + (y - k)^2 = r^2$$
$$(x - 1)^2 + (y - 0)^2 = 5^2$$
$$\text{or} \quad (x - 1)^2 + y^2 = 25$$

We will find x-intercepts by letting $y = 0$ and y-intercepts when $x = 0$.

$$(x - 1)^2 + 0 = 25$$
$$x - 1 = \pm 5$$
$$x = 1 \pm 5$$

The x-intercepts are therefore $(6,0)$ and $(-4,0)$. If $x = 0$ we get

$$(0 - 1)^2 + y^2 = 25$$
$$y^2 = 24$$
$$y = \pm 2\sqrt{6}$$

and conclude that the y-intercepts are $(0,2\sqrt{6})$, and $(0,-2\sqrt{6})$.

9. We will find the midpoint of AB and use that and the coordinates of point C
    to find the desired equation.

9. (cont) $\qquad x_m = \dfrac{1 + 6}{2} = \dfrac{7}{2} \qquad y_m = \dfrac{2 + 1}{2} = \dfrac{3}{2}$

$$m = \dfrac{8 - \dfrac{3}{2}}{7 - \dfrac{7}{2}} = \dfrac{\dfrac{13}{2}}{\dfrac{7}{2}} = \dfrac{13}{7}$$

and

$$y - 8 = \dfrac{13}{7} (x - 7)$$

$$7y - 56 = 13x - 91$$

$$13x - 7y - 35 = 0 \quad \text{as required.}$$

11. In intercept form the equation becomes

$$\frac{5x}{30} + \frac{6y}{30} = \frac{30}{30}$$

$$\frac{x}{6} + \frac{y}{5} = 1$$

The area then is:

$$A = \frac{1}{2} b \cdot h$$

$$= \frac{1}{2} (6)(5)$$

$$= 15 \text{ sq. units}$$

13. 1

15. $x + \sqrt{2}\, y - 2 = 0$ becomes

$$\sqrt{2}\, y = -x + 2 \quad \text{or}$$

$$y = \frac{-1}{\sqrt{2}} x + \frac{2}{\sqrt{2}} \quad \text{in slope-intercept form.}$$

Here $m = -\dfrac{1}{\sqrt{2}}$ so using $m = \tan$

$$\tan \theta = -\frac{1}{\sqrt{2}}$$

$$\theta = \tan^{-1}\left(-\frac{1}{\sqrt{2}}\right)$$

$$\theta = 144.7° \quad \text{using a calculator.}$$

17. 1.25 radians

19. (a)
$$d = \frac{|1(-2) + (-3)(3) + (-3)|}{\sqrt{1^2 + (-3)^2}}$$

$$= \frac{|-2 - 9 - 3|}{\sqrt{10}}$$

$$= \frac{14}{\sqrt{10}} \quad \text{or} \quad \frac{7\sqrt{10}}{5}$$

(b) We rewrite the equation as

$$-3y = -x + 3$$

$$y = \frac{1}{3}x - 1$$

Then

$$d = \frac{|\frac{1}{3}(-2) + (-1) - (3)|}{\sqrt{1 + (\frac{1}{3})^2}}$$

$$= \frac{|-\frac{2}{3} - 1 - 3|}{\sqrt{\frac{10}{9}}}$$

$$= \frac{\frac{14}{3}}{\frac{\sqrt{10}}{3}} \quad \text{or} \quad \frac{7\sqrt{10}}{5} \quad \text{as before.}$$

21. Its radius will be the perpendicular distance from the center to the line.

$$d = \frac{|\frac{1}{2}(1) + (5) - (3)|}{\sqrt{1 + (\frac{1}{2})^2}}$$

$$= \frac{|\frac{5}{2}|}{\sqrt{\frac{5}{4}}} = \frac{5}{2} \cdot \frac{2}{\sqrt{5}} = \sqrt{5} \quad \text{units as required.}$$

23. 32.5 sq. units

25. Lets follow the work of example 5 on page 517.
     If the required slope is m, we can write the equation of the tangent line
     as
$$y - (-5) = m(x - 0)$$
     or $$y = mx - 5$$

At the point of tangency, its distance from the center is $\sqrt{4}$ or 2. So,

25. (cont)

$$d = \frac{|m \cdot x_0 + b - y_0|}{\sqrt{1 + m^2}}$$

becomes

$$2 = \frac{|m(3) - 5 - 0|}{\sqrt{1 + m^2}}$$

$$2\sqrt{1 + m^2} = |3m - 5| \quad \text{square both sides and get}$$

$$4(1 + m^2) = 9m^2 - 30m + 25$$

$$4 + 4m^2 = 9m^2 - 30m + 25$$

$$0 = 5m^2 - 30m + 21$$

Using the quadratic formula we find

$$m = \frac{15 \pm 2\sqrt{30}}{5}$$

and a calculator gives us values of 0.81 and 5.19.

27. $\frac{12}{5}$ units

29. We need a sketch here. In fact, you should be encouraged to sketch almost every problem as an aid to understanding and solving.

If we use a and b for the indicated distances then since (2,6) is to be a midpoint,

$$2 = \frac{2 + a + 0}{2} \quad \text{or} \quad a = 2$$

and

$$6 = \frac{0 + 6 + b}{2} \quad \text{or} \quad b = 6.$$

The x and y-intercepts are then 4 and 12 respectively and the equation will be

$$\frac{x}{4} + \frac{y}{12} = 1$$

or

$$3x + y - 12 = 0$$

31.

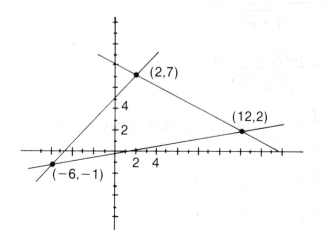

We need to solve for the points of intersection. Using the first two lines as an example we have:

$$\begin{cases} y = x + 5 \\ x + 2y = 16 \end{cases}$$

or $\begin{cases} -x + y = 5 \\ x + 2y = 16 \end{cases}$

$\therefore\ 3y = 21$

$y = 7$ so

$x = 2$

The other two vertices are as indicated. We will use $A = \frac{1}{2} b \cdot h$, so let's find the perpendicular distance from (2,7) to the opposite side, and the length of that side.

$$d = \frac{\left|\frac{1}{6}(2) + 0 - 7\right|}{\sqrt{1 + (\frac{1}{6})^2}} = \frac{\frac{20}{3}}{\frac{\sqrt{37}}{6}} = \frac{40}{\sqrt{37}} \quad \text{(a useful form here)}$$

We find also that the distance formula gives a base of $3\sqrt{37}$. The area is then

$$= \frac{1}{2}(3\sqrt{37})\left(\frac{40}{\sqrt{37}}\right)$$

$$= 60 \text{ sq. units}$$

33. $5\sqrt{2}$ units

43.

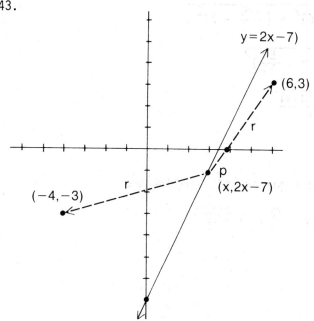

It is required that the distance from the center to each given point be equal to a radius. Recall that any point on the line has coordinates given by $(x, 2x - 7)$. So,

$$\sqrt{(x - 6)^2 + (2x - 7 - 3)^2} = \sqrt{(x + 4)^2 + (2x - 7 + 3)^2}$$

$$(x - 6)^2 + (2x - 10)^2 = (x + 4)^2 + (2x - 4)^2 \qquad \text{(squaring)}$$

$$x^2 - 12x + 36 + 4x^2 - 40x + 100 = x^2 + 8x + 16 + 4x^2 - 16x + 16$$

$$-52x + 136 = -8x + 32$$

$$-44x = -104$$

$$x = \frac{26}{11}$$

and

$$y = 2\left(\frac{26}{11}\right) - 7 = \frac{-25}{11}$$

Our circle now looks like this

$$\left(x - \frac{26}{11}\right)^2 + \left(y + \frac{25}{11}\right)^2 = r^2$$

Again, using the distance formula with these center coordinates and either endpoint will give us a radius.

43. (cont) $d = \sqrt{(\frac{26}{11} - 6)^2 + (\frac{-25}{11} - 3)^2}$

$$= \sqrt{(\frac{-40}{11})^2 + (\frac{-58}{11})^2}$$

$$= \sqrt{\frac{1600 + 3364}{121}}$$

$$= \sqrt{\frac{4964}{121}}$$

We can stop because the equation requires r^2, and we get

$$(x - \frac{26}{11})^2 + (y + \frac{25}{11})^2 = \frac{4964}{121} .$$

47. $m = -\frac{A}{B}$; $b = -\frac{C}{B}$

EXERCISE SET 9.2

1.   focus: (0, 1); directrix: $y = -1$; focal width: 4

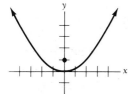

Since $x^2 = 4y$, $4p = 4$ or $p = 1$ and we can identify the focus directrix. Recall that the focal width, $4p$, is the distance across the parabola at the focus. Here it is 4.

3.   focus: $(-2, 0)$; directrix: $x = 2$; focal width: 8

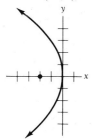

$y^2 = -8x$

$4p = -8$

$p = -2$

5.   focus: $(0, -5)$; directrix: $y = 5$; focal width: 20

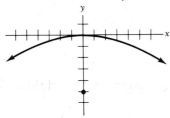

7.   focus: $(-7, 0)$; directrix: $x = 7$; focal width: 28

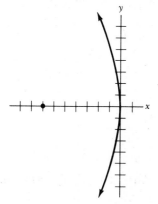

9.   focus: $\left(0, \frac{3}{2}\right)$; directrix: $y = -\frac{3}{2}$; focal width: 6

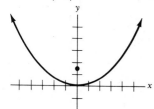

11.   focus: $\left(0, \frac{7}{16}\right)$; directrix: $y = -\frac{7}{16}$; focal width: $\frac{7}{4}$

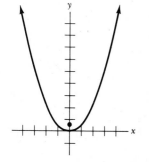

13. Given that the focus is at $(0,3)$, we see that $p = +3$ and $4p = 12$. Since the parabola opens up, it has the $x^2 = 4py$ form, and its equation must be $x^2 = 12y$.

15. $y^2 = 128x$

17. If it passes through $(5,6)$ and $(5,-6)$ it must open to the right. Its form is therefore $y^2 = 4px$.

Substituting for x and y we get

$$(6)^2 = 4p(5)$$
$$4p = \frac{36}{5}$$

The required equation is therefore

$$y^2 = \frac{36}{5} x.$$

19. $y^2 = -9x$

21.

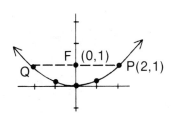

$x^2 = 4y$ so $4p = 4$ or $p = 1$

The sketch shows us that point Q must be at $(-2,1)$.

23. $\frac{1369}{144}$ units (≈ 9.51)

27. 11.25 ft.

29.

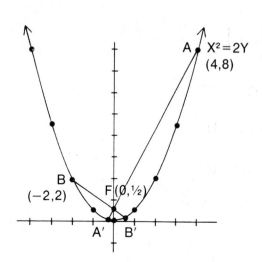

This is a rather long problem. Not difficult, but requiring careful work on many small steps. First we need to find the coordinates of A' and B'. We will use A(4,8) and $P(0,\frac{1}{2})$ to find the equation of AA' first.

$$m = \frac{8 - \frac{1}{2}}{4 - 0} = \frac{15}{8}$$

and

$$y - \frac{1}{2} = \frac{15}{8}(x - 0)$$

$$y = \frac{15}{8}x + \frac{1}{2}$$

Now let's find the point of intersection of this line and the parabola. To do this, we solve the system

$$y = \frac{15}{8}x + \frac{1}{2}$$
$$x^2 = 2y \qquad \text{by substitution.}$$

$$x^2 = 2(\frac{15}{8}x + \frac{1}{2})$$

$$x^2 = \frac{15}{4}x + 1$$

$$4x^2 - 15x - 4 = 0$$

$$(4x + 1)(x - 4) = 0$$

$x = -\frac{1}{4}$ and 4 are roots. We already knew the 4, because it's the given end of AA'. But, the $x = -\frac{1}{4}$ is new, and gives

$$2y = (-\frac{1}{4})^2$$

$$2y = \frac{1}{16}$$

$$y = \frac{1}{32}$$

for the corresponding y coordinate. Using the same technique we find B' to be at $(\frac{1}{2},\frac{1}{8})$.

(a) Now we are going after line AB'. We know its endpoints are $(4,8)$ and $(\frac{1}{2},\frac{1}{8})$. Its slope is

29. (cont)
$$m = \frac{8 - \frac{1}{8}}{4 - \frac{1}{2}} = \frac{9}{4} \text{ ,}$$

and from point-slope we get

$$y - 8 = \frac{9}{4} (x - 4)$$

or

$$4y - 32 = 9x - 36$$

and

$$9x - 4y - 4 = 0$$

as our result.

(b) Using the same technique we get

$$9x + 8y + 2 = 0$$

as the equation for BA'.

(c) Subtracting equation (b) from (a) gives

$$-12y - 6 = 0$$

or

$$y = -\frac{1}{2}$$

so the y-coordinate of the point of intersection is $-\frac{1}{2}$ which is the equation of the directrix. This is what we were asked to establish.

31. (a) The focus is at $(0, \frac{1}{4})$, so

$$m = \frac{4 - \frac{1}{9}}{2 - 0} = \frac{15}{8}$$

and

$$y - \frac{1}{4} = \frac{15}{8} (x - 0)$$

or

$$y = \frac{15}{8} x + \frac{1}{4} \text{ .}$$

This is line PQ and we solve the system consisting of this line and the parabola to get point Q.

31. (cont)
$$x^2 = \frac{15}{8}x + \frac{1}{4}$$

$$8x^2 - 15x - 2 = 0$$

$$(8x + 1)(x - 2)$$

$x = -\frac{1}{8}$ and $x = 2$ are the results. The new value for x, $-\frac{1}{8}$, is the one of interest. There $y = \frac{1}{64}$. That is point Q, $(-\frac{1}{8}, \frac{1}{64})$.

(b)
$$x_m = \frac{2 - \frac{1}{8}}{2} = \frac{15}{16}$$

and

$$y_m = \frac{4 + \frac{1}{64}}{2} = \frac{257}{128}.$$

These are the coordinates of the midpoint.

(c)

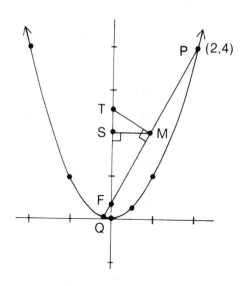

The focal width of $x^2 = y$ is 1. Now we want to show that $\overline{TS} = \frac{1}{2}$. Let's make a geometrical argument. $\overline{SM}$ is an altitude to the hypotenuse of right $\triangle TMF$. Therefore

$$\frac{\overline{TS}}{\overline{SM}} = \frac{\overline{SM}}{\overline{SF}}$$

or

$$\frac{\overline{TS}}{\frac{15}{16}} = \frac{\frac{15}{16}}{\left(\frac{257}{128} - \frac{1}{4}\right)}$$

cross multiplying,

$$\overline{TS} = \frac{\frac{225}{256}}{\frac{225}{128}} = \frac{1}{2}$$

The result is clearly one-half of it, as required.

33. Following the method outlined on page 525-6 we write the equation of the tangent at (4,2) as

$$y - 2 = m(x - 4)$$

and solve this system

$$x^2 = 8y$$

33. (cont)

$$x^2 = 8[m(x - 4) + 2]$$
$$x^2 = 8mx - 32m + 16$$
$$x^2 - 16 - 8mx + 32m = 0$$
$$x^2 - 16 - 8m(x - 4) = 0$$
$$(x - 4)[(x + 4) - 8m] = 0$$

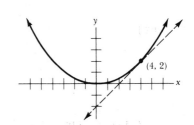

$x = 4$ and $x = 8m - 4$ are the roots.

We want only one x, namely 4, for this

solution, since the line must intersect the parabola only once to be tangent.

Therefore we set $8m - 4$ equal to 4 and solve

$$8m - 4 = 4$$
$$m = 1$$

If $m = 1$,

$$y - 2 = 1(x - 4)$$

or

$$y = x - 2.$$

35.

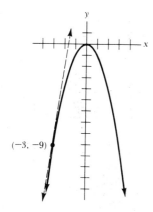

$$y + 9 = m(x + 3)$$
$$y = mx + 3m - 9 \text{ is the line}$$
$$x^2 = -y \text{ is the parabola}$$

Solve.

$$x^2 = -mx - 3m + 9$$

$$x^2 - 9 + mx + 3m = 0$$
$$(x + 3)(x - 3) + m(x + 3) = 0$$
$$(x + 3)[x - 3 + m] = 0$$

$x = -3$ and $x = -m + 3$ are the roots.

We require that

$$-m + 3 = -3$$

which means

$$m = 6.$$

The line is therefore

$$y + 9 = 6(x + 3)$$

or

$$y = 6x + 9.$$

37.

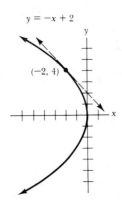

$y = -x + 2$

$(-2, 4)$

39. The sketch in the book will have the following coordinates. 0 is the origin.

B is at $(x, \frac{x^2}{4p})$ and A is $(-x, \frac{x^2}{4p})$. We require that $\overline{AB} = \overline{OB}$. That is

$$2x = \sqrt{(x - 0)^2 + (\frac{x^2}{4p} - 0)^2}$$

$$2x = \sqrt{x^2 + \frac{x^4}{16p^2}} \qquad \text{squaring}$$

$$4x^2 = x^2 + \frac{x^4}{16p^2}$$

$$0 = -3x^2 + \frac{x^4}{16p^2}$$

$$0 = -48x^2p^2 + x^4$$

$$0 = x^2(-48p^2 + x^2)$$

so $x^2 = 0$ or $x = 0$ is one root and $x^2 = 48p^2$ or $x = \pm4\sqrt{3}\, p$ is the
other.

The distance from A to B is therefore

$$2(4\sqrt{3}\, p) \quad \text{or} \quad 8\sqrt{3}\, p \quad \text{units.}$$

To find the area we note that this is an equilateral triangle. Half of it
is a 30° - 60° - 90° triangle whose height will be $\sqrt{3}$ times its base.
The height is therefore $\sqrt{3} \cdot 4\sqrt{3}\, p$ or 12p.
Our area is

39. (cont) $\frac{1}{2}$ $(8\sqrt{3} \ p)(12p)$

                                        $= 48\sqrt{3} \ p^2$ sq. units.

45. x-intercept = 4p

49. (a) -1
     (b) -2
     (c) -3

Exercise Set 9.3

1. We know that the sum of the distances from a point on the ellipse to the
    foci is 12. That is, 2a = 12 or a = 6.
    Also, since the eccentricity = $\frac{2}{3}$

$$\frac{c}{a} = \frac{2}{3} \quad \text{or} \quad \frac{c}{6} = \frac{2}{3}$$

    and

$$c = 4.$$

    Therefore the distance between the foci is 2c or 8 units.

3. $\frac{4}{5}$

5. $2a = 10; \ 2b = 4; \ \text{foci:} \ (\pm \ \sqrt{21}, \ 0); \ e = \frac{\sqrt{21}}{5}$ $4x^2 + 25y^2 = 100$

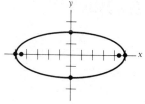

                                                        becomes

$$\frac{x^2}{25} + \frac{y^2}{4} = 1$$

                                                        in standard form. By inspection 2a = 10,
                                                        2b = 4.

$$c^2 = a^2 - b^2$$
$$c^2 = 21$$

    so

$$c = \pm\sqrt{21} \quad \text{for the foci}$$

    and

$$e = \frac{\sqrt{21}}{5}$$

7. $2a = 10$; $2b = 6$; foci: $(\pm 4, 0)$; $e = \dfrac{4}{5}$

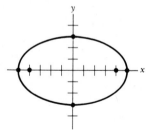

9. $2a = \sqrt{6}$; $2b = 2$; foci: $\left(\pm \dfrac{\sqrt{2}}{2}, 0\right)$; $e = \dfrac{\sqrt{3}}{3}$

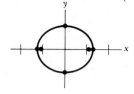

11. $2a = 10$; $2b = 2$; foci: $(0, \pm 2\sqrt{6})$; $e = \dfrac{2\sqrt{6}}{5}$

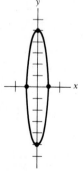

13. $2a = 4$; $2b = \dfrac{4}{3}$; foci: $\left(0, \pm \dfrac{4\sqrt{2}}{3}\right)$; $e = \dfrac{2\sqrt{2}}{3}$

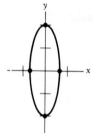

$9x^2 + y^2 = 4$ becomes

$$\frac{9x^2}{4} + \frac{y^2}{4} = 1 \quad \text{or}$$

$$\frac{x^2}{\frac{4}{9}} + \frac{y^2}{4} = 1$$

Note that a^2 here is the y^2 denominator.

$2a = 2\sqrt{4} = 4$ and $2b = 2\sqrt{\dfrac{4}{9}} = \dfrac{4}{3}$.

13. (cont)

$$c^2 = 4 - \frac{4}{9} \qquad e = \frac{c}{a}$$

$$c^2 = \frac{32}{9} \qquad\qquad = \frac{2\sqrt{2}}{3}$$

$$c = \pm \frac{4\sqrt{2}}{3}$$

15.

$$2a = 8;\ 2b = \frac{20}{3};\ \text{foci: } \left(0,\ \pm\frac{2\sqrt{11}}{3}\right);\ e = \frac{\sqrt{11}}{6}$$

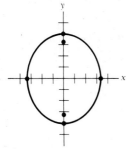

17. The foci are at $(0,\pm1)$ so $c = 1$.
    The vertices are at $(0,\pm4)$ so $a = 4$.
    Then

$$b^2 = a^2 - c^2$$
$$= 16 - 1$$
$$= 15$$

The equation must be

$$\frac{x^2}{15} + \frac{y^2}{16} = 1$$

or

$$16x^2 + 15y^2 = 240.$$

19. Foci at $(0,\pm2)$ mean $c = 2$.
    Minor axis end points at $(\pm5,0)$ mean $b = 5$.
    Therefore

$$a^2 = b^2 + c^2$$
$$= 25 + 4$$
$$= 29,$$

and the equation is

$$\frac{x^2}{25} + \frac{y^2}{29} = 1$$

or

19. (cont) $29x^2 + 25y^2 = 725.$

21. These axes define a as 10 and b as 4 so we get the equations directly.

$$\frac{x^2}{100} + \frac{y^2}{16} = 1 \quad \text{or} \quad 4x^2 + 25y^2 = 400.$$

23. The center at the origin puts the other end of the minor axis at (8,0).
    This is a vertical ellipse, that is it's taller than it is wide. Since
    $b = 8$ and $e = \frac{3}{5}$ we have these two equations relating c and a

$$e = \frac{c}{a} = \frac{3}{5} \quad \text{or} \quad c = \frac{3}{5} a$$

and

$$a^2 = c^2 + b^2 \quad \text{or} \quad a^2 = c^2 + 64.$$

Substituting gives

$$a^2 = \left(\frac{3}{5} a \right)^2 + 64$$

$$a^2 = \frac{9}{25} a^2 + 64$$

$$\frac{16}{25} a^2 = 64$$

$$a^2 = \frac{64 \cdot 25}{16}$$

$$a = \pm 10$$

Our equation must be

$$\frac{x^2}{64} + \frac{y^2}{100} = 1 \quad \text{or} \quad 25x^2 + 16y^2 = 1600.$$

25. (a) The tangent formula on page 537 gives us

$$\frac{x_1 x}{a^2} + \frac{y_1 y}{b^2} = 1$$

for the equation of the tangent at the point $(x_1 y_1)$. Substituting
we find

$$\frac{4x}{\frac{52}{3}} + \frac{2y}{52} = 1$$

or

$$12x + 2y = 52$$

or

$$6x + y = 26$$

25. (cont)

finally $y = -6x + 26.$

(b) The intercepts of this tangent line are $(0,26)$ and $(\frac{13}{2},0)$ so the area is

$$\frac{1}{2}(26)(\frac{13}{2}) = \frac{169}{2} \text{ sq. units.}$$

27. (b) $3x + 10\sqrt{6}y - 75 = 0$

(c) $d_1 = \dfrac{63}{\sqrt{609}}$, $d_2 = \dfrac{87}{\sqrt{609}}$

31. points are $\left(\pm \dfrac{ab}{\sqrt{a^2 + b^2}}, \pm \dfrac{ab}{\sqrt{a^2 + b^2}}\right)$

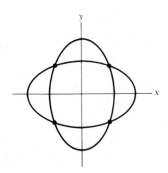

35. (b) $(-\frac{20}{7}, -\frac{18}{7})$

EXERCISE SET 9.4

1.
vertices: $(\pm 2, 0)$; foci: $(\pm\sqrt{5}, 0)$; $e = \dfrac{\sqrt{5}}{2}$; transverse axis = 4; conjugate axis = 2; asymptotes: $y = \pm\frac{1}{2}x$

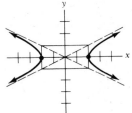

We start by dividing through by 4 to put the equation into standard form.

$$\frac{x^2}{4} - \frac{y^2}{1} = 1$$

We see that $a = \sqrt{4} = 2$ and $b = \sqrt{1} = 1$, so we can calculate c and then e.

1. (cont)
$$c^2 = a^2 + b^2 \qquad e = \frac{c}{a}$$
$$c^2 = 4 + 1 \qquad e = \frac{\sqrt{5}}{2}$$
$$c = \sqrt{5}$$

The asymptotes will be $y = \pm \dfrac{b}{a} x$ or $y = \pm \dfrac{1}{2} x$.

3.

vertices: (0 ± 2); foci: $(0, \pm\sqrt{5})$; $e = \dfrac{\sqrt{5}}{2}$; transverse
axis $= 4$; conjugate axis $= 2$; asymptotes: $y = \pm 2x$

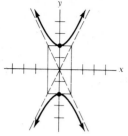

5.

vertices: $(\pm 5, 0)$; foci: $(\pm\sqrt{41}, 0)$; $e = \dfrac{\sqrt{41}}{5}$; transverse
axis $= 10$; conjugate axis $= 8$; asymptotes: $y = \pm\dfrac{4}{5}x$

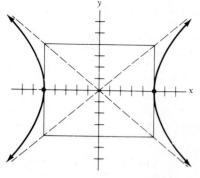

7.

vertices: $(0, \pm 1)$; foci: $(0, \pm\sqrt{2})$; $e = \sqrt{2}$; transverse
axis = 2; conjugate axis = 2; asymptotes: $y = \pm x$

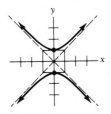

9.

vertices: $(0, \pm 5)$; foci: $(0, \pm\sqrt{29})$; $e = \dfrac{\sqrt{29}}{5}$; transverse

axis = 10; conjugate axis = 4; asymptotes: $y = \pm\dfrac{5}{2}x$

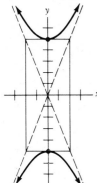

$4y^2 - 25x^2 = 100$ becomes

$$\frac{y^2}{25} - \frac{x^2}{4} = 1, \quad \text{a hyperbola}$$

opening up and down.

$c^2 = 25 + 4 \qquad e = \dfrac{c}{a}$

$c = \sqrt{29} \qquad\qquad e = \dfrac{\sqrt{29}}{5}$

Asymptotes:

$y = \pm \dfrac{a}{b} x$

$y = \pm \dfrac{5}{2} x$

Note that the slope ($\dfrac{a}{b}$ or $\dfrac{b}{a}$) changes between "vertical" and "horizontal" hyperbolas.

11. The foci are at $(\pm 4, 0)$ so $c = 4$ and we have an $Ax^2 - By^2 = c$ hyperbola. Since the vertices are $(\pm 1, 0)$, $a = 1$ and we can find b.

$$c^2 = a^2 + b^2$$
$$16 = 1 + b^2$$
$$15 = b^2$$
$$\sqrt{15} = b$$

11. (cont)
    Our equation will be $\dfrac{x^2}{1} - \dfrac{y^2}{15} = 1$ or $15x^2 - y^2 = 15$ in the required form.

13. The slope of the asymptotes, $\pm\dfrac{1}{2}$, tells us that the ratio $\dfrac{b}{a} = \dfrac{1}{2}$ in this hyperbola. Also, since the vertices are $(\pm2,0)$, $a = 2$. The required ratio is therefore

$$\frac{b}{2} = \frac{1}{2} \quad \text{and} \quad b = 1.$$

The equation is

$$\frac{x^2}{4} - \frac{y^2}{1} = 1 \quad \text{or} \quad x^2 - 4y^2 = 4 \quad \text{as required.}$$

15. $2x^2 - 5y^2 = 10$

17. The vertices are at $(0,\pm7)$ so we know it is a "vertical" hyperbola.

Its equation will be $\dfrac{y^2}{49} - \dfrac{x^2}{b^2} = 1$, but we also know that $(1,9)$ is a point satisfying the equation. We use it to find b.

$$\frac{9^2}{49} - \frac{1^2}{b^2} = 1$$

$$81b^2 - 49 = 49b^2$$

$$-49 = -32b^2$$

$$b^2 = \frac{49}{32} \qquad \text{that's all we need}$$

$$\frac{y^2}{49} - \frac{32x^2}{49} = 1 \quad \text{or} \quad y^2 - 32x^2 = 49 \quad \text{as required.}$$

19. Here, $2a$ is 6, so a is 3. Also $2b = 2$, so b is 1. The foci are on the y-axis, and we have

$$\frac{y^2}{3^2} - \frac{x^2}{1^2} = 1 \quad \text{or} \quad y^2 - 9x^2 = 9 \quad \text{as required.}$$

23. (a) Let's substitute

$$5(6)^2 - 4(5)^2 = 80$$
$$5(36) - 4(25)$$
$$180 - 100$$
$$80 \quad \text{yes!}$$

(b)
$$\frac{5y^2}{80} - \frac{4x^2}{80} = \frac{80}{80}$$

$$\frac{y^2}{16} - \frac{x^2}{20} = 1$$

so $a = 4$ and $b = 2\sqrt{5}$.

$$c^2 = a^2 + b^2$$
$$= 16 + 20$$
$$= 36$$

so $c = 6$ and the foci will be at $(0, \pm 6)$.

(c)
$$\overline{F_1P} = \sqrt{(5 - 0)^2 + (6 - 6)^2} = 5$$

$$\overline{F_2P} = \sqrt{(5 - 0)^2 + (6 - (-6))^2}$$

$$= \sqrt{25 + 144} = 13$$

(d)
$$|\overline{F_1P} - \overline{F_2P}| = |5 - 13|$$
$$= |-8|$$
$$= 8$$
$$= 2a \quad \text{as required.}$$

27. (a) and (b): $\sqrt{2}$

37. By substitution

$$16x^2 - 9(\tfrac{4}{3} x - 1)^2 = 144$$

$$16x^2 - 9(\tfrac{16}{9} x^2 - \tfrac{8}{3} x + 1) = 144$$

$$16x^2 - 16x^2 + 24x - 9 = 144$$

$$24x = 153$$

$$x = \frac{51}{8}$$

$$y = \frac{4}{3} \cdot \frac{51}{8} - 1$$

$$= \frac{17}{2} - 1$$

$$= \frac{15}{2}$$

Therefore $(\frac{51}{8} , \frac{15}{2})$ is

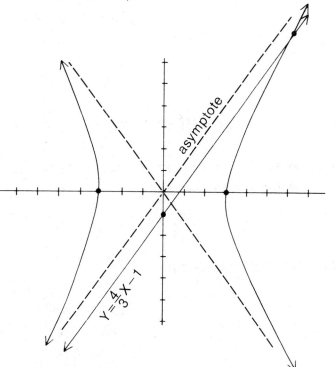

37. (cont)

   the one point of intersection.

EXERCISE SET 9.5

1.

vertex: (2, 3); axis: $y = 3$; focus: (3, 3); directrix: $x = 1$

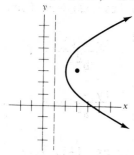

3.

vertex: (4, 2); axis: $x = 4$; focus: $\left(4, \frac{9}{4}\right)$; directrix: $y = \frac{7}{4}$

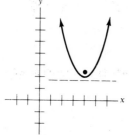

Compare the equation with its standard form.

$$(x - h)^2 = 4p(y - k)$$
$$(x - 4)^2 = (y - 2)$$

We see that the vertex is at (4,2) and that $4p = 1$. The focal length, p, is $\frac{1}{4}$.

5.

center: (5, −1); vertices: (0, −1), (10, −1); foci: (1, −1), (9, −1); $e = \frac{4}{5}$; transverse axis: 10; conjugate axis: 6

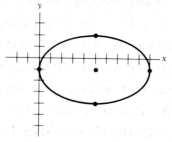

Compare.

$$\frac{(x - h)^2}{a^2} + \frac{(y - k)^2}{b^2} = 1$$

$$\frac{(x - 5)^2}{5^2} + \frac{(y + 1)^2}{3^2} = 1$$

The center is clearly at (5,-1). We see that a is 5 and b is 3, so we can calculate c and then the eccentricity.

5. (cont)

$$a^2 = c^2 + b^2 \qquad e = \frac{c}{a}$$

$$25 = c^2 + 3 \qquad e = \frac{4}{5}$$

$$16 = c^2$$

$$4 = c$$

7.

center: $(-4, 1)$; vertices: $(-7, 1)$, $(-1, 1)$; foci: $(-9, 1)$, $(1, 1)$; $e = \frac{5}{3}$; transverse axis: 6; conjugate axis: 8

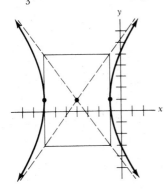

Again, we compare the given equation to its standard form

$$\frac{(x - h)^2}{a^2} - \frac{(y - k)^2}{b^2} = 1$$

$$\frac{(x + 4)^2}{3^2} - \frac{(y - 1)^2}{4^2} = 1$$

The center is at $(-4,1)$, a is 3, and b is 4. Here

$$c^2 = a^2 + b^2 \qquad e = \frac{5}{3}$$
$$c^2 = 25$$
$$c = 5$$

9. Can you see in advance that this is an ellipse? Look at the theorem above the problems on page 559.

$$3x^2 - 6x \qquad + 4y^2 + 16 \qquad = -7$$

$$3(x^2 - 2x + 1) + 4(y^2 + 4y + 4) = -7 + 3 + 16$$

$$3(x - 1)^2 \qquad + 4(y + 2)^2 \qquad = 12$$

$$\frac{(x - 1)^2}{4} + \frac{(y + 2)^2}{3} \qquad = 1$$

In the second step we added 3 and 16 on the right because, on the left, the 1 and 4 in parentheses are multiplied by 3 and 4 respectively. From this point our work repeats what we have done earlier in this section. Locate the center and build the ellipse away from it using a and b. Find the foci using $a^2 = c^2 + b^2$.

center: $(1, -2)$; foci: $(0, -2)$, $(2, -2)$; major axis: 4; minor axis: $2\sqrt{3}$

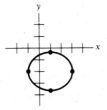

11.

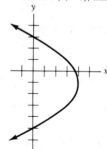

vertex: $(4, -1)$; axis: $y = -1$; focus: $(3, -1)$; directrix: $x = 5$

$$y^2 + 2y \qquad = -4x + 14$$

$$y^2 + 2y + 1 = -4x + 15 + 1$$

$$(y + 1)^2 = -4(x - 4)$$

This is a parabola with a vertex at $(4,-1)$. It opens left, and since $4p = -4$, $p = -1$. That means the focus will be at $(3,-1)$. The directrix will be one unit to the right of the vertex.

13.

center: $(1, 5)$; vertices: $(-2, 5)$, $(4, 5)$; foci: $(-4, 5)$, $(6, 5)$;
asymptotes: $y = \frac{4}{3}x + \frac{11}{3}$, $y = -\frac{4}{3}x + \frac{19}{3}$

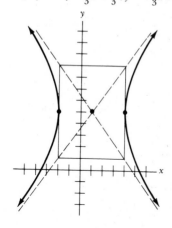

$$16(x^2 - 2x) \qquad - 9(y^2 - 10y) \qquad = 353$$

$$16(x^2 - 2x + 1) - 9(y^2 - 10y + 25) = 353 + 16 - 255$$

$$16(x - 1)^2 \qquad - 9(y - 5)^2 \qquad = 144$$

or

$$\frac{(x - 1)^2}{9} - \frac{(y - 5)^2}{16} = 1$$

This equation translates into the information and graph.

15. one point: $(4,6)$

17. two lines intersecting at $(5,1)$:
$3x + 4y = 19$ and $3x - 4y = 11$

19. center: $(0,-4)$; vertices: $(0,1)$, $(0,-9)$; foci: $(0,-4 + \sqrt{26})$, $(0,-4 - \sqrt{26})$; asymptotes: $y = \pm 5x - 4$

21. no graph

25. We start with $y = \sin x - \cos x$ and we want to substitute $y = y' + k$ and $x = x' + h$ and translate the original function into the function $y' = \sqrt{2} \sin x$.

$$y' + k = \sin(x' + h) - \cos(x' + h), \quad \text{now expand,}$$

$$y' + k = \sin x' \cdot \cos h + \cos x' \cdot \sin h - \cos x' \cdot \cos h + \sin x' \cdot \sin h$$
$$= \sin x'(\cos h + \sin h) + \cos x'(\sin h - \cos h)$$

or

$$\sqrt{2} \sin x' + k = \sin x'(\cos h + \sin h) + \cos x'(\sin h - \cos h)$$

Look carefully at this required equation. It will be true if 3 conditions are met.

(1) The coefficients of $\sin x'$ are equal, $\sqrt{2} = \cos h + \sin h$;

(2) The coefficient of $\cos x'$ is zero, $\sin h - \cos h = 0$; and $k = 0$.

Adding

$$\sin h + \cos h = \sqrt{2}$$
$$\sin h - \cos h = 0$$

we get

$$2 \sin h = \sqrt{2}$$
$$\sin h = \frac{\sqrt{2}}{2}$$
$$h = \frac{\pi}{4} \text{ or } \frac{3}{4}\pi$$

The second root will not check, however.

We want $k = 0$ and $h = \frac{\pi}{4}$.

A second approach is to look at graphs of $y = \sin x - \cos x$ and $y' = \sqrt{2} \sin x$.

The two will coincide if we shift $y = \sin x - \cos x$ left $\frac{\pi}{4}$ units.

$f(x + \frac{\pi}{4})$ will work.

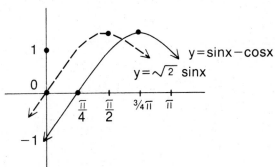

Exercise Set 9.6

1. Since

$$x = x' \cos \theta - y' \sin \theta$$

and

$$y = x' \sin \theta + y' \cos \theta,$$

substitution gives

$$
\begin{aligned}
x &= \sqrt{3} \cdot \cos 30° - 2 \cdot \sin 30° \\
&= \sqrt{3} \cdot \frac{\sqrt{3}}{2} - 2 \cdot \frac{1}{2} \\
&= \frac{3}{2} - 1 \\
&= \frac{1}{2}
\end{aligned}
$$

and

$$
\begin{aligned}
y &= \sqrt{3} \cdot \sin 30° + 2 \cdot \cos 30° \\
&= \sqrt{3} \cdot \frac{1}{2} + 2 \cdot \frac{\sqrt{3}}{2} \\
&= \frac{\sqrt{3}}{2} + \sqrt{3} \\
&= \frac{3\sqrt{3}}{2}
\end{aligned}
$$

The coordinates in the $x - y$ system are $\left(\frac{1}{2}, \frac{3\sqrt{3}}{2}\right)$.

3. $(2,0)$

5. Here

$$x' = x \cos \theta + y \sin \theta$$

and

$$y' = -x \sin \theta + y \cos \theta.$$

Therefore

$$x' = -3 \cdot \cos\left(\sin^{-1} \frac{5}{13}\right) + 1 \cdot \sin\left(\sin^{-1} \frac{5}{13}\right)$$

or

$$x' = -3 \cdot \frac{12}{13} + 1 \cdot \frac{5}{13} = -\frac{31}{13}$$

and

$$y' = 3 \cdot \frac{5}{13} + 1 \cdot \frac{12}{13} = \frac{27}{13}$$

The coordinates with respect to the $x' - y'$ system are $\left(-\frac{31}{13}, \frac{27}{13}\right)$.

7. Applying the rule that $\cot 2\theta = \dfrac{A - C}{B}$ where θ is the required angle, and A, B, and C are the numerical coefficients of the x^2, xy, and y^2 terms respectively, we have

$$\cot 2\theta = \frac{25 - 18}{-24} = -\frac{7}{24} .$$

If we are fortunate and recognize this as the cot of a special angle, then we can write $\sin \theta$ and $\cos \theta$ directly.

However, that is not the case here, and we proceed.

$$\cot 2\theta = -\frac{7}{24}$$

$$\tan 2\theta = -\frac{24}{7}$$

Now, since

$$1 + \tan^2 x = \sec^2 x$$

$$1 + \left(-\frac{24}{7}\right)^2 = \sec^2 2\theta$$

or

$$\sec^2 2\theta = \frac{625}{49}$$

and

$$\sec 2\theta = \pm \frac{25}{7} .$$

Now, we chose between the signs by looking back at $\cot 2\theta$. It was negative, so 2θ must lie in the second quadrant and hence $\sec 2\theta$ will also be negative. We have

$$\sec 2\theta = -\frac{25}{7}$$

so

$$\cos 2\theta = -\frac{7}{25} ,$$

and we are ready to determine $\sin \theta$ and $\cos \theta$ by use of the proper identities.

$$\sin \theta = \pm\sqrt{\frac{1 - \cos 2\theta}{2}} \quad \text{and} \quad \cos \theta = \pm\sqrt{\frac{1 + \cos 2\theta}{2}} .$$

$$\sin \theta = \sqrt{\frac{1 - \left(-\frac{7}{25}\right)}{2}} \quad \text{and} \quad \cos \theta = \sqrt{\frac{1 + \left(-\frac{7}{25}\right)}{2}}$$

$$= \sqrt{\frac{\frac{32}{25}}{2}} \qquad\qquad\qquad = \sqrt{\frac{\frac{18}{25}}{2}}$$

$$= \sqrt{\frac{16}{25}} = \frac{4}{5} \qquad\qquad = \sqrt{\frac{9}{25}} = \frac{3}{5}$$

7. (cont)

These are the required answers. We chose the positive square root here because since 2θ is a second quadrant angle, θ is first quadrant and both $\sin \theta$ and $\cos \theta$ are positive.

9. $\sin \theta = \dfrac{3}{5}$; $\cos \theta = \dfrac{4}{5}$

11.

$$\cot 2\theta = \frac{A - C}{B}$$

$$= \frac{1 - (-1)}{-2\sqrt{3}}$$

$$= -\frac{1}{\sqrt{3}}$$

This is a nice result because we recognize that $\cot 2\theta = -\dfrac{1}{\sqrt{3}}$ means that $2\theta = 120°$ or $\theta = 60°$. Now, we can write $\sin \theta = \dfrac{\sqrt{3}}{2}$ and $\cos \theta = \dfrac{1}{2}$ directly.

13. $\sin \theta = \dfrac{7\sqrt{2}}{34}$; $\cos \theta = \dfrac{23\sqrt{2}}{34}$

15. $\dfrac{y'^2}{9} - \dfrac{x'^2}{9} = 1$

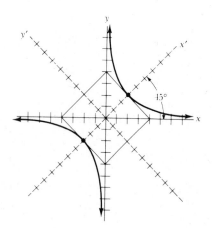

17. $\dfrac{x'^2}{(\frac{1}{3})^2} - \dfrac{y'^2}{1^2} = 1$

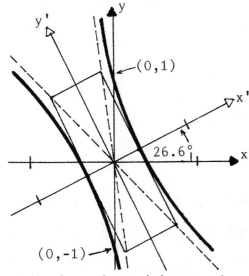

(0,1)

26.6°

x

(0,-1)

Graphing the equation requires that we not only find the angle of rotation which eliminates the xy term, but go past that to find the new $x' - y'$ equation. Here we have $7x^2 + 8xy + y^2 - 1 = 0$, so

$$\cot 2\theta = \dfrac{7 - 1}{8} = \dfrac{3}{4}$$

$$\tan 2\theta = \dfrac{4}{3}$$

$$\sec^2 2\theta = 1 + \left(\dfrac{4}{3}\right)^2$$

$$\sec^2 2\theta = \dfrac{25}{9}$$

and

$$\sec 2\theta = \dfrac{5}{3} .$$

We chose the positive root because $\cot 2\theta > 0$ so 2θ is less than $90°$. We proceed

$$\cos 2\theta = \dfrac{3}{5}$$

$$\sin \theta = \sqrt{\dfrac{1 - (\frac{3}{5})}{2}} = \dfrac{\sqrt{5}}{5}$$

and

$$\cos \theta = \sqrt{\dfrac{1 + \frac{3}{5}}{2}} = \dfrac{2\sqrt{5}}{5}$$

A calculator will show us that

$$\sin^{-1} \dfrac{\sqrt{5}}{5} \approx 26.6°.$$

We know that

$$x = x' \cos \theta - y' \sin \theta$$

and

$$y = x' \sin \theta + y' \cos \theta,$$

so now substitute

$$7x^2 + 8xy + y^2 - 1 = 0$$

becomes

17. (cont)

$$7\left[x'\,\frac{2\sqrt{5}}{5} - y'\,\frac{\sqrt{5}}{5}\right]^2 + 8\left[x'\,\frac{2\sqrt{5}}{5} - y'\,\frac{\sqrt{5}}{5}\right]\left[x'\,\frac{\sqrt{5}}{5} + y'\,\frac{2\sqrt{5}}{5}\right]$$

$$+ \left[x'\,\frac{\sqrt{5}}{5} + y'\,\frac{2\sqrt{5}}{5}\right]^2 - 1 = 0$$

and we must expand and collect similar terms.

$$7\left[\frac{4}{5}x'^2 - \frac{4}{5}x'y' + \frac{1}{5}y'^2\right]^2 + 8\left[\frac{2}{5}x'^2 + \frac{3}{5}x'y' - \frac{2}{5}y'^2\right]$$

$$+ \left[\frac{1}{5}x'^2 + \frac{4}{5}x'y' + \frac{4}{5}y'^2\right] - 1 = 0$$

$$\frac{28}{5}x'^2 - \frac{28}{5}x'y' + \frac{7}{5}y'^2 + \frac{16}{5}x'^2 + \frac{24}{5}x'y' - \frac{16}{5}y'^2 + \frac{1}{5}x'^2$$

$$+ \frac{4}{5}x'y' + \frac{4}{5}y'^2 - 1 = 0$$

Notice that if everything has gone according to plan the sum of the x' - y' terms will be zero. That is the case here. We now combine similar terms to get

$$9x'^2 - y'^2 = 1$$

or

$$\frac{x'^2}{(\frac{1}{3})^2} - \frac{y'^2}{(1)^2} = 1 \quad \text{in standard form.}$$

We construct a new set of x'y' axes rotated 26.6° and follow the old rules to sketch this hyperbola.

19. $x'^2 = \frac{1}{5}$

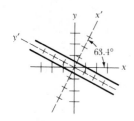

21. We follow the same procedure as in problem 17.

$$\cot 2\theta = \frac{9 - 16}{-24} = \frac{7}{24}$$

from which we get $\sin \theta = \frac{3}{5}$ and $\cos \theta = \frac{4}{5}$. Again we calculate

21. (cont) $\sin^{-1} \frac{3}{5} \approx 36.9°$.

After substituting we will have

$$9\left[\frac{4}{5} x' - \frac{3}{5} y'\right]^2 - 24\left[\frac{4}{5} x' - \frac{3}{5} y'\right]\left[\frac{3}{5} x' + \frac{4}{5} y'\right] + 16\left[\frac{3}{5} x' + \frac{4}{5} y'\right]^2$$

$$- 400\left[\frac{4}{5} x' - \frac{3}{5} y'\right] - 300\left[\frac{3}{5} x' + \frac{4}{5} y'\right] = 0.$$

Now we carefully expand and collect similar terms and get

$$25y' - 500x' = 0$$

or

$$y'^2 = 20x', \quad \text{a parabola.}$$

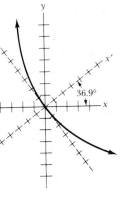

The graph, on our rotated x' - y' axes, completes the problem. Be sure to apply our rules about the focus and focal width as an aid to sketching. See section 9.2 if you have forgotten.

23.

$$\frac{\left(x' + \frac{2}{\sqrt{5}}\right)^2}{1} - \frac{\left(y' + \frac{1}{\sqrt{5}}\right)^2}{4} = 1$$

25. $\dfrac{(x'-1)^2}{1} + \dfrac{(y'+1)^2}{\frac{1}{2}} = 1$

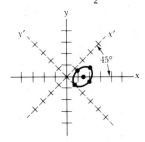

27. $(y' - \sqrt{2})^2 = 2\sqrt{2}\left(x' - \dfrac{11\sqrt{2}}{2}\right)$

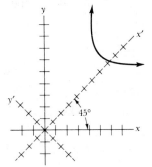

29. $\dfrac{x'^2}{1} + \dfrac{y'^2}{\frac{7}{2}} = 1$

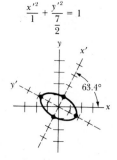

31. Again, $\cot 2\theta = \dfrac{17 - 8}{-12} = -\dfrac{3}{4}$, and we follow the old argument to conclude that $\sin \theta = \dfrac{2}{\sqrt{5}}$ and $\cos \theta = \dfrac{1}{\sqrt{5}}$. We will leave these with radicals in the denominator as an aid to later calculations. Observe that if we square denominators inside parentheses and factor carefully then

31. (cont)

$$17\left[\frac{1}{\sqrt{5}}x' - \frac{2}{\sqrt{5}}y'\right]^2 - 12\left[\frac{1}{\sqrt{5}}x' - \frac{2}{\sqrt{5}}y'\right]\left[\frac{2}{\sqrt{5}}x' + \frac{1}{\sqrt{5}}y'\right]$$

$$+ 8\left[\frac{2}{\sqrt{5}}x' + \frac{1}{\sqrt{5}}y'\right]^2 - 80 = 0$$

becomes

$$\frac{17}{5}(x' - 2y')^2 - \frac{12}{5}(x' - 2y')(2x' + y') + \frac{8}{5}(2x' + y')^2 - 80 = 0$$

We could have used this idea in earlier problems. Multiplying and combining gives us the ellipse $5x^2 + 20y^2 = 80$ or

$\frac{x'^2}{16} + \frac{y'^2}{4} = 1$. The graph, rotated $\approx 63.4°$ is as indicated. Note the intercepts on the $x' - y'$ axes.

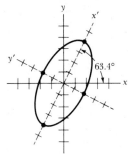

33. This time we are missing an x^2 term, but that will only simplify the algebra.

$$\cot 2\theta = \frac{0 - (-4)}{3} = \frac{4}{3}$$

and

$$\sin \theta = \frac{1}{\sqrt{10}}, \quad \cos \theta = \frac{3}{\sqrt{10}}.$$

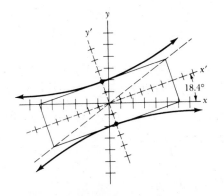

Taking advantage of the shortcut from the last problem, we write

$$\frac{3}{10}(3x' - y')(x' + 3y') - \frac{4}{10}(x' + 3y')^2$$

$$+ 18 = 0,$$

which leads us to

$$\frac{y'^2}{4} - \frac{x'^2}{36} = 1$$

33. (cont)

when expanded and simplified. The graph, rotated ≈ 18.4° to the new x'y'
axes follows from what we already know about graphing hyperbolas.

35. $x'^2 = 4y'$

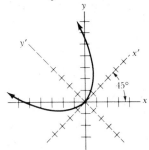

37. $\dfrac{x'^2}{6} + \dfrac{y'^2}{\frac{2}{3}} = 1$

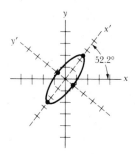

39. Start with $3x^2 - 2xy + 3y^2 + 2 = 0$

$$\cot 2\theta = \frac{3 - 3}{-2} = 0.$$

This is nice because it means $\tan 2\theta$ is not defined $\left(\frac{1}{0}\right)$. The tan is
not defined at 90°, therefore we conclude $2\theta = 90°$ and $\theta = 45°$. We
have $\sin \theta = \cos \theta = \dfrac{1}{\sqrt{2}}$.
Now substituting,

$$\frac{3}{2}(x' - y')^2 - \frac{2}{2}(x' - y')(x' + y') + \frac{3}{2}(x' + y')^2 + 2 = 0$$

When we expand and collect terms we find the result is

$$2x^2 + 4y^2 + 2 = 0,$$

an impossible situation since all these terms must be greater than or equal
to zero. Our conclusion is that there is no graph possible.

41. $x = x' \cos \theta - y' \sin \theta$; $y = x' \sin \theta + y' \cos \theta$

EXERCISE SET 9.7

1.   (a) $(3, \frac{2}{3}\pi)$ represents a set of polar coordinates of the form (r, θ).
          We recall that to convert we use

$$x = r \cos \theta \quad \text{and} \quad y = r \sin \theta$$
$$= 3 \cos \frac{2}{3}\pi \qquad\qquad = 3 \sin \frac{2}{3}\pi$$
$$= 3(-\frac{1}{2}) \qquad\qquad = 3(\frac{\sqrt{3}}{2})$$
$$= -\frac{3}{2} \qquad\qquad\qquad = \frac{3\sqrt{3}}{2}$$

The required coordinates are $(-\frac{3}{2}, \frac{3\sqrt{3}}{2})$.

(b)   Here
$$x = 4 \cos \frac{11}{6}\pi \quad \text{and} \quad y = 4 \sin \frac{11}{6}\pi$$
$$= 4(\frac{\sqrt{3}}{2}) \qquad\qquad = 4(-\frac{1}{2})$$
$$= 2\sqrt{3} \qquad\qquad\qquad = -2$$

$(2\sqrt{3}, -2)$ is our solution.

(c)   We could work it out as we have been doing, but let's just observe that
$\frac{11}{6}\pi$ and $-\frac{\pi}{6}$ are the same θ so our solution is the same as part (b).

3.   (a) $(0,1)$
     (b) $(0,1)$
     (c) $\left(\frac{\sqrt{2 + \sqrt{2}}}{2}, \frac{\sqrt{2 - \sqrt{2}}}{2} \right)$

5.   Now we use $x^2 + y^2 = r^2$ and $\tan \theta = \frac{y}{x}$.

(a) $(-1)^2 + (-1)^2 = r^2 \qquad \tan \theta = \frac{-1}{-1}$
$$r^2 = 2 \qquad\qquad\qquad = \frac{\pi}{4} \text{ or } \frac{5}{4}\pi$$
$$r = \sqrt{2}$$

The coordinates are $(\sqrt{2}, \frac{5}{4}\pi)$.   Why did we choose $\frac{5}{4}\pi$?

7. $$r = 2 \cos \theta$$

$$\sqrt{x^2 + y^2} = 2\, \frac{x}{\sqrt{x^2 + y^2}}$$

Now cross multiply to get

$$x^2 + y^2 = 2x$$

$$x^2 - 2x \quad + y^2 = 0 \quad \text{complete the square}$$

$$x^2 - 2x + 1 + y^2 = 1$$

$$(x - 1)^2 \quad + y^2 = 1$$

A circle, center at $(1,0)$ with a radius of 1.

9. $x^4 + x^2 y^2 - y^2 = 0$

11. $$r = 3 \cos 2\theta$$

$$\sqrt{x^2 + y^2} = 3\left[\frac{x^2}{x^2 + y^2} - \frac{y^2}{x^2 + y^2} \right]$$

using $\cos 2\theta = \cos^2 \theta = \sin^2 \theta$.

$$\sqrt{x^2 + y^2} = \frac{3(x^2 - y^2)}{x^2 + y^2}$$

Now square both sides.

$$x^2 + y^2 = \frac{9(x^2 - y^2)^2}{(x^2 + y^2)^2}$$

$$(x^2 + y^2)^3 = 9(x^2 - y^2)^2$$

$$x^6 + 3x^4 y^2 + 3x^2 y^4 + y^6 = 9x^4 - 18x^2 y^2 + 9y^4$$

or finally

$$x^6 - 9x^4 + 3x^4 y^2 + 18x^2 y^2 + 3x^2 y^4 - 9y^4 + y^6 = 0$$

Now admit it, wasn't $r = 3 \cos \theta$ cleaner?

13.
$$r^2 = \frac{8}{2 - \sin^2 \theta}$$

or

$$r^2(2 - \sin^2 \theta) = 8$$

$$(x^2 + y^2)\left(2 - \frac{y^2}{x^2 + y^2}\right) = 8$$

$$(x^2 + y^2)\left[\frac{2(x^2 + y^2) - y^2}{(x^2 + y^2)}\right] = 8$$

cancelling $(x^2 + y^2)$ we get

$$2x^2 + 2y^2 - y^2 = 8 \quad \text{or}$$

$$2x^2 + y^2 - 8 = 0.$$

Do you recognize this conic section? Can you put it in the standard form for an ellipse?

15. $x + 2y - 1 = 0$

17. Substituting $x = r \cos \theta$ and $y = r \sin \theta$ in $3x - 4y = 2$ gives

$$3(r \cos \theta) - 4(r \sin \theta) = 2$$

or factoring

$$r(3 \cos \theta - 4 \sin \theta) = 2.$$

Solving for r,

$$r = \frac{2}{3 \cos \theta - 4 \sin \theta} .$$

Since $3x - 4y = 2$ is a line, this is the polar form for a line.

19. $r = \tan^2 \theta \cdot \sec \theta$

21. $r^2 = \dfrac{1}{2 \sin \theta \cos \theta}$

23. $r^2 = \dfrac{9}{9 \cos^2 \theta \sin^2 \theta}$

25. Let's make a table for $r = 3 \cos \theta$, but while we do it recall problem 7 and what its graph turned out to be.

25.   (cont)

θ	0	$\frac{\pi}{6}$	$\frac{\pi}{4}$	$\frac{\pi}{3}$	$\frac{\pi}{2}$	$\frac{2\pi}{3}$	$\frac{3\pi}{4}$	$\frac{5\pi}{6}$	π
r = 3 cos θ	3	$\frac{3\sqrt{3}}{2}$	$\frac{3\sqrt{2}}{2}$	$\frac{3}{2}$	0	$-\frac{3}{2}$	$-\frac{3\sqrt{2}}{2}$	$-\frac{3\sqrt{3}}{2}$	-3
	3	2.6	2.1	1.5	0	-1.5	-2.1	-2.6	-3

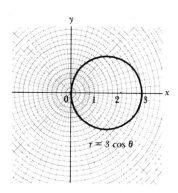

$r = 3 \cos \theta$

We really need calculator approximations for some of the values to simplify plotting them, so a third row has been added here. Note that taking θ from 0 to π has given us the entire graph. Did you think to consider symmetry? Since cos(-θ) = cos θ, we have symmetry with respect to the x-axis and $0 \leq \theta \leq \frac{\pi}{2}$ would have been sufficient.

27.   r = 1 - cos θ

This time we will make a point of considering f(-θ). It does equal f(θ) since, again, cos(-θ) = cos θ. Therefore taking θ from 0 to π will be adequate.

Our table of values looks like this

θ	0	$\frac{\pi}{6}$	$\frac{\pi}{4}$	$\frac{\pi}{3}$	$\frac{\pi}{2}$	$\frac{2}{3}\pi$	$\frac{3}{4}\pi$	$\frac{5}{6}\pi$	π
r = 1 - cos θ	0	$1 - \frac{\sqrt{3}}{2}$	$1 - \frac{\sqrt{2}}{2}$	$\frac{1}{2}$	1	$\frac{3}{2}$	$1 + \frac{\sqrt{2}}{2}$	$1 + \frac{\sqrt{3}}{2}$	2
	0	.1	.3	.5	1	1.5	1.7	1.9	2

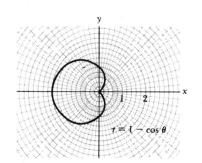

$r = 1 - \cos \theta$

The result is this cardioid. We reflect it across the x-axis to complete the graph.

29.

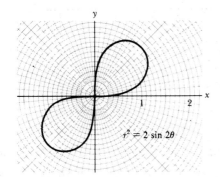

31.

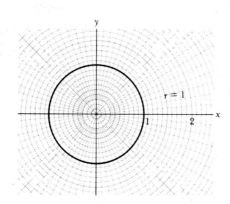

33.

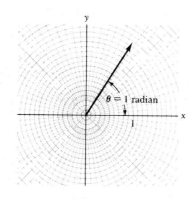

35. r = 2 sin 2θ

θ	0	$\frac{\pi}{6}$	$\frac{\pi}{4}$	$\frac{\pi}{3}$	$\frac{\pi}{2}$	$\frac{2\pi}{3}$	$\frac{3\pi}{4}$	$\frac{5\pi}{6}$	π
r	0	$\sqrt{3}$	2	$\sqrt{3}$	0	$-\sqrt{3}$	-2	$-\sqrt{3}$	0

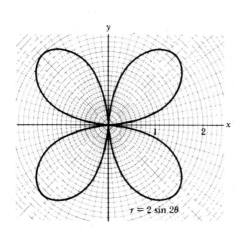

You may want to add some smaller values of θ here, say $\frac{\pi}{12}$ and $\frac{5}{12}\pi$, to help give shape to the graph. It turns out to be this interesting four leafed rose. Note that θ from 0 to π gives us the points in the first and fourth quadrant and we can reflect it across the y-axis to complete the curve. This is because replacing r with -r and θ with (-θ) gives us the same equation.

37.

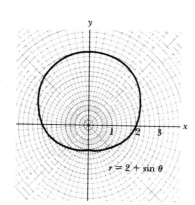

39.

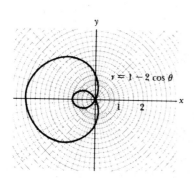

41.

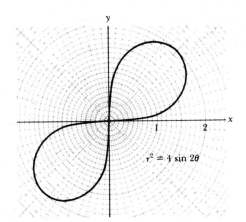

$r^2 = 4 \sin 2\theta$

43.

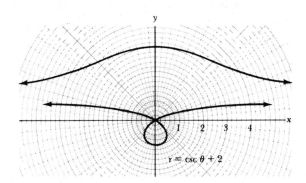

$r = \csc \theta + 2$

45.

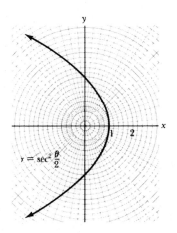

$r = \sec^2 \dfrac{\theta}{2}$

Chapter 10   Additional Topics in Algebra

1. We will follow the two step procedure presented by the author in his sample solutions in the text.

    Here P_n denotes the statement

    $$1 + 2 + \cdots + n = \frac{n(n + 1)}{2} \, .$$

    Step 1: We must check that P_1 is true.

    $$1 = \frac{1(2)}{2}$$

    $$\text{or} \quad 1 = 1$$

    Step 2: Assuming that P_k is true we must show that P_{k+1} is true. Thus we assume that

    $$1 + 2 + \cdots + k = \frac{k(k + 1)}{2} \tag{1}$$

    we must show that

    $$1 + 2 + \cdots + k + k + 1 = \frac{(k + 1)[(k + 1) + 1]}{2}$$

    Adding $k + 1$ to the right side of equation (1) gives

1. (cont)

$$1 + 2 + \cdots + k + k + 1 = \frac{k(k + 1)}{2} + k + 1$$

Our strategy will be to simplify on the right side:

$$\frac{k(k + 1)}{2} + (k + 1) = \frac{k(k + 1) + 2(k + 1)}{2}$$

$$= \frac{k^2 + k + 2k + 2}{2}$$

$$= \frac{k^2 + 3k + 2}{2}$$

$$= \frac{(k + 1)(k + 2)}{2}$$

$$= \frac{(k + 1)[(k + 1) + 1]}{2}$$

which is what we wished to show, and we conclude that P_n is true for all natural numbers n.

5.

$$1^2 + 2^2 + 3^2 + \cdots + n^2 = \frac{n(n + 1)(2n + 1)}{6} \,,$$

this is our proposition, P_n

Step 1:

$$1^2 = \frac{1(1 + 1)(2 \cdot 1 + 1)}{6}$$

$$= \frac{1(2)(3)}{6}$$

$$= 1$$

Step 2: Assuming that

$$1^2 + 2^2 + \cdots + k^2 = \frac{k(k + 1)(2k + 1)}{6}$$

we must show that

$$1^2 + 2^2 + \cdots + k^2 + (k + 1)^2 = \frac{(k + 1)[(k + 1) + 1][2(k + 1) + 1]}{6}$$

Again, we will go back and add $(k + 1)^2$ term to both sides of the assumed equation

5. (cont)

$$1^2 + 2^2 + \cdots + k^2 + (k + 1)^2 = \frac{k(k + 1)(2k + 1)}{6} + (k + 1)^2$$

$$= \frac{k(k + 1)(2k + 1) + 6(k + 1)^2}{6}$$

$$= \frac{(k + 1)[k(2k + 1) + 6(k + 1)]}{6}$$

$$= \frac{(k + 1)[2k^2 + k + 6k + 6]}{6}$$

$$= \frac{(k + 1)(k + 2)(2k + 3)}{6} \quad \text{or}$$

$$= \frac{(k + 1)[(k + 1) + 1][2(k + 1) + 1]}{6}$$

as required.

9. P_n is the proposition that

$$3 + 3^2 + 3^3 + \cdots + 3^n = \frac{1}{2}(3^{n+1} - 3).$$

Step 1 asks us to verify that

$$3 = \frac{1}{2}(3^{1+1} - 3)$$

$$= \frac{1}{2}(9 - 3)$$

$$= 3$$

In Step 2 we assume
$$3 + 3^2 + 3^3 + \cdots + 3^k = \frac{1}{2}(3^{k+1} - 3)$$

and show

$$3 + 3^2 + 3^3 + \cdots + 3^k + 3^{k+1} = \frac{1}{2}(3^{k+1+1} - 3)$$

Let's add 3^{k+1} to both sides of our assumed equation

$$3 + 3^2 + 3^3 + \cdots + 3^k + 3^{k+1} = \frac{1}{2}(3^{k+1} - 3) + 3^{k+1}$$

$$= \frac{3^{k+1} - 3 + 2 \cdot 3^{k+1}}{2}$$

$$= \frac{3 \cdot 3^{k+1} - 3}{2}$$

$$= \frac{3^{k+1+1} - 3}{2}$$

9. (cont)

as required. The proposition is established.

11. Step 1: Show that our proposition is true for n = 1.

$$\sin(\tfrac{\pi}{4} + 1 \cdot \pi) = (-1)^1 \tfrac{\sqrt{2}}{2}$$

$$\sin(\tfrac{5}{4} \pi) = - \tfrac{\sqrt{2}}{2}, \quad \text{yes.}$$

Step 2: Assuming that

$$\sin(\tfrac{\pi}{4} + k\pi) = (-1)^k \tfrac{\sqrt{2}}{2}$$

we want to show that

$$\sin(\tfrac{\pi}{4} + (k + 1)\pi) = (-1)^{k+1} \tfrac{\sqrt{2}}{2}$$

Working on the left side,

$$\sin(\tfrac{\pi}{4} + (k + 1)\pi) = \sin(\tfrac{\pi}{4} + k\pi + \pi)$$

$$= \sin[(\tfrac{\pi}{4} + k\pi) + \pi]$$

$$= \sin(\tfrac{\pi}{4} + k\pi)(-1) + \cos(\tfrac{\pi}{4} + k\pi)(0)$$

But from P_k this is

$$\left[(-1)^k \tfrac{\sqrt{2}}{2}\right](-1)$$

which is $(-1)^{k+1} \tfrac{\sqrt{2}}{2}$ as we wanted to establish. So P_{k+1} follows from P_k, and our induction proof is complete.

19. Step 1: P_1 is the statement that

$$(2 \cdot 1 - 1)(2 \cdot 1 + 1) = \frac{1(4 \cdot 1^2 + 6 \cdot 1 - 1)}{3}$$

$$\text{or} \qquad 3 = 3$$

Step 2: We assume P_k, that is

$$1 \times 3 + 3 \times 5 + 5 \times 7 + \cdots + (2k - 1)(2k + 1) = \frac{k(4k^2 + 6k - 1)}{3}$$

and show that P_{k+1} is true. The right side of P_k with the next term added looks like this

19. (cont)

$$\frac{k(4k^2 + 6k - 1)}{3} + [2(k + 1) - 1][2(k + 1) + 1]$$

If we expand, add using a common denominator, and collect similar terms, this equals

$$\frac{4k^3 + 18k^2 + 23k + 9}{3} \qquad (*)$$

The right side of P_{k+1} should look like

$$\frac{(k + 1)[4(k + 1)^2 + 6(k + 1) - 1]}{3} , \qquad (**)$$

By multiplying out (**) now, you'll see it equals (*). Thus P_{k+1} is established and our proposition is true.

31. Step 1 requires us to show that it is true for the first natural number greater than or equal to 2:

$$2^2 + 4 < (2 + 1)^2$$
$$8 < 9 \quad \text{true.}$$

Step 2: We take P_k to be

$$k^2 + 4 < (k + 1)^2 \quad \text{for} \quad k \geq 2,$$

and show that

$$(k + 1)^2 + 4 < [(k + 1) + 1]^2 \quad \text{for} \quad k \geq 2,$$
$$\text{or} \quad k^2 + 2k + 5 < k^2 + 4k + 4.$$

This is true whenever

$$1 < 2k$$
$$\text{or} \quad \frac{1}{2} < k$$

which is true for $k \geq 2$. The induction proof is complete.

33. (a)

n	1	2	3	4	5
f(n)	$\frac{1}{2}$	$\frac{2}{3}$	$\frac{3}{4}$	$\frac{4}{5}$	$\frac{5}{6}$

(b) The pattern suggests that $f(6)$ will be $\frac{6}{7}$ and calculations confirm this.

$$\frac{5}{6} + \frac{1}{6(7)} = \frac{35 + 1}{42}$$
$$= \frac{36}{42}$$
$$= \frac{6}{7}$$

(c) It looks like $f(n) = \frac{n}{n + 1}$.

Step 1 is done because $f(1) = \frac{1}{2}$ from the table.

$f(k)$ is the statement

$$\frac{1}{1 \times 2} + \frac{1}{2 \times 3} + \cdots + \frac{1}{k(k + 1)} = \frac{k}{k + 1}$$

and we assume this and show that it leads to the conclusion that

$$\frac{1}{1 \times 2} + \frac{1}{2 \times 3} + \cdots + \frac{1}{k(k + 1)} + \frac{1}{(k + 1)(k + 2)} = \frac{k + 1}{k + 2}.$$

Let's add $\frac{1}{(k + 1)(k + 2)}$ to both sides of $f(k)$. The right side will then be

$$\frac{k}{k + 1} + \frac{1}{(k + 1)(k + 2)} = \frac{k(k + 2) + 1}{(k + 1)(k + 2)}$$
$$= \frac{k^2 + 2k + 1}{(k + 1)(k + 2)}$$
$$= \frac{(k + 1)(k + 1)}{(k + 1)(k + 2)}$$
$$= \frac{k + 1}{k + 2}$$

which is what we wished to show. P_{k+1} is established and the proof is complete.

43. P_1 is the simple statement that 4 is a factor of $5^1 + 3$ or 8.
Step 2 requires us to assume that $5^n + 3$ is divisible by 4 and show that then $5^{n+1} + 3$ must also be divisible by 4. Incidentally, try some terms for yourself to see that it is plausible.

43. (cont)

It is

To show that it is true let's look at the difference between

$$5^{n+1} + 3 \quad \text{and} \quad 5^n + 3.$$

It is

$$(5^{n+1} + 3) - (5^n + 3)$$
$$\text{or} \quad 5^{n+1} - 5^n.$$

Factoring gives $5^n(5 - 1)$ which is $4(5^n)$. This is clearly divisible by 4. Since $5^n + 3$ is divisible by hypothesis and $5^{n+1} + 3$ is larger by a multiple of 4 our proposition is true.

45. We wish to prove that

$$\log_{10}(a_1 a_2 \cdots a_n) = \log_{10} a_1 + \log_{10} a_2 + \cdots + \log_{10} a_n$$

Step 1 is easily satisfied since $\log_{10} a_1 = \log_{10} a_1$.
For Step 2 we assume the truth for $n = k$ and show that this implies that

$$\log_{10}(a_1 a_2 \cdots a_k a_{k+1}) = \log_{10} a_1 + \log_{10} a_2 + \cdots + \log_{10} a_k + \log_{10} a_{k+1}$$

Now,

$$\log_{10}[a_1 a_2 \cdots a_k a_{k+1}] = \log_{10}[(a_1 a_2 \cdots a_k) \cdot a_{k+1}]$$
$$= \log_{10}(a_1 a_2 \cdots a_k) + \log_{10} a_{k+1}$$

but the first part of this sum is $\log_{10} a_1 + \log_{10} a_2 + \cdots + \log_{10} a_k$ by the induction hypothesis. The Principal of Mathematical Induction allows us to conclude that P_n is true for all natural numbers n.

Exercise Set 10.2

1.
$$
\begin{array}{c}
1 \\
1 \quad 1 \\
1 \quad 2 \quad 1 \\
1 \quad 3 \quad 3 \quad 1 \\
1 \quad 4 \quad 6 \quad 4 \quad 1 \\
1 \quad 5 \quad 10 \quad 10 \quad 5 \quad 1 \\
1 \quad 6 \quad 15 \quad 20 \quad 15 \quad 6 \quad 1 \\
1 \quad 7 \quad 21 \quad 35 \quad 35 \quad 21 \quad 7 \quad 1 \\
1 \quad 8 \quad 28 \quad 56 \quad 70 \quad 56 \quad 28 \quad 8 \quad 1 \\
1 \quad 9 \quad 36 \quad 84 \quad 126 \quad 126 \quad 84 \quad 36 \quad 9 \quad 1
\end{array}
$$

3. $a^9 - 9a^8b + 36a^7b^2 - 84a^6b^3 + 126a^5b^4 - 126a^4b^5 + 84a^3b^6 - 36a^2b^7 + 9ab^8 - b^9$

5. The expansion of $(a + b)^5$ has the form $a^6 + 6a^5b + 15a^4b^2 + 20a^3b^3 + 15a^2b^4 + 6ab^5 + b^6$. The coefficients can be found by looking back to a table like the answer to problem 1 or by recreating Pascal's triangle from time to time.

$$
\begin{array}{c}
1 \\
1 \quad 1 \\
1 \quad 2 \quad 1 \\
1 \quad 3 \quad 3 \quad 1 \\
1 \quad 4 \quad 6 \quad 4 \quad 1 \\
1 \quad 5 \quad 10 \quad 10 \quad 5 \quad 1 \\
1 \quad 6 \quad 15 \quad 20 \quad 15 \quad 6 \quad 1
\end{array}
$$

and so on.

Remember each element is the sum of the elements diagonally above it. Now, since we actually want to expand $(1 + 2x)^6$, we let $a = 1$ and $b = 2x$.

5. (cont)

$$1^6 + 6(1)^5(2x) + 15(1)^4(2x)^2 + 20(1)^3(2x)^3 + 15(1)^2(2x)^4 + 6(1)(2x)^5 + (2x)^6 \quad \text{or}$$

$$1 + 12x + 60x^2 + 160x^3 + 240x^4 + 192x^5 + 64x^6.$$

7. $243x^{10} - 405x^8y + 270x^6y^2 - 90x^4y^3 + 15x^2y^4 - y^5$

9.   Our expansion for $(a + b)^4$ gives coefficients of 1   4   6   4   1   and the complete expansion is

$$a^4 + 4a^3b + 6a^2b^2 + 4ab^3 + b^4.$$

Now we substitute and get

$$(\sqrt{x})^4 + 4(\sqrt{x})^3(-\sqrt{y}) + 6(\sqrt{x})^2(-\sqrt{y})^2 + 4(\sqrt{x})(-\sqrt{y})^3 + (-\sqrt{y})^4 \quad \text{or}$$

$$x^2 - 4x^{3/2}y^{1/2} + 6xy - 4x^{1/2}y^{3/2} + y^2.$$

11. $\frac{1}{8} x^3 - \frac{1}{4} x^2y + \frac{1}{6} xy^2 - \frac{1}{27} y^3$

13.   Our expansion using Pascal's triangle is

$$a^7 + 7a^6b + 24a^5b^2 + 35a^4b^3 + 35a^3b^4 + 24a^2b^5 + 7ab^6 + b^7$$

so substitution yields

$$(ab^2)^7 + 7(ab^2)^6c + 24(ab^2)^5c^2 + 35(ab^2)^4c^3 + 35(ab^2)^3c^4$$
$$+ 24(ab^2)^2c^5 + 7(ab^2)c^6 + c^7$$

or

$$a^7b^{14} + 7a^6b^{12}c + 24a^5b^{10}c^2 + 35a^4b^8c^3 + 35a^3b^6c^4$$
$$+ 24a^2b^4c^5 + 7ab^2c^6 + c^7$$

as required.

15. $x^8 + 8\sqrt{2} x^7 + 56x^6 + 112\sqrt{2} x^5 + 280x^4 + 224\sqrt{2} x^3 + 224x^2 + 64\sqrt{2} x + 16$

17.   The expansion for $(a + b)^3$ is easy, but we will have some simplifying to round out this problem.

17.
$$(a + b)^3 = a^3 + 3a^2b + 3ab^2 + b^3 \text{ so}$$
$$(\sqrt{2} - 1)^3 = (\sqrt{2})^3 + 3(\sqrt{2})^2(-1) + 3(\sqrt{2})(-1)^2 + (-1)^3$$
$$= 2\sqrt{2} - 6 + 3\sqrt{2} - 1$$

which becomes $5\sqrt{2} - 7$ when we combine similar terms. Be sure you remember that in problems like this b must be taken as (-1). The signs will alternate.

19. $109\sqrt{2} + 89\sqrt{3}$

21. We recall that in general n! means

$$n \cdot (n - 1) \cdot (n - 2) \cdots 2 \cdot 1$$
$$\text{or} \quad 1 \cdot 2 \cdots (n - 1) \cdot n,$$

where n is a natural number.

$$\frac{20!}{18!} \text{ then becomes } \frac{20 \cdot 19 \cdot 18 \cdot 17 \cdots 1}{18 \cdot 17 \cdot 16 \cdots 1}$$

which will reduce to $20 \cdot 19$ or 380. It would be a waste of time and effort to multiply this out instead of canceling.

23. $\frac{n(n - 2)!}{(n + 1)!}$ We will write out a few terms and look for ways to simplify.

$$\frac{n[1 \cdot 2 \cdots (n - 3) \cdot (n - 2)]}{1 \cdot 2 \cdots (n - 2) \cdot (n - 1) \cdot (n) \cdot (n + 1)}$$

We see that the factors in the numerator, including the n, all divide out with factors in the denominator leaving only $\frac{1}{(n - 1)(n + 1)}$ or $\frac{1}{n^2 - 1}$ as required.

25.

k	0	1	2	3	4	5	6	7	8
$\binom{8}{k}$	1	8	28	56	70	56	28	8	1

27. Taking n = 6 the binomial theorem yields

$$(a + b)^6 = \binom{6}{0}a^6 + \binom{6}{1}a^5b + \binom{6}{2}a^4b^2 + \binom{6}{3}a^3b^3 + \binom{6}{4}a^2b^4 + \binom{6}{5}ab^5 + \binom{6}{6}b^6.$$

27. (cont)

We recall that the binomial coefficient $\binom{n}{k}$ is defined by $\dfrac{n!}{k!(n-k)!}$.
That means for example that

$$\binom{6}{0} = \frac{6!}{0!(6-0)!}$$

$$= \frac{6!}{1(6)!} \quad \text{(Recall that } 0! = 1 \text{ by definition.)}$$

$$= 1$$

Also, to work out another coefficient, let's take

$$\binom{6}{3} = \frac{6!}{3!(6-3)!}$$

$$= \frac{6 \times 5 \times 4 \times 3 \times 2 \times 1}{(3 \times 2 \times 1)(3 \times 2 \times 1)}$$

$$= 20$$

Remember to cancel whenever possible. Evaluating the other coefficients in a similar manner, our expansion becomes

$$a^6 + 6a^5b + 15a^4b^2 + 20a^3b^3 + 15a^2b^4 + 6ab^5 + b^6$$

With $a = 1$ and $b = -\dfrac{1}{x}$, this becomes

$$1^6 + 6(1)^4\left(-\frac{1}{x}\right) + 15(1)^4\left(-\frac{1}{x}\right)^2 + 20(1)^3\left(-\frac{1}{x}\right)^3 + 15(1)^2\left(-\frac{1}{x}\right)^4$$

$$+ 6(1)\left(-\frac{1}{x}\right)^5 + \left(-\frac{1}{x}\right)^6$$

or

$$1 - \frac{6}{x} + \frac{15}{x^2} - \frac{20}{x^3} + \frac{15}{x^4} - \frac{6}{x^5} + \frac{1}{x^6} .$$

We all recognize that using Pascal's triangle to generate the coefficients is much easier than this expansion technique, but in turn the Binomial Theorem will make some later problems easier as we will see when we come to problem 33.

29. $a^{14}b^7 - 14a^{12}b^6c^2 + 84a^{10}b^5c^4 - 280a^8b^4c^6 + 560a^6b^3c^8 - 672a^4b^2c^{10}$
$$+ 448a^2bc^{12} - 128c^{14}$$

31. $28 - 16\sqrt{3}$

33. We find on page 594 that the rth term in the expansion of $(a + b)^n$ is simply $\binom{n}{r-1}a^{n-r+1}b^{r-1}$.

We want the 3rd term in the expansion of $(a - b)^{30}$. Any volunteers to write out 30 rows of Pascal's triangle? No, then let's use the Binomial theorem. We substitute to get

$$\binom{30}{3-1}(a^{30-3+1})[(-b)^{3-1}].$$

The coefficient is

$$\binom{30}{3-1} = \binom{30}{2}$$

$$= \frac{30 \cdot 29 \cdot 28 \cdots 1}{(2 \cdot 1)(28 \cdot 27 \cdot 26 \cdots 1)}$$

$$= \frac{30 \cdot 29}{2 \cdot 1}$$

$$= 435$$

35. $\dfrac{2300}{x^{41}}$ The complete answer is $435a^{28}b^2$ as required.

37. Again we use the fact that our r^{th} term is $\binom{n}{r-1}a^{n-r+1}b^{r-1}$. In this problem n is 12 and the exponent for a is $12 - 4 + 1$ and we want it to be 4. So,

$$12 - r + 1 = 4$$
$$\text{means} \qquad r = 9$$

The coefficient is therefore $\binom{12}{9-1}$ or $\binom{12}{8}$

$$\binom{12}{8} = \frac{12 \cdot 11 \cdot 10 \cdot 9 \cdots 1}{(8 \cdot 7 \cdot 6 \cdots 1)(4 \cdot 3 \cdot 2 \cdot 1)}$$

$$= \frac{12 \cdot 11 \cdot 10 \cdot 9}{4 \cdot 3 \cdot 2 \cdot 1}$$

$$= 11 \cdot 5 \cdot 9$$

$$= 495.$$

But, we must remember that we are expanding $(3a - 5x)^{12}$ so that the 495 will be multiplied by the appropriate powers of 3 and -5. When $r = 9$ we have $(3a)^4$ and $(-5x)^8$ as part of the expansion. The combined coefficient will then be $495 \cdot 3^4 \cdot (-5)^8$. That's big, too big for me. Let's leave it as

$$495 \cdot 3^4 \cdot 5^8.$$

39. We will follow example 8 on page 595. The rth term will be

$$(_{r-1}^{12})(x^2)^{12-r+1}(x^{-1})^{r-1} .$$

The coefficient will be just $(_{r-1}^{12})$. Simplifying the exponents of the
x term we have

$$(x^2)^{12-r+1}(x^{-1})^{r-1} = x^{24-2r+2} \cdot x^{-r+1}$$
$$= x^{27-3r}$$

and we want to know the r which makes this exponent 6.

$$27 - 3r = 6$$
$$-3r = -21$$
$$r = 7$$

The required coefficient is now obtained by substituting $r = 7$ in $(_{r-1}^{12})$

$$(_{7-1}^{12}) = (_{6}^{12})$$
$$= \frac{12 \cdot 11 \cdot 10 \cdots 1}{(6 \cdot 5 \cdot 4 \cdots 1)(6 \cdot 5 \cdot 4 \cdots 1)}$$
$$= \frac{12 \cdot 11 \cdot 10 \cdot 9 \cdot 8 \cdot 7}{6 \cdot 5 \cdot 4 \cdot 3 \cdot 2 \cdot 1}$$
$$= 924.$$

41. 16016

43. $(_{r-1}^{10})(\frac{B^2}{2})^{10-r+1}(3B^{-3})^{r-1}$ will be our r^{th} term. Its coefficient is
$(\frac{1}{2})^{10-r+1}(3)^{r-1}(_{r-1}^{10})$, and we will evaluate this when we find r.

$$(B^2)^{10-r+1} \cdot (B^{-3})^{r-1} = B^{20-2r+2} \cdot B^{-3r+3}$$
$$= B^{25-5r},$$

and we want to find r so that this exponent is -10

$$25 - 5r = -10$$
$$-5r = -35$$
$$r = 7$$

Substituting this back in the coefficient gives

43. (cont) $(\frac{1}{2})^4(3)^6(\begin{smallmatrix}10\\6\end{smallmatrix}) = \frac{1}{16}(729)(210)$

$$= \frac{76505}{8} \quad \text{as required.}$$

45. n = 22

47. $1792\sqrt{3}$

Exercise Set 10.3

1. Since $a_n = \frac{n}{n+1}$, we can write out the first five terms by setting n equal to the natural numbers 1 through 5

$$a_1 = \frac{1}{1+1} = \frac{1}{2}$$

$$a_2 = \frac{2}{2+1} = \frac{2}{3}$$

$$a_3 = \frac{3}{3+1} = \frac{3}{4}$$

$$a_4 = \frac{4}{4+1} = \frac{4}{5}$$

$$\text{and} \quad a_5 = \frac{5}{5+1} = \frac{5}{6}$$

Our sequence is $\frac{1}{2}, \frac{2}{3}, \frac{3}{4}, \frac{4}{5}, \frac{5}{6}$.

3. Again, letting n be successively 1 through 5 we get

$$a_1 = (1-1)^2$$

$$a_2 = (2-1)^2$$

$$a_3 = (3-1)^2$$

$$a_4 = (4-1)^2$$

$$a_5 = (5-1)^2$$

Our sequence is 0, 1, 4, 9, 16.

5. $2, \frac{9}{4}, \frac{64}{27}, \frac{625}{256}, \frac{7760}{3125}$

7. -1, 1, -1, 1, -1

9. sin x, -sin 2x, sin 3x, -sin 4x, sin 5x

11. 3, 6, 9, 12, 15

13. This "recursive" definition requires a little more care at first.

$$a_1 = 1$$

a_2 will equal $(1 + a_{2-1})^2$ which is
$$(1 + a_1)^2$$
$$\text{or } (1 + 1)^2$$
$$\text{or } \quad 4.$$

$$a_3 = (1 + a_2)^2$$
$$= (1 + 4)^2 = 25$$

$$a_4 = (1 + a_3)^2$$
$$= (1 + 25)^2 = 676$$

$$a_5 = (1 + 676)^2 = 458{,}329$$

1, 4, 25, 676, 458,329 is the sequence.

15. 2, 2, 4, 8, 32

17. 1, 1, 2, 6, 24

19. 0, 1, 2, 4, 16

21. Given $a_n = 2^n$ we can see that the first five terms will be $2^1, 2^2, 2^3, 2^4,$ 2^5 and the sum becomes $2 + 4 + 8 + 16 + 32$ or 62.

23. 40

25. $-\dfrac{19}{30}$

27. The term for n = 3 is
$$a_3 = a_2^2 + a_1^2$$
$$= 2^2 + 1^2$$
$$= 5$$

27. (cont)
$$a_4 = a_3^2 + a_2^2$$
$$= 5^2 + 2^2$$
$$= 29$$

$$a_5 = a_4^2 + a_3^2$$
$$= 29^2 + 5^2$$
$$= 841 + 25$$
$$= 866$$

So, the sum of the first five terms is 903.

29. 278

31. When we write out the terms for this series we replace k with the natural numbers 1 through 5.
$$\sum_{k=1}^{5} k = 1 + 2 + 3 + 4 + 5 = 15$$

33. -35

35.
$$\sum_{n=1}^{3} (n - 1)x^{n-2} = (1 - 1)x^{1-2} + (2 - 1)x^{2-2} + (3 - 1)x^{3-2}$$
$$= \quad 0 \quad + \quad 1 \cdot x^0 \quad + \quad 2 \cdot x^1$$
$$= 1 + 2x$$

37. 121

39. $\tan 7x + \tan 8x + \tan 9x + \tan 10x$

41. $\sum_{j=1}^{5} (x^{j+1} - x^j) = (x^2 - x) + (x^3 - x^2) + (x^4 - x^3) + (x^5 - x^4) + (x^6 - x^5)$
$$= x^6 - x$$

43. The series $5 + 5^2 + 5^3 + \cdots + 5^n$.
We observe that we are adding the powers of 5 up to 5 to the nth. In summation or sigma notation this is written
$$\sum_{i=1}^{n} 5^i.$$

45. $\displaystyle\sum_{k=1}^{6} kx^k$ 47. $\displaystyle\sum_{j=1}^{n} \frac{1}{j}$

49. $\sin^2 x + \sin^3 2x + \sin^4 3x$ gives us an exponent which is one greater than the coefficient of x. We use

$$\sum_{n=1}^{3} \sin^{n+1} nx.$$

51. $\displaystyle\sum_{n=1}^{7} (-1)^{n+1} \frac{1}{2^n}$

EXERCISE SET 10.4

1. (a) To find the common difference, d, we simply subtract any term from the succeeding term.

Here that can be

$$3 - 1 = 2$$
$$\text{or} \quad 5 - 3 = 2$$
$$\text{or} \quad 7 - 5 = 2.$$

2 is the required common difference.

(b)

$$6 - 10 = -4$$
$$2 - 6 = -4$$
$$-2 - 2 = -4$$

The common difference is -4. It is not necessary to try all three pairs, but then we are told that this is an arithmetic sequence.

(c)

$$1 - \frac{2}{3} = \frac{4}{3} - 1 = \frac{5}{3} - \frac{4}{3} = \frac{1}{3},$$

the common difference.

(d)

$$1 + \sqrt{2} - 1 = \sqrt{2}$$
$$(1 + 2\sqrt{2}) - (1 + \sqrt{2}) = \sqrt{2}$$

Here, $\sqrt{2}$ is the common difference.

3. We can see that $a = 10$ and $d = 11$ so using $a_n = a + (n - 1)d$ we find
    the 12th term to be

    $$a_{12} = 10 + (12 - 1)11$$
    $$= 10 + 121$$
    $$= 131$$

5. 501

7. 998

9. Following example 2 from the text we see that this information will give us
    two equations in two unknowns to solve. With $a_4 = -6$ and $a_{10} = 5$:

    $$-6 = a + (4 - 1)d \quad \text{or} \quad -6 = a + 3d$$
    $$\text{and} \quad 5 = a + (10 - 1)d \quad \text{or} \quad 5 = a + 9d$$

    The system is therefore

    $$a + 3d = -6$$
    $$a + 9d = 5 \quad \text{subtracting we get}$$
    $$-6d = -11$$
    $$d = \frac{11}{6}$$

    so

    $$a + 3(\frac{11}{6}) = -6$$
    $$a + \frac{11}{2} = -6$$
    $$a = -6 - \frac{11}{2}$$
    $$a = -\frac{23}{2}$$

    The first term is $-\frac{23}{2}$ and the common difference is $\frac{11}{6}$.

11. Since we know $a_{60} = 105$ and $d = 5$,

    $$105 = a + (60 - 1)5$$
    $$105 = a + 295$$
    $$-190 = a$$

    The first term is -190.

13. This problem can be done by careful reasoning as follows. From a_7 to a_{15} there are 8 increments or common differences, and since these 8d's amount to -1, each is $-\frac{1}{8}$.

There must be a way to arrive at the same conclusion systematically. Try this.

$$a_{15} = a + (15 - 1)d$$
$$a_7 = a + (7 - 1)d$$

or

$$a_{15} = a + 14d$$
$$a_7 = a + 6d$$

now subtract

$$a_{15} - a_7 = 8d.$$

But since $a_{15} - a_7 = -1$

$$-1 = 8d$$

or $d = -\frac{1}{8}$ as required.

15. 500, 500

17. We can see the first and last terms and count the number of terms as thirteen. Using the formula

$$S_n = \frac{n}{2}(a + a_n) \quad \text{we have}$$
$$S_n = \frac{13}{2}\left(\frac{\pi}{3} + \frac{13}{3}\pi\right)$$
$$= \frac{13}{2} \cdot \frac{14}{3}\pi$$
$$= \frac{91}{3}\pi \quad \text{for the sum.}$$

19. $a_1 = \frac{1}{2}$

21. Again we can use $S_n = \frac{n}{2}(a + a_n)$

$$S_{16} = \frac{16}{2}[4 + (-100)]$$
$$= 8(-96)$$
$$= -768$$

21. (cont)

Using this result in $s_n = \frac{n}{2}[2a + (n - 1)d]$ gives

$$-768 = \frac{16}{2}[2(4) + (16 - 1)d]$$

$$-768 = 8(8 + 15d)$$

$$-768 = 64 + 120d$$

$$-832 = 120d$$

$$-\frac{104}{15} = d \quad \text{as required.}$$

23. Solving this problem is first a matter of choosing the correct equation in which to substitute, and then solving simultaneously. We know that $a_8 = 5$ and $s_{10} = 20$. So

$$a_n = a + (n - 1)d \quad \text{becomes}$$
$$5 = a + 7d$$

also $s_n = \frac{n}{2}[2a + (n - 1)d]$ becomes

$$20 = \frac{10}{2}[2a + 9d].$$

$$\text{or} \quad 4 = 2a + 9d.$$

Solve this system by addition-subtraction.

$$a + 7d = 5$$
$$2a + 9d = 4$$

$$2a + 14d = 10$$
$$2a + 9d = 4$$

$$5d = 6$$
$$d = \frac{6}{5}$$

And substituting

$$a = 5 - 7\left(\frac{6}{5}\right)$$
$$a = -\frac{17}{5}$$

The first term is $-\frac{17}{5}$ and the common difference is $\frac{6}{5}$.

25. $\sum\limits_{k=1}^{20} (4k + 3)$ is the series $7 + 11 + 15 + \cdots + 83$. We can use either sum formula.

$$S_{20} = \frac{20}{2}(7 + 83)$$
$$= 900$$

27. If we follow the suggestion and let the terms be $x - d$, x, and $x + d$, our problem says

$$(x - d) + x + (x + d) = 30$$
$$\text{and} \qquad x(x + d)(x - d) = 360$$

The first is equivalent to $3x = 30$ or $x = 10$. The second equation is therefore

$$10(10 + d)(10 - d) = 360$$
$$100 - d^2 = 36$$
$$d^2 = 64$$
$$d = \pm 8$$

Picking the positive root gives the series $2, 10, 18$. The other root yields $18, 10, 2$ which also satisfies the conditions of the problem.

29. We have

$$x - d + x + x + d = 6,$$
$$\text{so} \qquad 3x = 6$$
$$\text{and} \qquad x = 2$$

Also

$$(x - d)^3 + x^3 + (x + d)^3 = 132,$$
$$\text{so} \qquad (2 - d)^3 + 2^3 + (2 + d)^3 = 132.$$

Expanding we get

$$8 - 12d + 6d^2 - d^3 + 8 + 8 + 12d + 6d^2 + d^3 = 132$$
$$\text{or} \qquad 12d^2 = 108$$
$$d^2 = 9$$
$$d = \pm 3.$$

The sequence is $-1, 2, 5$ or the reverse.

31. (b) $-3(2 + 3\sqrt{2})$

EXERCISE SET 10.5

1. The terms will be 9, x, 4. Since in a geometric sequence the ratio of successive terms is constant, we have

$$\frac{x}{9} = \frac{4}{x}$$

$$\text{or} \quad x^2 = 36$$

$$x = \pm 6$$

Since the common ratio is positive, the second term is 6.

3. 20, 100

5. 1

7. The formula on page 611 tells us that $a_n = ar^{n+1}$ and we substitute after finding the common ratio. Computing

$$\frac{\frac{4}{9}}{\frac{2}{3}} \quad \text{we get} \quad \frac{2}{3} .$$

Let's confirm this ratio with the second and third terms.

$$\frac{\frac{8}{27}}{\frac{4}{9}} = \frac{8}{27} \cdot \frac{9}{4} = \frac{2}{3} \quad \text{also.}$$

The common ratio is therefore $\frac{2}{3}$. So we have

$$a_8 = \frac{2}{3} \left(\frac{2}{3}\right)^{8-1}$$

$$= \frac{2}{3} \left(\frac{2}{3}\right)^7$$

$$= \frac{256}{6561}$$

the required eighth term.

9. We are given that a_1 or $a = 1$ and $a_7 = 4096$. Substituting gives

$$4096 = 1 \cdot r^{7-1}$$

so

$$r^6 = 4096$$

$$r = \sqrt[6]{4096}$$

$$r = 4$$

The common ratio is 4.

11. 7161

13. The sum of a geometric series is

$$S_n = \frac{a(1 - r^n)}{1 - r} .$$

We see that each term is multiplied by $\sqrt{2}$ to produce the next term. In other words, the common ratio is $\sqrt{2}$. Also $32 = (\sqrt{2})^{10}$; we go from $(\sqrt{2})^0$ to $(\sqrt{2})^{10}$. There are eleven terms.
So

$$S_n = \frac{1(1 - \sqrt{2}^{11})}{1 - \sqrt{2}}$$

$$= \frac{1 - 32\sqrt{2}}{1 - \sqrt{2}}$$

Rationalizing the denominator gives $63 + 31\sqrt{2}$ for the sum. Note that we can look at this series as

$$\sum_{n=0}^{10} (\sqrt{2})^n \quad \text{or} \quad \sum_{n=1}^{11} (\sqrt{2})^{n-1}$$

15. $\sum\limits_{k=1}^{6} (\frac{3}{2})^k$ can be evaluated directly by writing out the six terms, finding a common denominator and adding. But, we will use the sum formula for a finite geometric series.

$$S_n = \frac{a(1 - r^n)}{1 - r}$$

$$S_n = \frac{\frac{3}{2}\left[1 - (\frac{3}{2})^6\right]}{1 - \frac{3}{2}}$$

15. (cont)

$$= \frac{\frac{3}{2}(1 - \frac{729}{64})}{(1 - \frac{3}{2})}$$

$$= \frac{\frac{3}{2}(-\frac{665}{64})}{-\frac{1}{2}}$$

$$= \frac{1995}{64}$$

17. 0.011111

19. In this infinite series the common ratio is $-\frac{4}{9}$ divided by $\frac{2}{3}$, or $-\frac{2}{3}$, clearly less than 1.

So,

$$S = \frac{a}{1 - r}$$

$$= \frac{\frac{2}{3}}{1 - (-\frac{2}{3})}$$

$$= \frac{\frac{2}{3}}{\frac{5}{3}}$$

$$= \frac{2}{5} \quad \text{as required.}$$

21. Each ratio here is $\frac{1}{1.01}$ so

$$S = \frac{1}{1 - \frac{1}{1.01}}$$

$$= \frac{1}{\frac{1.01 - 1}{1.01}}$$

$$= \frac{1.01}{.01}$$

$$= 101 \quad \text{for our sum.}$$

23. The repeating decimal 0.555... can be viewed as the infinite geometric series $\frac{5}{10} + \frac{5}{100} + \frac{5}{1000} + \cdots$ where the common ratio is $\frac{1}{10}$. Applying the formula for such a sum gives

23. (cont) .

$$s = \frac{\frac{5}{10}}{1 - \frac{1}{10}}$$

$$= \frac{\frac{5}{10}}{\frac{9}{10}}$$

$$= \frac{5}{9} \quad \text{as required.}$$

Do you recall that we worked on similar problems in the first section of Chapter one? A nice way to round out the volume, I think.

25. $0.1\overline{23}$ can be viewed as

$$\frac{1}{10} + \frac{23}{1000} + \frac{23}{100,000} + \cdots$$

If we take $\frac{23}{1000}$ as our first term the common ratio is $\frac{1}{100}$ and our sum is

$$s = \frac{1}{10} + \frac{\frac{23}{1000}}{1 - \frac{1}{100}}$$

$$= \frac{1}{10} + \frac{\frac{23}{1000}}{\frac{99}{100}}$$

$$= \frac{1}{10} + \frac{23}{990}$$

$$= \frac{99 + 23}{990}$$

$$= \frac{122}{990} \quad \text{or} \quad \frac{61}{495} \quad \text{as required.}$$

27. $\frac{16}{37}$

29. We follow the hint and use $\frac{a}{r}$, a, ar as our terms. Then we are told that

$$\frac{a}{r} \cdot a \cdot ar = -1000$$

$$\text{so} \qquad a^3 = -1000$$

$$\text{and} \qquad a = -10$$

Also

$$\frac{a}{r} + a + ar = 15$$

29. (cont)

Substituting gives

$$-\frac{10}{r} - 10 - 10r = 15$$

$$-\frac{10}{r} - 10r = 25$$

$$-10 - 10r^2 = 25r$$

$$2r^2 + 5r + 2 = 0$$

$$(2r + 1)(r + 2) = 0$$

from which we have $r = -\frac{1}{2}$ and $r = -2$.

Taking $a = -10$ and $r = -\frac{1}{2}$ our sequence is

$$\frac{-10}{-\frac{1}{2}}, -10, -10(-\frac{1}{2})$$

or   20, -10, 5.

Using $r = -2$ we get

$$\frac{-10}{-2}, -10, -10(-2)$$

or   5, -10, 20 for the sequence.

SOLUTIONS TO CHAPTER ONE TEST

1. (a) $m = \frac{4-1}{-2-4} = -\frac{1}{2}$. Then, using the point $(4,1)$ as (x_1,y_1),

we find from the point-slope formula that $y-1 = -\frac{1}{2}(x-4)$. Solving for y,

we obtain $y = -\frac{1}{2}x + 3$.

(b) The y-intercept of the line $y = -\frac{1}{2}x + 3$ is 3. To find the

x-intercept, set $y = 0$ in the equation $y = -\frac{1}{2}x + 3$ to obtain $0 = -\frac{1}{2}x + 3$.

This yields $\frac{1}{2}x = 3$, and consequently $x = 6$. The x and y-intercepts are

therefore 6 and 3, respectively.

2.

3. (a) $(4x+1)|(3x-2) = 0$ The solutions are $-\frac{1}{4}$ and $\frac{2}{3}$
        $4x+1=0 | 3x-2 = 0$
        $x = -\frac{1}{4} | x = 2/3$

(b) $x = \frac{-1 \pm \sqrt{1-4(2)(1)}}{2(1)} = \frac{-1 \pm \sqrt{-7}}{2}$ The solutions are therefore $\frac{-1 \pm i\sqrt{7}}{2}$

4. Let $x = 3.4747\cdots$. Then $100x = 347.\overline{47}$ and $100x - x = 344$.

Therefore $99x = 344$ and consequently $x = \frac{344}{99}$, as required.

5. To find the slope of the line $3x+5y = -1$, solve for y to get
$y = -\frac{3}{5}x - \frac{1}{5}$. The slope of this line is therefore $-\frac{3}{5}$. But the slope of the
other line, $y=(3/5)x+9$, is $3/5$. So the slopes are not equal, and therefore
the lines are not parallel.

6. The midpoint is $(\frac{2+8}{2}, \frac{3+(-7)}{2})$), or $(5,-2)$. The distance d from

$(0,0)$ to $(5,-2)$ is $d = \sqrt{(5-0)^2+(-2-0)^2} = \sqrt{29}$, as required.

7. $(3+i)(4-i)+5-8i = 12+i-i^2+5-8i = 12+i-(-1)+5-8i = 18-7i$.

8. Subtracting 8 from both sides yields $-3x \leqslant -7$. Now dividing by -3 yields
$x \geqslant 7/3$. The solution set therefore consists of all real numbers x such
that $x \geqslant 7/3$.

10. $\frac{5-6i}{2-i} \cdot \frac{2+i}{2+i} = \frac{10-7i-6i^2}{4-i^2} = \frac{10-7i+6}{4+1} = \frac{16}{5} - \frac{7}{5}i$.

11. (a) $\sqrt{ab} \leqslant \frac{a+b}{2}$, for all nonnegative numbers a and b. Equality holds exact-

ly when $a=b$.

(b) Using the values a=11 and b=10 in the above inequality, we find

that $\sqrt{(11)(10)} \leqslant \frac{11+10}{2}$. Thus $\sqrt{110} \leqslant \frac{21}{2}$. Furthermore, since a $\neq$ b

in this case, we can write $\sqrt{110} < \frac{21}{2}$, or $\sqrt{110} < 10.5$, as required.

12. (a) $m = \frac{3-4}{-1-(-7)} = \frac{-1}{6}$.

    (b) $m = \frac{(x+h)^2-x^2}{(x+h)-x} = \frac{x^2+2xh+h^2-x^2}{h} = \frac{2xh+h^2}{h} = 2x+h$

13. Multiplying the inequality by -1 yields 4 > 1-2x > -6. Therefore
3 > -2x > -7. Finally, dividing by -2 we obtain $-\frac{3}{2} < x < \frac{7}{2}$. The
solution set is therefore the open interval $(-\frac{3}{2}, \frac{7}{2})$.

14.

x	-3	-2	-1	0	1	2	3	4
y	3	2	1	0	-1	0	1	2

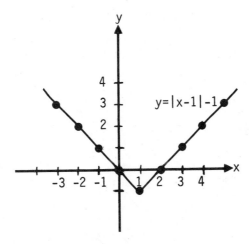

15. From the point-slope formula we obtain y-(-2) = -4[x-(-3)].
Upon simplification this becomes y = -4x-14.

16. $\frac{z+\bar{z}}{2} = \frac{(a+bi)+(a-bi)}{2} = \frac{2a}{2} = a$.

17. $\left| 3-5 \right| + \left| -4 \right| - \left| \left| -2 \right| - \left| -3 \right| \right| = 2+4-\left| 2-3 \right| = 5$.

18. (a) $(x-1)^2+y^2 = 25$
    (b) Setting x = 0 yields $(0-1)^2+y^2 = 25$.
        Thus $y^2=24$ and $y = \pm\sqrt{24} = \pm\sqrt{4}\sqrt{6} = \pm2\sqrt{6}$

19. First complete the square to put the equation of the circle in standard
    form: $x^2+8x+16+y^2-2y+1 = 8+16+1$. Thus $(x+4)^2+(y-1)^2 = 5^2$. The center of
    the circle is therefore $(-4,1)$. So the slope of the radius drawn to the
    point $(-7,5)$ is $\dfrac{5-1}{-7-(-4)} = -\dfrac{4}{3}$. Since the tangent is perpendicular to this
    radius, the slope of the tangent must be $\dfrac{3}{4}$. The equation of the tangent
    is then $y-5 = \dfrac{3}{4}[x-(-7)]$. Upon simplification this becomes $y = \dfrac{3}{4}x + \dfrac{41}{4}$.

20. First compute z^2: $z^2 = (1-i)^2 = 1-2i+i^2 = -2i$

    Next compute $\dfrac{z}{\bar{z}}$: $\dfrac{z}{\bar{z}} = \dfrac{1-i}{1+i} \cdot \dfrac{1-i}{1-i} = \dfrac{1-2i+i^2}{1-i^2} = \dfrac{-2i}{2} = -i$.

    Thus $z^2+\dfrac{z}{\bar{z}} = -2i+(-i) = -3i$, as required.

SOLUTIONS TO CHAPTER TWO TEST

1. The quantity 12-3x must be nonnegative. Therefore we require $12-3x \geqslant 0$, or $-3x \geqslant -12$, or $x \leqslant 4$. Thus the domain of $y = \sqrt{12-3x}$ consists of all real numbers x for which $x \leqslant 4$.

2. In order to determine the range of $y = \frac{4-x}{3x+1}$, we solve for x, as follows:

$$y = \frac{4-x}{3x+1} \implies 3xy+y = 4-x$$

$$\implies 3xy+x = 4-y$$

$$\implies x(3y+1) = 4-y$$

$$\implies x = \frac{4-y}{3y+1} .$$

Thus the range of the function of $y = \frac{4-x}{3x+1}$ consists of all real numbers except $y = -\frac{1}{3}$.

3. (a) $f(-1) = 3(-1)^2-2(-1) = 5$ (b) $f(1-\sqrt{2}) = 3(1-\sqrt{2})^2-2(1-\sqrt{2})$

$$= 3(1-2\sqrt{2}+2)-2+2\sqrt{2}$$

$$= 7-4\sqrt{2} .$$

4. $\frac{g(x+h)-g(x)}{h} = \frac{2(x+h)^2+1-(2x^2+1)}{h}$

$$= \frac{2x^2+4xh+2h^2+1-2x^2-1}{h}$$

$$= \frac{4xh+2h^2}{h}$$

$$= 4x+2h$$

5. $\frac{F(x)-F(a)}{x-a} = \frac{(1/x)-(1/a)}{x-a}$

$$= \frac{xa}{xa}[\frac{(1/x)-(1/a)}{x-a}]$$

$$= \frac{a-x}{xa(x-a)}$$

$$= \frac{-1}{xa} .$$

6. (a) $f(-2)$ is larger than $f(2)$, for as the given graph indicates, $f(-2)$ is positive, whereas $f(2)$ is negative.

(b) $f(-3) = 0$

7. The graph does not represent a function $y = f(x)$.

8.

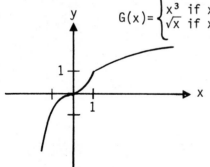

$$G(x) = \begin{cases} x^3 & \text{if } x < 1 \\ \sqrt{x} & \text{if } x \geqslant 1 \end{cases}$$

9.

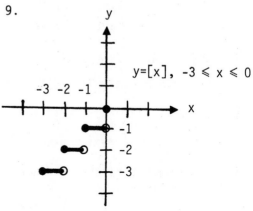

$y = [x], \ -3 \leqslant x \leqslant 0$

10.

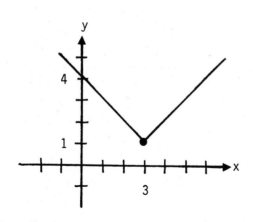

11.

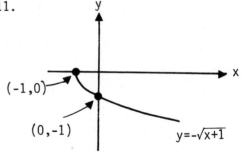

$(-1,0)$

$(0,-1)$

$y = -\sqrt{x+1}$

12.

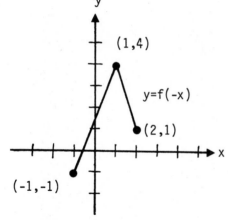

$(1,4)$

$y = f(-x)$

$(2,1)$

$(-1,-1)$

13. (a) $(f+g)(x) = f(x)+g(x) = (2x^2-5x+1)+(1+5x) = 2x^2+2$

(b) $(\frac{f}{g})(1) = \frac{f(1)}{g(1)} = \frac{2(1)^2-5(1)+1}{1+5(1)} = \frac{-2}{6} = -\frac{1}{3}$

14. (a) $(f\circ g)(x) = f[g(x)] = f(2x-3) = 3(2x-3)^2 = 12x^2-36x+27$

(b) $f[g(0)] = 12(0)^2-36(0)+27 = 27$

15. $C = f\circ g$, where $f(x) = x^3$ and $g(x) = 6x^2-x$.

CHECK: $(f\circ g)(x) = f[g(x)] = f(6x^2-x)=(6x^2-x)^3 = C(x)$, as required.

16. To compute the inverse function for $F(x) = 1-2x$, first write $y = 1-2x$. Next switch x and y to obtain $x = 1-2y$. Now solve for y to obtain

$y = \frac{1-x}{2}$. Thus $F^{-1}(x) = \frac{1-x}{2}$.

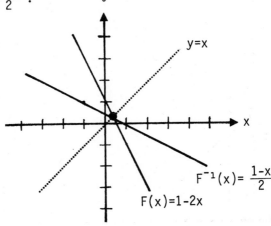

17.

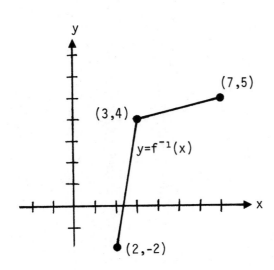

18. $F = Ka$. Using F=120 and a=10, we have $120 = K(10)$, and consequently $K = 12$.
    The law of variation is then $F = 12a$. Now if a=15, we obtain $F = 12(15) = 180$.
    That is, $F = 180$.

19. $T = \dfrac{K}{U^2}$. Using T=5 and U=4, we have $5 = \dfrac{K}{16}$, and consequently K=80. The
    law of variation then is $T = \dfrac{80}{U^2}$. Now if U=5, we obtain $T = \dfrac{80}{25} = \dfrac{16}{5}$.
    That is, $T = \dfrac{16}{5}$.

20. The law of variation is $F = \dfrac{KmM}{d^2}$, where F is the force, m and M are the
    masses, and d is the separation distance. If we replace m by 2m, M by 2M,
    and d by $\dfrac{d}{2}$, we obtain: $F = \dfrac{k(2m)(2M)}{(\frac{d}{2})^2} = 16(\dfrac{KmM}{d^2})$.
    The new force is therefore 16 times greater than the original force.

SOLUTIONS TO CHAPTER THREE TEST

1. x-coordinate of vertex: $x = \dfrac{-b}{2a} = \dfrac{-6}{2(3)} = -1$

    y-coordinate of vertex: $y = 3(-1)^2 + 6(-1) - 10 = -13.$

    Since the parabola is U-shaped upward, the vertex is the lowest point. Therefore the required coordinates are $(-1, -13)$.

2. $d = \sqrt{[x-(-1)]^2 + (y-0)^2}$

    $= \sqrt{(x+1)^2 + (\sqrt{1-x^2})^2}$

    $= \sqrt{x^2 + 2x + 1 + 1 - x^2}$

    $= \sqrt{2x+2}$

3. The graph of G is a line passing through the points $(1,-2)$ and $(-2,-11)$. The slope here is $m = \dfrac{-2-(-11)}{1-(-2)} = 3.$ Thus the equation of the line is

    $y-(-2) = 3(x-1)$, or $y = 3x-5$. Therefore $G(x) = 3x-5$, and we have $G(0) = 3(0)-5 = -5$.

4. If x and y are the two numbers, we have $x+y = \sqrt{3}$. Thus $y = \sqrt{3} -x$, and the product can be written $x(\sqrt{3} -x)$, or $\sqrt{3} x -x^2$.

5. First solve the equation $x^2-5x = 0$. We have $x(x-5) = 0$, and therefore $x=0$ or $x=5$. The solutions of the inequality $x^2-5x \geqslant 0$ are then $x \leqslant 0$ or $x \geqslant 5$.

6. The graph of $h = -16t^2 + 256t + 100$ is a parabola that is U-shaped downward. Thus the second coordinate of the vertex will give us the maximum value for h. Using the vertex formula, we have:

    $t = \dfrac{-256}{2(-16)} = 8$ seconds. Therefore $h = -16(8)^2 + 256(8) + 100$. After carrying

    out the arithmetic, we obtain $h = 1124$ feet. This is the maximum height. It is attained when $t = 8$ seconds.

7. The inequality can be written $x^2+2x-6 \leqslant 0$. By using the quadratic formula, we find that the solutions of the equation $x^2+2x-6 = 0$ are $x = -1\pm\sqrt{7}$. The solution set of the inequality is therefore the closed interval $[-1-\sqrt{7}, \ -1+\sqrt{7}]$.

8. We have $20\pi = 2\pi r^2 + 2\pi rh$, or equivalently, $10 = r^2+rh$. Solving this last equation for h gives us $h = (10-r^2)/r$. The volume therefore is

    $V = \pi r^2 h = \pi r^2 \left(\dfrac{10-r^2}{r}\right)$. Thus $V = \pi(10r-r^3)$.

9. Let $(x,2x-4)$ represent a point on the line $y = 2x-4$. Then the distance from $(0,1)$ to $(x,2x-4)$ is:

$$d = \sqrt{(x-0)^2+(2x-4-1)^2} \quad = \sqrt{5x^2-20x+25}.$$

We want to determine a value for x such that this distance is as small as possible. As explained in the text, it is simplest to work with the square of this distance; the same x-value that minimizes the square of the distance will also minimize the distance itself. Thus we want to determine x such that the function $F(x) = 5x^2-20x+25$ is a minimum. Since the graph here is a parabola that opens upward, we can use the vertex formula to find the required x-value. We have:

$$x = -\frac{b}{2a} = \frac{20}{10} = 2. \quad \text{Now if } x=2, \text{ we have}$$

$y = 2x-4 = 2(2)-4 = 0$. The required point is therefore $(2,0)$.

10. vertex: $x = \frac{-b}{2a} = -\frac{4}{2} = -2$. Therefore $y = (-2)^2+4(-2)-5 = -9$.

x-intercepts: $x^2+4x-5 = 0 \implies (x+5)(x-1) = 0 \implies x = -5$ or $x = 1$.

y-intercept: -5

axis of symmetry: $x = -2$.

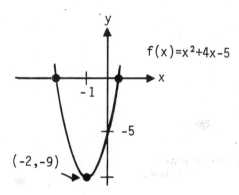

$f(x)=x^2+4x-5$

$(-2,-9)$

11. The function indeed has a maximum value since its graph is a parabola that is U-shaped downward. The x-coordinate of the vertex is

$$x = -\frac{b}{2a} = \frac{-100}{2(-2)} = 25. \quad \text{The required } y\text{-value is then } y = -2(25)^2+100(25)=1250.$$

This is the maximum value of the function.

12. Multiplying by the quantity $(x+2)^2$ gives us:

$$4(x+2)^2 \leqslant 3(x+2)$$

$$4(x+2)^2-3(x+2) \leqslant 0$$

$$(x+2)[4(x+2)-3] \leqslant 0$$

$$(x+2)(4x+5) \leqslant 0$$

The solutions of the equation $(x+2)(4x+5)=0$ are $x = -2$ and $x = -\frac{5}{4}$. Thus the solution set for the inequality $(x+2)(4x+5) \leqslant 0$ is the interval $[-2,-\frac{5}{4}]$. However, for the original inequality, $4 \quad \frac{3}{x+2}$, notice that x cannot be -2. Therefore the solution set here is the interval $(-2,-\frac{5}{4}]$.

13. $x = \dfrac{-b}{2a} = \dfrac{9}{2(3)} = \dfrac{3}{2}$.

14.

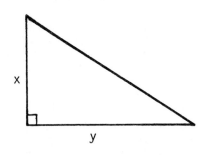

Let x and y denote the lengths of the two shorter sides. Then x+y = 12, and we have y = 12-x. The area of the triangle is therefore:

$$A = \tfrac{1}{2}xy = \tfrac{1}{2}x(12-x)$$

$$= 6x - \tfrac{1}{2}x^2$$

The x-value that maximizes this quadratic function is:

$$x = -\frac{b}{2a} = \frac{-6}{2(-\tfrac{1}{2})} = 6.$$

The corresponding y-value then is 12-6, or 6. Finally, letting h denote the length of the hypotenuse, we have $h^2 = 6^2 + 6^2 = 72$, and consequently $h = \sqrt{72} = 6\sqrt{2}$. The lengths of the three sides of the triangle are therefore x=6 cm, y=6 cm, and h=6$\sqrt{2}$ cm.

15. Using the Pythagorean Theorem, we have $x^2 + w^2 = 24^2$, or $x^2 = 576 - w^2$. Thus $x = \sqrt{576 - w^2}$. The perimeter P is then given by:

$$P = 2x + 2w$$

$$= 2\sqrt{576 - w^2} + 2w.$$

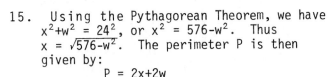

16. $m = \dfrac{y-(-1)}{x-0} = \dfrac{y+1}{x} = \dfrac{x^2+1}{x}$.

That is, $m = \dfrac{x^2+1}{x}$. This is not a quadratic function.

17. The inequality can be written $(2x-3)^2 \leq 0$. Since the square of a real number is never negative, the only solution here occurs when 2x-3 = 0. Thus x = 3/2 is the only solution.

18. $R = xp = x(-\frac{1}{8}x+100) = -\frac{1}{8}x^2 + 100x$. The x-value that maximizes this quadratic function is $x = \dfrac{-b}{2a} = \dfrac{-100}{2(-1/8)} = 400$. The corresponding revenue then is $-\frac{1}{8}(400)^2 + 100(400)$. After carrying out the arithmetic, we find that this maximum revenue is $20,000.

19. Let A denote the total area.

Then $A = \pi r^2 + (\frac{20-x}{4})^2$.

The circumference of the
circle is x; therefore
$2\pi r = x$, or $r = x/2\pi$.
Using this r-value, the area
equation becomes:

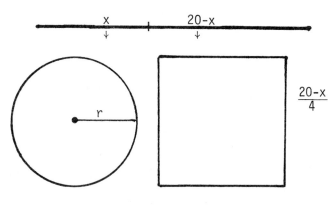

$A = \pi(\frac{x}{2\pi})^2 + (\frac{20-x}{4})^2$

$= \frac{x^2}{4\pi} + \frac{400-40x+x^2}{16}$

$= \frac{x^2}{4\pi} + 25 - \frac{5}{2}x + \frac{x^2}{16}$

$= (\frac{1}{4\pi} + \frac{1}{16})x^2 - \frac{5}{2}x + 25.$

This is a quadratic function. Since the coefficient of x^2 is positive, the
vertex formula will give us the x-value that minimizes this function.

We have: $x = \frac{-b}{2a} = \frac{-(-5/2)}{2(\frac{1}{4\pi} + \frac{1}{16})} = \frac{5}{4(\frac{1}{4\pi} + \frac{1}{16})}$

$= \frac{5}{\frac{1}{\pi} + \frac{1}{4}} \cdot \frac{4\pi}{4\pi} = \frac{20\pi}{4+\pi}$

Thus when $x = \frac{20\pi}{4+\pi}$, the total area A will be a minimum.

20. $\frac{f(x+h)-f(x)}{h} = \frac{a(x+h)^2+b(x+h)+c-ax^2-bx-c}{h}$

$= \frac{2axh+ah^2+bh}{h}$

$= 2ax+ah+b$

SOLUTIONS TO CHAPTER FOUR TEST

1. $\frac{1}{2}$ |

	6	-5	7	-2	-2
		3	-1	3	$\frac{1}{2}$
	6	-2	6	1	-3/2

According to the Remainder Theorem, $f(\frac{1}{2})$ is equal to the remainder when $f(x)$ is divided by $x-\frac{1}{2}$. Therefore $f(\frac{1}{2}) = -3/2$.

2. Since $x = -3$ is a root, it follows from the Factor Theorem that $x+3$ is a factor of $x^3+x^2-11x-15$. By means of synthetic division, or long division, we obtain $x^3+x^2-11x-15 = (x+3)(x^2-2x-5)$. The reduced equation is then $x^2-2x-5=0$. The roots of this reduced equation can be determined by means of the quadratic formula. We have:

$$x = \frac{2\pm\sqrt{4-4(-5)}}{2}$$

$$= \frac{2\pm\sqrt{24}}{2} = \frac{2\pm2\sqrt{6}}{2} = 1\pm\sqrt{6}$$

The roots of the given equation are therefore -3, $1+\sqrt{6}$, and $1-\sqrt{6}$.

3. The curve crosses the y-axis at $(0,32)$.

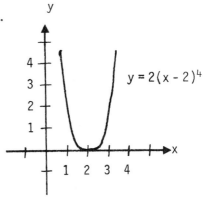

4. factors of 6: ±1, ±2, ±3, ±6
   factors of 2: ±1, ±2

   The possibilities for rational roots are the fractions whose numerators are factors of 6 and whose denominators are factors of 2. Thus the possibilities are ±1, $\pm\frac{1}{2}$, ±2, ±3, $\pm 3/2$, ±6.

5. The general form for a quadratic function with zeros r_1 and r_2 is $f(x) = a_2(x-r_1)(x-r_2)$. Thus we have $f(x) = a_2(x-1)(x+8)$. Since the y-intercept is -24, we have $f(0)=-24$ and consequently $-24 = a_2(-1)(8)$. Therefore $a_2=3$, and the function is $f(x) = 3(x-1)(x+8)$. This can be written $f(x) = 3x^2+21x-24$.

6. $y = (x-4)(x-1)(x+1)$

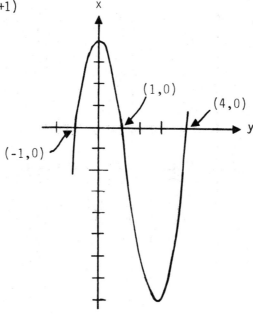

x

$(1,0)$

$(4,0)$

y

$(-1,0)$

7. (a) $2x^5 + 3x^4 - 5x^3 = x^3(2x^2 + 3x - 5)$

    $$= x^3(2x+5)(x-1)$$

    (b) $2x^5 + 3x^4 - 5x^3 = 0$

    $x^3(2x+5)(x-1) = 0$

$x^3 = 0$	$2x+5 = 0$	$x-1 = 0$
$x = 0$	$x = -\dfrac{5}{2}$	$x = 1$

    The roots of the equation are 0, $-\dfrac{5}{2}$, and 1.

8. $-1 \,\big|\;\; 4 \quad\;\; 1 \quad -8 \quad\;\; 3$

    $\underline{\qquad\quad -4 \quad\;\; 3 \quad\;\; 5}$

    $\qquad\;\; 4 \quad -3 \quad -5 \quad\;\; 8$

    Thus, when $4x^3 + x^2 - 8x + 3$ is divided by $x+1$, the quotient is $4x^2 - 3x - 5$ and the remainder is 8. We can also write this result as:
    $4x^3 + x^2 - 8x + 3 = (x+1)(4x^2 - 3x - 5) + 8$.

9. (a) The Factor Theorem: Suppose $f(x)$ is a polynomial. If $f(r)=0$, then $x-r$ is a factor of $f(x)$. Conversely, if $x-r$ is a factor of $f(x)$, then $f(r)=0$.

    (b) The Fundamental Theorem of Algebra: Every polynomial equation of degree one or more has at least one root among the complex numbers. (This root may be a real number.)

10. $y = \dfrac{x}{(x+2)(x-4)}$

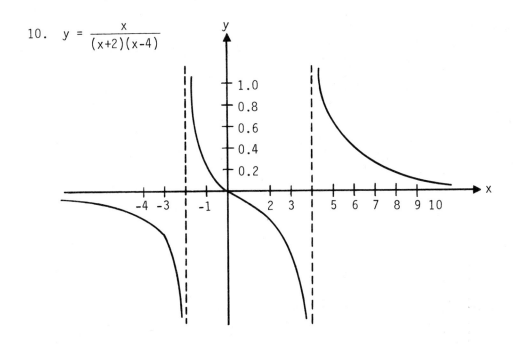

11. $f(0) = -1$ $\left.\begin{array}{l} f(2) = -1 \\ f(3) = 8 \end{array}\right\}$ Sign change

$f(1) = -2$

This shows that there is a root between x=2 and x=3. To obtain a preliminary estimate for the location of the root, we use linear interpolation. The equation of the line passing through (2,-1) and (3,8) is found to be y=9x-19. The x-intercept here is $x = \dfrac{19}{9} \approx 2.1$ By synthetic division we find that f(2.1) ≈ -0.5. Notice now that both f(2) and f(2.1) are negative, although f(2.1) is closer to zero than f(2). This suggests that we look at f(2.1), f(2.2), and so on. The results are as follows:

$f(2.1) \approx -.06$

$\left.\begin{array}{l} f(2.2) \approx -.03 \\ f(2.3) \approx +.59 \end{array}\right\}$ Sign change

Since f(2.2) is negative and f(2.3) is positive, we conclude that there is a root between 2.2 and 2.3.

12. By the Congugate Roots Theorem, we have four roots: 1+i, 1-i, 3-2i, 3+2i. The corresponding factors of the polynomial are [x-(1+i)], [x-(1-i)], [x-(3-2i)], and [x-(3+2i)]. By multiplying the first two of these factors, we find that x^2-2x+2 is a factor of the original polynomial. Similarly, by multiplying the second pair of factors, we find that $x^2-6x+13$ is a factor of the original polynomial. The product of x^2-2x+2 and $x^2-6x+13$ is $x^4-8x^3+27x^2-38x+26$.

12. (continued)

Now we use long division to divide the original polynomial by
$x^4-8x^3+27x^2-38x+26$. The quotient is found to be $x+2$, and the remainder
is 0. Thus $x = -2$ is also a root of the given equation. The five roots
are then -2, $1\pm i$, and $3\pm 2i$.

13.

$$
\begin{array}{r}
x^2 + 2x\ -\ 1 \\
x^2 + 0x + 1\ \overline{\smash{\big)}\ x^4 + 2x^3 + 0x^2 - x + 6} \\
\underline{x^4 + 0x^3 +\ \ x^2} \\
2x^3\ -\ x^2\ - x \\
\underline{2x^3 + 0x^2\ + 2x} \\
-x^2\ \ - 3x + 6 \\
\underline{-x^2\ \ - 0x - 1} \\
- 3x + 7
\end{array}
$$

Thus $q(x) = x^2+2x-1$ and $R(x) = -3x+7$

14. First we determine the roots of the equation $2x^2-6x+5 = 0$. By means of
the quadratic formula we obtain: $r_1 = (3+i)/2$ and $r_2 = (3-i)/2$. The
factored form of the polynomial is then:
$$a_n(x-r_1)(x-r_2) = 2[x-(3+i)/2][x-(3-i)/2].$$

15. (a) ± 1, ± 2, ± 3, ± 4, ± 6, ± 8, ± 12, ± 24

(b) To show that 2 is a upper bound for the roots of the given equation,
we first use synthetic division to divide x^4-x^3+24 by $x-2$.

$$
\begin{array}{r|rrrrr}
2 & 1 & -1 & 0 & 0 & 24 \\
  &   & 2 & 2 & 4 & 8 \\
\hline
  & 1 & 1 & 2 & 4 & 32
\end{array}
$$

The numbers in the third line of the synthetic division are 1, 1, 2, 4, and
32. Since each of these is nonnegative, the Upper Bound Theorem
tells us that 2 is an upper bound for the roots of the given equation.

(c) ± 1, ± 2.

(d) By substitution (or synthetic division), we find that $x = -2$ satisfies
the given equation. The values 1, -1, and 2 do not satisfy the equation.

16. (a)

$$
\begin{array}{r}
3 \\
x + 2\ \overline{\smash{\big)}\ 3x + 5} \\
\underline{3x + 6} \\
-1
\end{array}
$$

This shows that: $\dfrac{3x+5}{x+2} = 3 - \dfrac{1}{x+2}$, as required.

16. (continued)

(b)

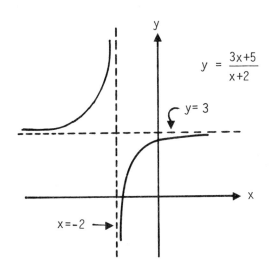

$$y = \frac{3x+5}{x+2}$$

y = 3

x = -2

17. (a) $x^3+8 = x^3+2^3 = (x+2)(x^2-2x+4)$

(b) Using the factorization in part (a), we conclude that x+2=0 or $x^2-2x+4 = 0$. From the equation x+2=0 we obtain x=-2. The equation $x^2-2x+4 = 0$ can be solved using the quadratic formula. We have:

$$x = \frac{2\pm\sqrt{4-4(4)}}{2} = \frac{2\pm\sqrt{-12}}{2} = \frac{2\pm2i\sqrt{3}}{2} = 1\pm i\sqrt{3}$$

The solutions of the given equation are therefore -2, $1+i\sqrt{3}$, and $1-i\sqrt{3}$.

18. The possibilities for rational roots are ±1, $\pm\frac{1}{2}$, $\pm 3/1$, $\pm 3/2$.

After using synthetic division to test the various possibilities, we find that 3/2 is a root.

The synthetic division in this case looks as follows:

3/2 |	2	-1	-1	-3
		3	3	3
	2	2	2	0

The reduced equation is then $2x^2+2x+2 = 0$, or $x^2+x+1 = 0$. By means of the quadratic formula, we find that the roots here are $(-1\pm i\sqrt{3})/2$.

The roots of the given equation are therefore $\frac{3}{2}$, $\frac{-1+i\sqrt{3}}{2}$, and $\frac{-1-i\sqrt{3}}{2}$.

19. Let $f(x) = 3x^4+x^2-5x-1$. Then f(x) has one sign change. It follows therefore (by Descartes' rule) that the equation f(x)=0 has exactly one positive root. For negative roots we consider the polynomial $f(-x) = 3x^4+x^2+5x-1$. There is one sign change here, so f(x)=0 has at most one negative root. Now if f(x)=0 had no negative roots, it would then have to have one positive root and three complex roots. This is not possible because complex roots occur in pairs. We conclude therefore that the equation f(x)=0 has one positive root, one negative root, and two complex roots.

20.

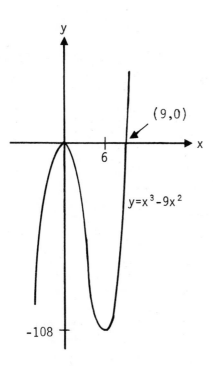

$y = x^3 - 9x^2$

SOLUTIONS TO CHAPTER FIVE TEST

1. $\log_5 126$ is slightly larger than 3 because $5^3=125$. But $\log_{10} 999$ is slightly less than 3 because $10^3=1000$. Therefore $\log_5 126$ is larger than $\log_{10} 999$.

2. $y = 3^{-x} - 3$
   Domain: all real numbers
   Range: $y > -3$
   x-intercept: -1
   y-intercept: -2
   Asymptote: $y = -3$

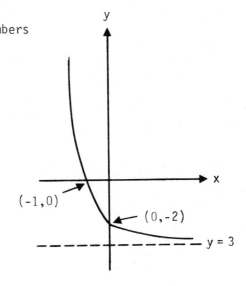

3. (a) $32^{-4/5} = (2^5)^{-4/5} = 2^{-4} = \dfrac{1}{2^4} = \dfrac{1}{16}$

   (b) $(2^a - 1)^2 = (2^a)^2 - 2(2^a)(1) + (-1)^2$

   $\qquad\qquad = 2^{2a} - 2^{a+1} + 1$

4. The growth law in this case is $N = 8000e^{kt}$. When $t=4$, we are given that $N=10000$. Therefore $10000 = 8000e^{4k}$, or $1.25 = e^{4k}$. The logarithmic form of this last equation is $\ln(1.25) = 4k$. Thus $k = \dfrac{\ln(1.25)}{4}$. Now to determine when the population will reach 12000, we replace N by 12000 in the growth law to obtain $12000 = 8000e^{kt}$, where k is $\dfrac{\ln(1.25)}{4}$. We then have $1.5 = e^{kt}$ and consequently $\ln(1.5) = kt$, or $t = \dfrac{\ln(1.5)}{k}$. Using the value found for k, we thus have:

   $$t = \frac{\ln(1.5)}{\left[\frac{\ln 1.25}{4}\right]} = \frac{4\ln(1.5)}{\ln(1.25)} \text{ hours.}$$ With a calculator we find that $t \approx 7.27$

   hours. This is about 7 hours and 16 minutes.

5. Let $A = \log_{10} 2$. Then $10^A = 2$. Taking the natural logarithm of both sides in the last equation, we have $\ln 10^A = \ln 2$. Therefore $A \ln 10 = \ln 2$, and consequently $A = \dfrac{\ln 2}{\ln 10}$, as required.

6. The function is not one-to-one.

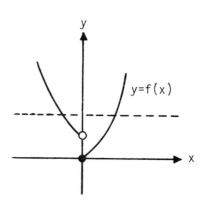

7. $2^{10} \approx 10^3$. Therefore $(2^{10})^6 \approx (10^3)^6$, and consequently $2^{60} \approx 10^{18}$.

8. The equation can be rewritten $\ln(x+1) - \ln(x-1) = 1$. Therefore $\ln \dfrac{x+1}{x-1} = 1$. To solve for x, we write this last equation in exponential form: $e^1 = \dfrac{x+1}{x-1}$. This yields $ex - e = x + 1$, or $ex - x = e + 1$. Therefore $x(e-1) = e+1$, and consequently $x = \dfrac{e+1}{e-1}$. (By checking, we find that this value indeed satisfies the original equation.)

9. Use the formula $A = P[1 + (r/n)]^{nt}$ with $A = 10000$, $P = 5000$, $r = .08$, and $n = 1$. This yields $10000 = 5000(1 + .08)^t$, or $2 = (1.08)^t$. Therefore $\ln 2 = t \ln(1.08)$, and consequently $t = \dfrac{\ln 2}{\ln 1.08} \approx \dfrac{0.7}{0.07} = 10$ years.

10. (a) By factoring, we find that the given equation can be written $e^x(x-2) = 0$. Since $e^x \neq 0$, we must have $x - 2 = 0$, and therefore $x = 2$.

    (b) Multiplying the given equation by $(x^2+1)^{1/3}$ yields $(x^2+1)^{3/3} - 3(x^2+1)^0 = 0$. That is, $x^2 + 1 - 3 = 0$. Therefore $x^2 = 2$, and $x = \pm\sqrt{2}$.

11. $\dfrac{a^{-2} - b^{-2}}{a^{-1} - b^{-1}} \cdot \dfrac{a^2 b^2}{a^2 b^2} = \dfrac{b^2 - a^2}{ab^2 - a^2 b} = \dfrac{(b-a)(b+a)}{ab(b-a)} = \dfrac{b+a}{ab}$

12. Let $\log_9 \dfrac{1}{27} = x$. Then $9^x = \dfrac{1}{27}$. This can be rewritten as $(3^2)^x = 3^{-3}$ or $3^{2x} = 3^{-3}$. Therefore $2x = -3$, and we obtain $x = -\dfrac{3}{2}$.

13. $\ln \dfrac{A^2\sqrt{B}}{C^3}$ $= \ln A^2 + \ln B^{\frac{1}{2}} - \ln C^3$

$\qquad = 2\ln A + \tfrac{1}{2}\ln B - 3\ln C$

$\qquad = 2a + \tfrac{1}{2}b - 3c.$

14. (a) If the half-life is 13 years, then $N=\tfrac{1}{2}N_0$ when $t=13$. The equation
$N=N_0e^{kt}$ therefore becomes $\tfrac{1}{2}N_0=N_0e^{13k}$. Thus $\tfrac{1}{2}=e^{13k}$. In logarithmic form,
this equation becomes $13k=\ln\tfrac{1}{2}$; therefore $k = \dfrac{\ln\tfrac{1}{2}}{13} \approx -0.0533$.

(b) When $t=100$ we have $N=N_0e^{100k}$. Using the value of k from part (a),

we have: $\qquad\qquad\qquad N = N_0e^{100(\ln\tfrac{1}{2}/13)}.$

This can be simplified as follows:
$$N = N_0(e^{\ln\tfrac{1}{2}})^{100/13}$$
$$= N_0(\tfrac{1}{2})^{100/13} \approx 0.00483 N_0$$

15. $3\log_{10}x - \log_{10}(1-x) = \log_{10}x^3 - \log_{10}(1-x)$

$\qquad\qquad = \log_{10}\left(\dfrac{x^3}{1-x}\right).$

16. The given equation can be written $e^{2-x} = \dfrac{12}{5}$. The logarithmic form of
this equation is $\ln\dfrac{12}{5} = 2-x$. Therefore $x=2-\ln\dfrac{12}{5}$. (The answer can also
be written $x=2-\ln12+\ln5$.)

17. The formula in this case is $N=2e^{0.02t}$, where N is in units of one million,
and $t=0$ corresponds to the year 1980. Using $N=3$, we have
$3=2e^{0.02t}$, or $1.5=e^{0.02t}$. To solve for t, write this last equation in
logarithmic form. This yields $0.02t = \ln 1.5$, and therefore
$t = \dfrac{\ln 1.5}{0.02} \approx \dfrac{0.40}{0.02} = 20$ years. Now adding 20 to 1980, we can estimate that
the population will reach 3 million in the year 2000.

18. $\ln e + \ln\sqrt{e} + \ln 1 + e^{\ln10} = 1+\tfrac{1}{2}+0+10$

$\qquad\qquad\qquad\qquad = \dfrac{23}{2}.$

19. $\left(\dfrac{64a^{-12}b^4}{27a^4b^{-6}}\right)^{-\frac{1}{2}} = \left(\dfrac{64b^{10}}{27a^{16}}\right)^{-\frac{1}{2}} = \left(\dfrac{27a^{16}}{64b^{10}}\right)^{\frac{1}{2}}$

$\qquad\qquad = \dfrac{(27)^{\frac{1}{2}}a^8}{(64)^{\frac{1}{2}}b^5} = \dfrac{3\sqrt{3}\,a^8}{8b^5}$

20. From Section 5.5, the formula for estimating doubling time is $T_2 \approx \frac{0.7}{r}$.
     Thus we have $T_2 \approx \frac{0.7}{0.1} = 7$ years. Since the doubling time is approximately
     7 years, we can set up the following table relating the amount A and the
     time t.

t	0	7	14	21
A	1000	2000	4000	8000

By plotting these points, we obtain the following graph:

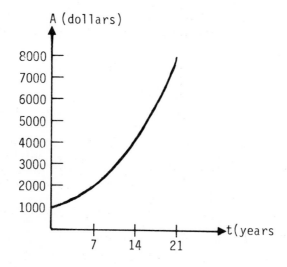

SOLUTIONS TO CHAPTER SIX TEST

1. $\cos 30° = \sqrt{3}/2$

    $\tan 60° = \sqrt{3}$

    $\sin^2 7° + \cos^2 7° = 1$

2. (a) $\sin(-270°) = 1$ (b) $\cos 540° = -1$ (c) $\cot 450° = 0$

3. $(2\cos\theta+3)(\cos\theta+4)$

4. $A = \frac{1}{2}ab\sin\theta = \frac{1}{2}(5)(6)\sin 135° = 15(\sqrt{2}/2) = (15\sqrt{2})/2$ cm².

5. $a^2 = b^2+c^2-2bc \cos A$

    $= 5^2+3^2-2(5)(3)\cos 120°$

    $= 34-30(-\frac{1}{2})$

    $= 49.$ Thus $a = \sqrt{49} = 7$cm.

6. Let θ denote the angle opposite the side of length 4 cm. Then we have (by the Law of Cosines) $4^2=2^2+3^2-2(2)(3)\cos\theta$. Solving here for $\cos\theta$, we find that $\cos\theta = -\frac{1}{4}$. Since this answer is negative, θ is not an acute angle. (When θ is in standard position, the terminal ray will be in the second quadrant.)

7. (a) $\cos 330° = \sqrt{3}/2$ (b) $\tan 135° = -1$

8. $\cos^2\theta = 1-\sin^2\theta = 1-(-1/3)^2 = 8/9$. Therefore $\cos\theta = \pm\sqrt{8/9} = (\pm 2\sqrt{2})/3$. We choose the positive root here because cosine is positive in the given range $270°<\theta<360°$. Thus $\cos\theta = (2\sqrt{2})/3$. For $\cot\theta$, we have $\cot\theta = (\cos\theta)/(\sin\theta) = (2\sqrt{2}/3)/(-1/3) = -2\sqrt{2}$.

9. By means of the Pythagorean Theorem, we find that the length of the third side of the triangle is 4 units. Thus we have $\tan\theta = $ opposite/adjacent$=3/4$.

10. For convenience let $\tan\theta = T$. Then we have

    $$\frac{\frac{T+1}{T} + 1}{\frac{T-1}{T} - 1} \cdot \frac{T}{T} = \frac{T+1+T}{T-1-T} = \frac{2T+1}{-1} = -2T-1.$$

    The given expression therefore becomes $-2\tan\theta-1$.

11. Let x denote the length of the side opposite the 30° angle. Using the law of sines, we have:

$$\frac{\sin 30°}{x} = \frac{\sin 45°}{20\sqrt{2}}$$

$$\frac{1}{2x} = \frac{\sqrt{2}/2}{20\sqrt{2}}$$

$$\frac{1}{2x} = \frac{1}{40}$$

Therefore 2x=40, and x=20cm.

12. Let y denote the required height. Then we have $\sin 60° = y/10$. Therefore $\sqrt{3}/2 = y/10$, or $2y = 10\sqrt{3}$. Thus $y = 5\sqrt{3}$ ft.

13. $$\frac{\cos\theta + 1}{\csc\theta + \cot\theta} = \frac{\cos\theta + 1}{(1/\sin\theta)+(\cos\theta)/(\sin\theta)} \quad \frac{\sin\theta}{\sin\theta}$$

$$= \frac{(\cos\theta+1)(\sin\theta)}{1+\cos\theta}$$

$$= \sin\theta.$$

14. The x-coordinate of P is $\overline{AP}$. Since θ is in standard position, it follows that $\overline{AP}=\cos\theta$. Now notice that angle APB also equals θ; this is because AP is parallel to the x-axis. Thus in right triangle APB we have

$$\sin\theta = \frac{\overline{AB}}{\overline{AP}} = \frac{\overline{AB}}{\cos\theta} \,. \quad \text{Therefore } \overline{AB} = \sin\theta\cos\theta.$$

Also in right triangle APB we have $\cos\theta = \dfrac{\overline{BP}}{\overline{AP}} = \dfrac{\overline{BP}}{\cos\theta} \,. \quad \text{Therefore } \overline{BP} = \cos^2\theta.$

15. $$\frac{\sin\theta}{1+\cos(180°-\theta)} = \frac{\sin\theta}{1-\cos\theta}$$

$$= \frac{\sin\theta}{1-\cos\theta} \cdot \frac{1+\cos\theta}{1+\cos\theta}$$

$$= \frac{\sin\theta(1+\cos\theta)}{1-\cos^2\theta}$$

$$= \frac{\sin\theta(1+\cos\theta)}{\sin^2\theta}$$

$$= \frac{1+\cos\theta}{\sin\theta} = \frac{1+\cos\theta}{\sin(180°-\theta)}$$

16. $$\frac{(\cos\theta + \sin\theta)^2}{1+2\sin\theta\cos\theta} = \frac{\cos^2\theta+2\cos\theta\sin\theta+\sin^2\theta}{1+2\sin\theta\cos\theta} = \frac{1+2\cos\theta\sin\theta}{1+2\sin\theta\cos\theta} = 1.$$

17. Since $\sin 15° = \sqrt{1-\cos^2 15°}$, we first need to compute $\cos^2 15°$. Using the given expression, we have:

$$\cos^2 15° = [\tfrac{1}{4}(\sqrt{6} + \sqrt{2})]^2 = (1/16)(6+2\sqrt{12}+2)$$

$$= (1/16)(8+4\sqrt{3}) = (2\sqrt{3})/4$$

Therefore $\quad\quad\quad\quad \sin 15° = \sqrt{1-(2+\sqrt{3})/4} = \sqrt{(4-2-\sqrt{3})/4} = \dfrac{\sqrt{2-\sqrt{3}}}{2}$.

18. We have $\overline{SP} = 2$, $\overline{SV} = 8$, and angle VSP = 45°. Applying the law of cosines in triangle VSP therefore gives us:

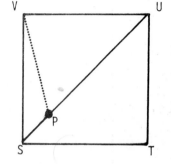

$$\overline{PV}^2 = 8^2+2^2-2(8)(2)\cos 45°$$

$$= 68-32(\sqrt{2}/2)$$

$$= 68-16\sqrt{2}$$

We then have

$$\overline{PV} = \sqrt{68-16\sqrt{2}} = 2\sqrt{17-4\sqrt{2}} \text{ cm.}$$

19. In right triangle ABC we have $\tan 55° = \overline{CB}/50$, and therefore $\overline{CB}=50\tan 55°$. Also, in right triangle ABD we have $\tan 25° = \overline{DB}/50$, and therefore $\overline{DB} = 50\tan 25°$. Now we can write

$$\overline{CD} = \overline{CB} - \overline{DB}$$

$$= 50\tan 55°-50\tan 25°$$

$$= 50(\tan 55°-\tan 25°) \text{ cm.}$$

20. In the figure here, $\triangle OAB$ is one of the nine congruent triangles making up the given polygon. We have $\overline{OB} = \overline{OA} = 2$, and $\theta = \dfrac{360°}{9} = 40°$.

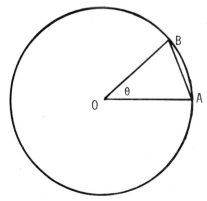

The area of $\triangle OAB$ can now be calculated using the formula $A = \tfrac{1}{2}ab\sin\theta$. We obtain $A = 2\sin 40°\text{m}^2$. Since there are nine such triangles, the area of the polygon is $18\sin 40°\text{m}^2$.

SOLUTIONS TO CHAPTER SEVEN TEST

1. (a) $-\sqrt{3}/2$ (b) $-\sqrt{3}$

2. x-intercepts: $\pm 1/6$

    high-point: $(0,3)$

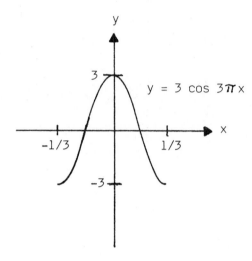

3. $\sin(\theta + \frac{3\pi}{2}) = \sin\theta \cos\frac{3\pi}{2} + \cos\theta \sin\frac{3\pi}{2} = 0 + (\cos\theta)(-1) = -\cos\theta$

4. (a) By means of the Pythagorean Theorem, we find that the third side of the
        triangle is 2. Thus we have

    $$\cos 2\beta = \cos^2\beta - \sin^2\beta = (\frac{1}{\sqrt{5}})^2 - (\frac{2}{\sqrt{5}})^2 = \frac{1}{5} - \frac{4}{5} = -\frac{3}{5}.$$

    (b) $\tan\frac{\alpha}{2} = \frac{\sin\alpha}{1 + \cos\alpha} = \frac{1/\sqrt{5}}{1 + (2\sqrt{5})} = \frac{1}{\sqrt{5} + 2}.$

    (An equivalent form for this answer is $\sqrt{5} - 2$.)

5. (a) Use the formula $s = r\theta$ with $r = \sqrt{5}$ and $\theta = 5\pi/12$. This yields
        $s = \sqrt{5}(5\pi/12) = 5\sqrt{5}\pi/12$ cm.

    (b) Use the formula $A = \frac{1}{2}r^2\theta$. This yields $A = (\frac{1}{2})(5)(5\pi/12) = 25\pi/24$ cm^2.

6. $\dfrac{1}{\sqrt{4 - t^2}} = \dfrac{1}{\sqrt{4 - 4\cos^2 x}} = \dfrac{1}{2\sqrt{1 - \cos^2 x}} = \dfrac{1}{2\sqrt{\sin^2 x}} = \dfrac{1}{2\sin x}$

    This can also be written $\frac{1}{2}\csc x$. (Note: The positive square root is
    appropriate here since $\sin x$ is positive throughout the given interval.)

7. To convert $\pi^2/180$ radians to degrees, multiply by $180°/\pi$. The result is $\pi°$. This is about 3.14°. Therefore an angle of $\pi^2/180$ radians is slightly larger than an angle of 3°.

8. The equation can be written $(2 \sin x + 1)(\sin x + 3) = 0$. Thus $2 \sin x + 1 = 0$ or $\sin x + 3 = 0$. In the first case we have $\sin x = -\tfrac{1}{2}$. Therefore x can be $7\pi/6$ or $11\pi/6$. In the second case we have $\sin x = -3$, which is impossible. Thus the only solutions in the given interval are $7\pi/6$ and $11\pi/6$.

9. $\sin(\beta - \alpha) = \sin \beta \cos \alpha - \cos \beta \sin \alpha = (4/5)(2/\sqrt{5}) - \cos \beta \sin \alpha$. Now we need to find $\cos \beta$ and $\sin \alpha$. We have $\cos \beta = -\sqrt{1 - (4/5)^2} = -\sqrt{9/25} = -3/5$. (The negative root was chosen because β is in the second quadrant, in which cosine is negative.) Similarly $\sin \alpha = -\sqrt{1 - (2/\sqrt{5})^2} = -\sqrt{1/5} = -1/\sqrt{5}$. Combining these results, we have

$$\sin(\beta - \alpha) = \frac{8}{5\sqrt{5}} - \left(-\frac{3}{5}\right)\left(\frac{-1}{\sqrt{5}}\right) = \frac{8}{5\sqrt{5}} - \frac{3}{5\sqrt{5}} = \frac{5}{5\sqrt{5}} = \frac{1}{\sqrt{5}}.$$

Thus, $\sin(\beta - \alpha) = \dfrac{1}{\sqrt{5}}$ or $\dfrac{\sqrt{5}}{5}$.

10. $\cos 4\theta = \cos[2(2\theta)] = 2 \cos^2 2\theta - 1$

$$= 2\left[2 \cos^2 \theta - 1\right]^2 - 1$$

$$= 2(4 \cos^4 \theta - 4 \cos^2 \theta + 1) - 1$$

$$= 8 \cos^4 \theta - 8 \cos^2 \theta + 1.$$

11. Since $1 + \tan^2 t = \sec^2 t$, we have $1 + \tan^2 t = 25/9$, and therefore $\tan^2 t = 16/9$. Thus $\tan t = 4/3$. (We chose the positive root since tangent is positive in the third quadrant.) It follows now that $\cot t = 3/4$.

12. First use an addition formula to expand $\sin(x + 30°)$:

$$\sin(x + 30°) = (\sin x)(\sqrt{3}/2) + (\cos x)(1/2)$$

The given equation then becomes

$$\frac{\sqrt{3}\ \sin x}{2} + \frac{\cos x}{2} = \sqrt{3}\ \sin x$$

$$\frac{\cos x}{2} = \frac{\sqrt{3}\ \sin x}{2}$$

$$\cos x = \sqrt{3}\ \sin x$$

Dividing now by $\sin x$, we obtain $\cot x = \sqrt{3}$. Therefore $x = 30°$.

13. amplitude: 1

period: π

phase shift: $\pi/2$

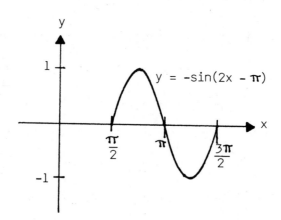

$y = -\sin(2x - \pi)$

14. Since $\pi < \theta < 3\pi/2$, we have $\pi/2 < \theta/2 < 3\pi/4$. Therefore $\sin \theta/2$ is
positive, and the appropriate half-angle formula is $\sin \theta/2 = \sqrt{(1 - \cos \theta)/2}$. Now since $\csc \theta = -3$, we have $\sin \theta = -1/3$. Then
$\cos \theta = \pm\sqrt{1 - (-1/3)^2} = \pm\sqrt{8/9} = \pm 2\sqrt{2}/3$. We want the negative root here
since θ itself is in the third quadrant. Thus $\cos \theta = -2\sqrt{2}/3$, and we
obtain $\sin \theta/2 = \sqrt{[1 - (-2\sqrt{2}/3)]/2} = \sqrt{(3 + 2\sqrt{2})/6}$.

15. $\sin 15° \cos 75° + \cos 15° \sin 75° = \sin(15° + 75°) = \sin 90° = 1$

16. Since angle $BPA = \theta$, it follows that angle $APC = \pi - \theta$. The area of the
shaded region can be found by subtracting the area of triangle APC from the
area of sector APC. Using A to denote the area of the shaded region, we
have therefore

$$A = \tfrac{1}{2}(\sqrt{2})^2(\pi - \theta) - \tfrac{1}{2}(\sqrt{2})(\sqrt{2})\sin(\pi - \theta)$$

$$= \pi - \theta - \sin(\pi - \theta)$$

$$= \pi - \theta - \sin \theta$$

17. The domain of the restricted sine function is the closed interval
     $[-\pi/2, \pi/2]$. The range of the restricted sine function is the closed
     interval $[-1,1]$. The domain of the inverse sine function is the closed
     interval $[-1,1]$. The range of the inverse sine function is the closed
     interval $[-\pi/2, \pi/2]$. The graphs of these two functions are shown in
     Figure 3(a) of Section 7.7 in the text.

18. (a) $\pi/10$ is in the domain of the restricted sine function, so the identity
          $\sin^{-1}(\sin x) = x$ is applicable. Therefore $\sin^{-1}(\sin \pi/10) = \pi/10$.

     (b) 2π is not in the domain of the restricted sine function, so the
          identity used in part (a) is not applicable. However, since
          $\sin 2\pi = 0$, we can write $\sin^{-1}(\sin 2\pi) = \sin^{-1}0 = 0$.

19. Let $\theta = \arcsin 3/4$. Then we can sketch a portrait
     of θ as shown.   By means of the Pythagorean
     Theorem, we find that the third side of this triangle
     is $\sqrt{7}$. Therefore $\cos \theta = \sqrt{7}/4$. That is,
     $\cos(\arcsin 3/4) = \sqrt{7}/4$.

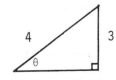

20. $\tan(\pi/4 + \theta/2) = \dfrac{\tan \pi/4 + \tan \theta/2}{1 - (\tan \pi/4)(\tan \theta/2)}$

$$= \frac{1 + \tan \theta/2}{1 - \tan \theta/2}$$

$$= \frac{1 + \dfrac{\sin \theta}{1 + \cos \theta}}{1 - \dfrac{\sin \theta}{1 + \cos \theta}} \cdot \frac{1 + \cos \theta}{1 + \cos \theta}$$

$$= \frac{1 + \cos \theta + \sin \theta}{1 + \cos \theta - \sin \theta} , \quad \text{as required.}$$

SOLUTIONS TO CHAPTER EIGHT TEST

1. In the equation $3x + 4y = 12$, replace y by $x^2 + 2x + 3$. After simplifying, we obtain $4x^2 + 11x = 0$. Thus $x(4x + 11) = 0$, and consequently
   $x = 0$ or $x = -11/4$. The corresponding y-values are now obtained from the
   equation $y = x^2 + 2x + 3$. When $x = 0$, we have $y = 3$. When $x = -11/4$,
   we have $y = (-11/4)^2 + 2(-11/4) + 3$. This simplifies to $y = 81/16$. The
   two solutions are therefore $(0,3)$ and $(-11/4, 81/16)$.

2. Multiplying the first equation by -3 and then adding the equations, we
   have $11y = -55$. Therefore $y = -5$. Then if $y = -5$, the equation
   $x - 2y = 13$ becomes $x + 10 = 13$. Consequently $x = 3$. The solution of
   the system is therefore $(3,-5)$. The system is consistent.

3. From the second equation subtract three times the first, and from the third
   subtract 4 times the first. This yields the equivalent system

$$\begin{cases} x + 4y - z = 0 \\ \quad\ -11y + 4z = -1 \\ \quad\ -20y + 9y = -7 \end{cases}$$

   Next, from the third equation in the new system, subtract 20/11 times the
   second equation. The resulting system is

$$\begin{cases} x + 4y - z = 0 \\ \quad\ -11y + 4z = -1 \\ \quad\quad \frac{19}{11} z = -\frac{57}{11} \end{cases}$$

   From the third equation here, we have $z = -57/19 = -3$. Substituting back
   into the second equation then yields $-11y + 4(-3) = -1$, or $-11y = 11$.
   Thus $y = -1$. Finally, using $y = -1$ and $z = -3$ in the first equation,
   we readily obtain $x = 1$. The solution therefore is $x = 1$, $y = -1$, and
   $z = -3$.

4. (a) $2A - B = \begin{pmatrix} 2 & -6 \\ 4 & -2 \end{pmatrix} - \begin{pmatrix} 0 & 4 \\ 1 & 3 \end{pmatrix} = \begin{pmatrix} 2 & -10 \\ 3 & -5 \end{pmatrix}$

   (b) $BA = \begin{pmatrix} 0 & 4 \\ 1 & 3 \end{pmatrix}\begin{pmatrix} 1 & -3 \\ 2 & -1 \end{pmatrix} = \begin{pmatrix} 8 & -4 \\ 7 & -6 \end{pmatrix}$

5.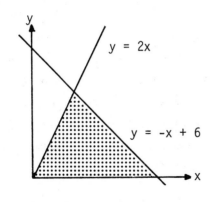

The base of the triangle is the x-inter-cept of the line $y = -x + 6$. To find this x-intercept, set $y = 0$ to obtain $0 = -x + 6$, or $x = 6$. The height of the triangle is the y-coordinate of the point where the two given lines meet. To find this coordinate, solve the equation $y = -x + 6$ for x to obtain $x = 6 - y$. Then we have $y = 2x = 2(6 - y)$. Thus $y = 12 - 2y$, from which we obtain $3y = 12$, and consequently $y = 4$. The area then is $A = \frac{1}{2}(6)(4) = 12$ square units.

6. $D = \begin{vmatrix} 2 & 3 \\ -5 & -4 \end{vmatrix} = 7,\quad D_x = \begin{vmatrix} 10 & 3 \\ -4 & -4 \end{vmatrix} = -28,\quad D_y = \begin{vmatrix} 2 & 10 \\ -5 & -4 \end{vmatrix} = 42.$

We have therefore $x = \dfrac{D_x}{D} = \dfrac{-28}{7} = -4$

$y = \dfrac{D_y}{D} = \dfrac{42}{7} = 6.$

The solution is $(-4,6)$.

7. coefficient matrix: $\begin{pmatrix} 1 & 1 & -1 \\ 2 & -1 & 2 \\ 1 & -2 & 1 \end{pmatrix}$

augmented matrix: $\left(\begin{array}{ccc|c} 1 & 1 & -1 & -1 \\ 2 & -1 & 2 & 11 \\ 1 & -2 & 1 & 10 \end{array} \right)$

8. $\begin{pmatrix} 1 & 1 & -1 & -1 \\ 2 & -1 & 2 & 11 \\ 1 & -2 & 1 & 10 \end{pmatrix} \xrightarrow[R_3 - R_1]{R_2 - 2R_1} \begin{pmatrix} 1 & 1 & -1 & -1 \\ 0 & -3 & 4 & 13 \\ 0 & -3 & 3 & 12 \end{pmatrix}$

$\xrightarrow[R_3 - R_2]{} \begin{pmatrix} 1 & 1 & -1 & -1 \\ 0 & -3 & 4 & 13 \\ 0 & 0 & -1 & -1 \end{pmatrix}$

This last matrix represents a system in echelon form. The system is

$$\begin{cases} x + y - z = -1 \\ -3y + 4z = 13 \\ -z = -1 \end{cases}$$

From the third equation we have z = 1. The second equation then yields
y = -3. Then from the first equation we obtain x = 3. The solution therefore is x = 3, y = -3, z = 1.

9. First solve the system

$$\begin{cases} x + y = 11 \\ 3x + 2y = 7 \end{cases}.$$

Using Cramer's rule, for instance, we find $D = -1$, $D_x = 15$, and $D_y = -26$.
Therefore $x = D_x/D = -15$ and $y = D_y/D = 26$. The intersection point then
is (-15,26). Next we find that the slope of the line 2x - 4y = 7 is 1/2.
Thus the slope of the perpendicular line is -2. Using the point-slope formula now, we have y - 26 = -2(x + 15). This can be rewritten y = -2x - 4.

10. Multiplying by $(x + 1)(x - 1)^2$ yields

$$x - 2 = A(x - 1)^2 + B(x + 1)(x - 1) + C(x + 1).$$

Let x = 1 in this identity yields -1 = 2C, and therefore C = -1/2.
Similarly, letting x = -1 in the identity to get -3 = 4A, and therefore
A = -3/4. To determine C now, we can replace A and B in the identity
by the values just determined. Then using x = 0, the identity becomes
-2 = -3/4 - B - 1/2. When we solve this for B we find B = 3/4. The
required values are therefore A = -3/4, B = 3/4, and C = -1/2.

11. (a) $\begin{vmatrix} 2 & -1 \\ 0 & 4 \end{vmatrix} = 8$ (b) -8

12. Factoring 4, 5, and 7 from the first, second, and third columns, respectively, we have

$$(4)(5)(7) \begin{vmatrix} 1 & -1 & 0 \\ -2 & 2 & 1 \\ 4 & 4 & 2 \end{vmatrix}.$$

Now add the first column to the second to obtain

$$140 \begin{vmatrix} 1 & 0 & 0 \\ -2 & 0 & 1 \\ 4 & 8 & 2 \end{vmatrix} = 140 \begin{vmatrix} 0 & 1 \\ 8 & 2 \end{vmatrix} = 140(-8) = -1120.$$

13. The system can be solved by the substitution method. An alternative procedure is as follows. The system can be rewritten

$$\begin{cases} x^2 + y^2 = 40 \\ 2xy = 24 \end{cases}$$

By adding these two equations we obtain $x^2 + 2xy + y^2 = 64$, or $(x + y)^2 = 64$. Therefore $x + y = \pm 8$. In the same manner, if we subtract the two equations we find that $(x - y)^2 = 16$, and consequently $x - y = \pm 4$. We now have four linear systems:

$$\begin{cases} x + y = 8 \\ x - y = 4 \end{cases} \quad \begin{cases} x + y = 8 \\ x - y = -4 \end{cases} \quad \begin{cases} x + y = -8 \\ x - y = 4 \end{cases} \quad \begin{cases} x + y = -8 \\ x - y = -4 \end{cases}$$

Each of these systems can be solved by inspection by using the addition-subtraction method. The solutions that result are $(6,2)$; $(2,6)$; $(-2,-6)$; $(-6,-2)$. These are the required solutions of the original system.

14. From the second equation subtract twice the first, and from the third subtract five times the first. The system becomes

$$\begin{cases} A + 2B + 3C = 1 \\ -5B - 7C = 0 \\ -5B - 7C = 0 \end{cases}$$

The third equation is redundant here, so we ignore it. From the second equation we find $B = -7C/5$. This allows us to solve the first equation for A in terms of C. The result is $A = (5 - C)/5$. The general solution of the system then is $\left((5 - C)/5, -7C/5, C\right)$, where C can be any real number.

15. $2X + B = 3A$

$2X = 3A - B$

$$X = \tfrac{1}{2}(3A - B) = \tfrac{1}{2}\left[\begin{pmatrix} 6 & 0 & -3 \\ 3 & 9 & 0 \end{pmatrix} - \begin{pmatrix} 1 & -4 & 6 \\ 2 & 1 & 1 \end{pmatrix}\right]$$

$$= \frac{1}{2} \begin{pmatrix} 5 & 4 & -9 \\ 1 & 8 & -1 \end{pmatrix} = \begin{pmatrix} 5/2 & 2 & -9/2 \\ 1/2 & 4 & -1/2 \end{pmatrix}$$

16.

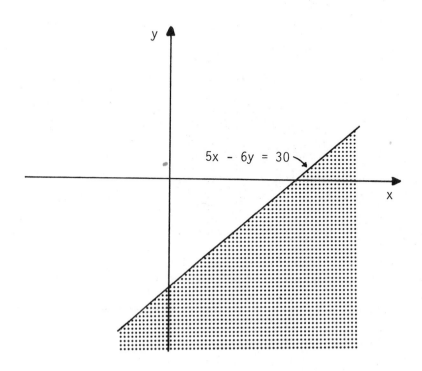

17. Since $(-2,-1)$ lies on the parabola, we have $-1 = 4P - 2Q - 5$. This simplifies to

$$2P - Q = 2. \qquad (1)$$

In the same fashion, since $(-1,-2)$ lies on the parabola, we have $-2 = P - Q - 5$. This simplifies to

$$P - Q = 3 \qquad (2)$$

Subtracting equation (2) from (1) we obtain $P = -1$. Then with the aid of equation (2) we obtain $Q = -4$. Thus $P = -1$ and $Q = -4$ (and the equation of the parabola is $y = -x^2 - 4x - 5$).

18.

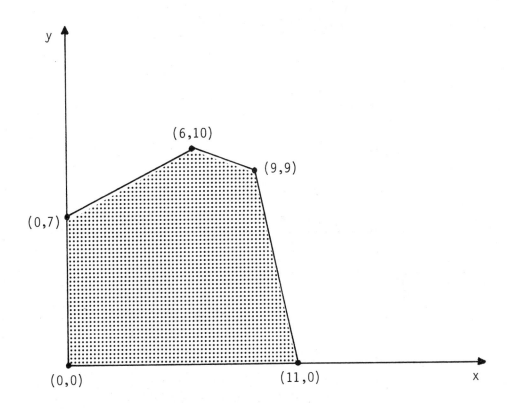

19.

x	y	C = 3x + y + 1
0	0	1
11	0	34
9	9	37 ←——— maximum value
6	10	29
0	7	8

The maximum value is 37.

20. First solve the system $\begin{cases} x - 2y = -3 \\ y = x \end{cases}$. This results in the intersection point (3,3). Since the line kx + 3y = -4 passes through this point, we have 3k + 3(3) = -4, and therefore 3k = -13, or k = -13/3.

SOLUTIONS TO CHAPTER NINE TEST

1. focus: (-3,0)

    directrix: x = 3

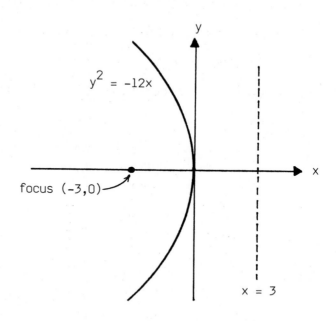

2. foci: $(\pm\sqrt{5},0)$

    asymptotes: $y = \pm\frac{1}{2}x$

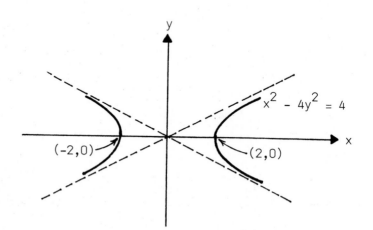

3. (a) $\cot 2\theta = \dfrac{A - C}{B} = \dfrac{1 - 3}{2\sqrt{3}} = -\dfrac{1}{\sqrt{3}}$.

    Since $\cot 2\theta = -1/\sqrt{3}$, we have $2\theta = 120°$, $\theta = 60°$.

(b) The rotation formulas are $x = x' \cos 60° - y' \sin 60° = \frac{1}{2}(x' - \sqrt{3}y')$,

and $y = x' \sin 60° + y' \cos 60° = \frac{1}{2}(\sqrt{3}x' + y')$. After substituting

these expressions for x and y in the given equation, and then

simplifying, we obtain $x'^2 + 6y' = 0$. This is the equation of a

parabola. The axis of the parabola is the y'-axis, as indicated in the

figure.

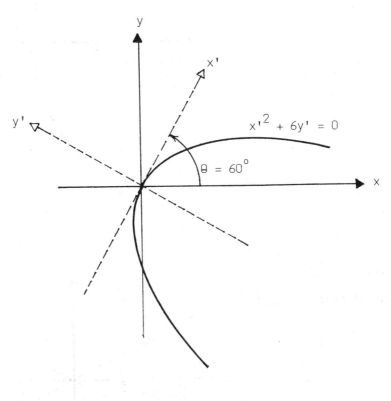

4. $\tan \theta = m = 1/\sqrt{3}$. Therefore $\theta = 30°$ (because the tangent of 30° is $1/\sqrt{3}$).

5. Let m denote the slope of the required tangent line. Then the equation of

the line is $y - 8 = m(x - 4)$. Now because this is the tangent line, the

system

$$\begin{cases} y - 8 = m(x - 4) & (1) \\ x^2 = 2y & (2) \end{cases}$$

must have exactly one solution, namely $(4,8)$. From equation (2) we have $y = x^2/2$. Then equation (1) becomes $x^2/2 - 8 = m(x - 4)$, and multiplying by 2 yields

$$x^2 - 16 = 2m(x - 4)$$
$$(x - 4)(x + 4) - 2m(x - 4) = 0$$
$$(x - 4)[(x + 4) - 2m] = 0$$

From this last equation we obtain $x = 4$ or $x = 2m - 4$. Now we equate these two x-values because the system is known to have but one solution. This yields $2m - 4 = 4$. Thus $2m = 8$, and consequently $m = 4$. With this value for m, the equation $y - 8 = m(x - 4)$ becomes $y - 8 = 4(x - 4)$, or $y = 4x - 8$. This is the required equation.

6. To determine the y-intercepts, we set $x = 0$ to obtain $(0 - 2)^2 + (y - 1)^2 = 9$. This can be written $(y - 1)^2 = 5$. Therefore $y - 1 = \pm\sqrt{5}$, and $y = 1 \pm \sqrt{5}$. From the figure it is clear that the tangent line at $(0,1 + \sqrt{5})$ has a positive slope. The slope of

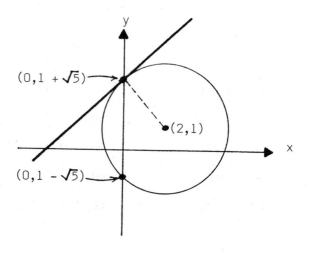

the radius drawn to this point is $\left[(1 + \sqrt{5}) - 1\right]/(0 - 2) = -\sqrt{5}/2$. Therefore the slope of the tangent is $2/\sqrt{5}$. The slope-intercept formula now yields $y = (2/\sqrt{5})x + (1 + \sqrt{5})$. After multiplying by $\sqrt{5}$ and rearranging, we obtain $2x - \sqrt{5}y + (\sqrt{5} + 5) = 0$, as required.

7. Since $e = \frac{1}{2}$ we have $c/a = \frac{1}{2}$, or $a = 2c$. But $c = 2$ because the foci are $(0,\pm2)$. Therefore $a = 4$. Now use the equation $c^2 = a^2 - b^2$ to determine b. The result is $b = 2\sqrt{3}$. The equation of the ellipse is

$$\frac{x^2}{(2\sqrt{3})^2} + \frac{y^2}{4^2} = 1.$$

8. This problem can be solved using the method in Example 5 of Section 9.1; however the following solution is shorter.

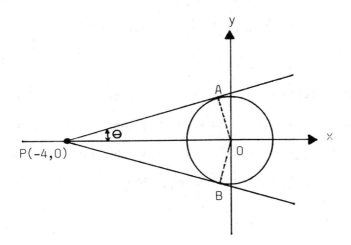

For the tangent line PA in the figure, we have $m = \tan \theta = \overline{OA}/\overline{PA} = 1/\overline{PA}$.

Now $\overline{PA}$ can be computed by means of the Pythagorean Theorem: $\overline{PA} = \sqrt{4^2 - 1^2} = \sqrt{15}$. Thus $m = 1/\sqrt{15}$. This is the slope of the tangent PA. From this result, and the fact that the triangles AOP and BOP are congruent, it follows that the slope of PB is $-1/\sqrt{15}$.

9. The slope of the line is $m = \tan 60° = \sqrt{3}$. Since the line passes through $(2,0)$, the equation is $y - 0 = \sqrt{3}(x - 2)$, or $y = \sqrt{3}x - 2\sqrt{3}$. To convert this to intercept form, we first write $\sqrt{3}x - y = 2\sqrt{3}$. Then dividing by $2\sqrt{3}$, we have $\dfrac{x}{2} + \dfrac{y}{(-2\sqrt{3})} = 1$, as required.

10. We have $c = 2$ because the foci are $(\pm 2,0)$. Since the asymptotes are $y = \pm(1/\sqrt{3})x$, we have $b/a = 1/\sqrt{3}$ and therefore $a = b\sqrt{3}$. Now using the

equation $c^2 = a^2 + b^2$, we obtain $4 = (b\sqrt{3})^2 + b^2$. Therefore $4b^2 = 4$, and consequently $b = 1$. Thus $a = 1(\sqrt{3}) = \sqrt{3}$. The required equation can now be written

$$\frac{x^2}{(\sqrt{3})^2} + \frac{y^2}{1^2} = 1.$$

11.

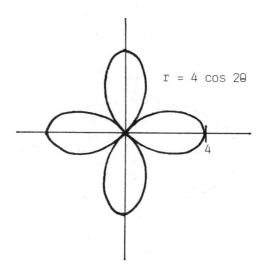

$r = 4 \cos 2\theta$

4

12. (a) Replace x by 6 and y by 5:

$$5(6)^2 - 4(5)^2 \overset{?}{=} 80$$

$$180 - 100 \overset{?}{=} 80$$

$$80 \overset{?}{=} 80 \quad \text{True}$$

This shows that $P(6,5)$ lies on the hyperbola $5x^2 - 4y^2 = 80$.

(b) The quantity $(\overline{F_1P} - \overline{F_2P})^2$ can be computed without determining the coordinates of F_1 and F_2. By definition we have $|\overline{F_1P} - \overline{F_2P}| = 2a$, for any point P on the hyperbola. Squaring both sides here yields $(\overline{F_1P} - \overline{F_2P})^2 = 4a^2$. Now to compute a, we convert the equation $5x^2 - 4y^2 = 80$ to standard form. The result is $\dfrac{x^2}{4^2} - \dfrac{y^2}{(2\sqrt{5})^2} = 1.$

Therefore $a = 4$ and we obtain $(\overline{F_1P} - \overline{F_2P})^2 = 4a^2 = 4(16) = 64$.

13. The standard form here is $\dfrac{x^2}{5^2} + \dfrac{y^2}{2^2} = 1$. Thus $a = 5$ and $b = 2$. The length of the major axis is $2a = 10$. The length of the minor axis is $2b = 4$. To compute c, we have $c = \sqrt{a^2 - b^2} = \sqrt{21}$. Therefore the coordinates of the foci are $(\pm\sqrt{21}, 0)$.

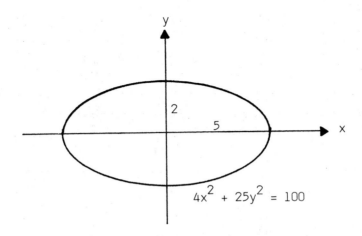

$$4x^2 + 25y^2 = 100$$

14. $r^2 = \sin 2\theta$

$$x^2 + y^2 = 2 \sin \theta \cos \theta$$

$$x^2 + y^2 = 2\left(\frac{y}{\sqrt{x^2 + y^2}}\right)\left(\frac{x}{\sqrt{x^2 + y^2}}\right)$$

$$x^2 + y^2 = \frac{2xy}{x^2 + y^2}$$

Now multiplying both sides by $x^2 + y^2$, we obtain $(x^2 + y^2)^2 = 2xy$. This answer can also be written $x^4 + 2x^2y^2 + y^4 - 2xy = 0$.

15. $d = \dfrac{|Ax_0 + By_0 + C|}{\sqrt{A^2 + B^2}} = \dfrac{|2(-1) + (-1)(0) - 1|}{\sqrt{4 + 1}} = \dfrac{3}{\sqrt{5}}$

This answer can also be written $3\sqrt{5}/5$.

16. By completing the square, we can rewrite the equation as $16(x - 2)^2 +$
    $(y + 1)^2 = 0$. The left side of this equation is clearly nonnegative.
    Furthermore, the left side equals zero only when $x = 2$ and $y = -1$. Thus
    the graph of the equation consists of the single point $(2,-1)$.

17.

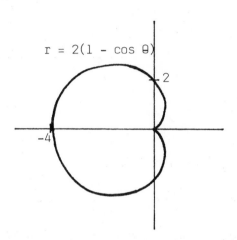

18.

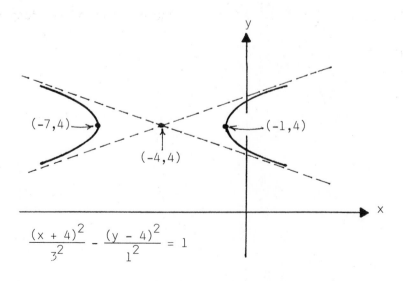

19. focal width: 8

vertex: (1,2)

[The focus is (1,4).]

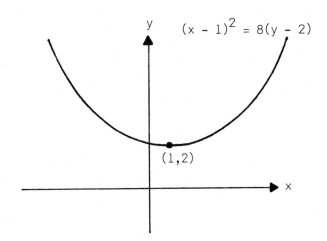

$(x - 1)^2 = 8(y - 2)$

(1,2)

20. The equation of the tangent line is $\dfrac{x_1 x}{a^2} + \dfrac{y_1 y}{b^2} = 1$. With $x_1 = -2$ and $y_1 = 4$, this becomes $\dfrac{-2x}{a^2} + \dfrac{4y}{b^2} = 1$. Now to determine a^2 and b^2, we divide both sides of the equation $x^2 + 3y^2 = 52$ by 52. This yields $\dfrac{x^2}{52} + \dfrac{y^2}{52/3} = 1$. Thus $a^2 = 52$ and $b^2 = 52/3$, and the equation of the tangent becomes $\dfrac{-2x}{52} + \dfrac{4y}{52/3} = 1$. When we simplify and solve for y, the result is $y = \dfrac{1}{6} x + \dfrac{13}{3}$. This is the equation of the tangent line, as required.

Solutions To Chapter Ten Test

1. The entries in the sixth row of Pascal's triangle are 1, 5, 10, 10, 5, 1.
   Thus we have

$$(2y + y)^5 = 2^5 + 5(2^4)y + 10(2^3)y^2 + 10(2^2)y^3 + 5(2)y^4 + y^5$$

$$= 32 + 80y + 80y^2 + 40y^3 + 10y^4 + y^5.$$

2. For $n = 1$ we have $1^2 = 1(1 + 1)(2 + 1)/6$. This is equivalent to $1 = 6/6$,
   which is surely true. This completes the first step in the induction proof.
   Now assume that $1^2 + 2^2 + \ldots + k^2 = k(k + 1)(2k + 1)/6$. (This is the
   induction hypothesis.) We must show that $1^2 + 2^2 + \ldots + k^2 + (k + 1)^2 =$
   $(k + 1)(k + 2)(2k + 3)/6$. By adding $(k + 1)^2$ to both sides of the equation
   in the induction hypothesis, we obtain

$$1^2 + 2^2 + \ldots + (k + 1)^2 = \frac{k(k + 1)(2k + 1)}{6} + (k + 1)^2$$

$$= (k + 1) \left[\frac{k(2k + 1)}{6} + k + 1 \right]$$

$$= (k + 1) \left(\frac{2k^2 + k}{6} + \frac{6k + 6}{6} \right)$$

$$= (k + 1) \left(\frac{2k^2 + 7k + 6}{6} \right)$$

$$= (k + 1) \left[\frac{(k + 2)(2k + 3)}{6} \right]$$

$$= \frac{(k + 1)(k + 2)(2k + 3)}{6} , \quad \text{as required.}$$

This completes the second step of the induction proof. It follows now, by
the Principle of Mathematical Induction, that the given equation is valid for
all natural numbers n.

3. (a) $\displaystyle\sum_{k=0}^{2} (10k - 1) = (0 - 1) + (10 - 1) + (20 - 1) = 27$

   (b) $\displaystyle\sum_{k=1}^{3} (-1)^k k^2 = (-1)^1(1)^2 + (-1)^2(2)^2 + (-1)^3(3)^2 = -6$

4. $S_{20} = \frac{n}{2}[2a + (n - 1)d] = \frac{20}{2}\left[\frac{4}{3} + (19)(1/3)\right] = 10\left(\frac{23}{3}\right) = \frac{230}{3}$

5. $a_1 = \frac{2^1}{1^2} = 2,\quad a_2 = \frac{2^2}{2^2} = 1,\quad a_3 = \frac{2^3}{3^2} = \frac{8}{9}$.

   This is not a geometric sequence.

6. (a) $S_n = \frac{a(1 - r^n)}{1 - r}$

   (b) $S_5 = \frac{(1/3)[1 - (1/3)^5]}{1 - (1/3)} = \frac{(1/3)(242/243)}{2/3} = \frac{121}{243}$

7. $\binom{n}{r-1} a^{n-r+1} y^{r-1} = \binom{14}{11} (x^2)^3 y^{11}$

   $\qquad = \frac{14!}{11!\ 3!}\ x^6 y^{11}$

   $\qquad = \frac{(14)(13)(12)}{6}\ x^6 y^{11}$

   $\qquad = 364 x^6 y^{11}$

8. The r-th term of the expansion is $\binom{9}{r-1} x^{9-r+1}(\sqrt{x})^{r-1}$. This can be rewritten $\binom{9}{r-1} x^{9-r+1} x^{(r-1)/2}$, which in turn becomes $\binom{9}{r-1} x^{(19-r)/2}$. Now if the coefficient of x is 8, we have $(19 - r)/2 = 8$, which implies that $r = 3$. In this case then, the required coefficient is $\binom{9}{2} = 36$.

9. $S_n = n\left(\frac{a + a_n}{2}\right) = 12\left(\frac{8 + 43/2}{2}\right) = 177$

10. $S = \frac{a}{1 - r} = \frac{9/10}{1 - (1/10)} = \frac{9/10}{9/10} = 1$.

11. The entries in the fifth row of Pascal's triangle are 1, 4, 6, 4, 1. Thus we have

$$(x^2 - 2y^3)^4 = (x^2)^4 + 4(x^2)^3(-2y^3) + 6(x^2)^2(-2y^3)^2 + 4(x^2)(-2y^3)^3 + (-2y^3)^4$$

$$= x^8 - 8x^6 y^3 + 24x^4 y^6 - 32x^2 y^9 + 16y^{12}.$$

12. The r-th term of the expansion is $\binom{11}{r-1} a^{11-r+1}(b^3)^{r-1}$. If the exponent of a is 3, we have $11 - r + 1 = 3$. Therefore $r = 9$. The coefficient in this case is $\binom{11}{8} = \frac{11!}{8!\,3!} = \frac{(11)(10)(9)}{6} = 165$.

13. $a_1 = 1$

   $a_2 = 1$

   $a_3 = (a_2)^2 + a_1 = 2$

   $a_4 = (a_3)^2 + a_2 = 4 + 1 = 5$

   $a_5 = (a_4)^2 + a_3 = 25 + 2 = 27$

   Thus $a_4 = 5$ and $a_5 = 27$.

14. Let r denote the common ratio. Then $4r^2 = 10$, and consequently $r = -\sqrt{5}/\sqrt{2} = -\sqrt{10}/2$. The sixth term is then $10(-\sqrt{10}/2) = -5\sqrt{10}$.

15. Using the formula $a_n = a + (n - 1)d$, we have $a_{16} = -1 + (15)(15) = 224$.

16. With $n = 3$ the inequality becomes $8 > 6$, which is certainly valid. That completes the first step of the induction proof. Now assume that $2^k > 2k$, for some integer $k > 3$. We must show that $2^{k+1} > 2(k + 1)$. Multiplying the inequality $2^k > 2k$ by 2 yields

$$2^{k+1} > 2(2k) = 2k + 2k > 2k + 2.$$

The last inequality follows from the fact that $2k > 2$ for all natural numbers $k > 3$. We have now $2^{k+1} > 2k + 2 = 2(k + 1)$. This completes the second step of the induction proof. It now follows by the Principle of Mathematical Induction that $2^n > 2n$ for $n \geq 3$.

17. $\frac{12!}{10!} = \frac{(12)(11)10!}{10!} = (12)(11) = 132$

18. $\binom{9}{3} = \frac{9!}{3! \ 6!} = \frac{(9)(8)(7)}{6} = 84$

19. When $n = 1$, the equation becomes $\cos(\theta + \pi) = -\cos \theta$. To see that this is correct, we expand $\cos(\theta + \pi)$ to obtain $\cos(\theta + \pi) = \cos \theta \cos \pi - \sin \theta \sin \pi = -\cos \theta$, as required. This completes the first step of the induction proof. Now assume that $\cos(\theta + k\pi) = (-1)^k \cos \theta$. We must show that $\cos[\theta + (k + 1)\pi] = (-1)^{k+1} \cos \theta$. We have

$$\cos[\theta + (k + 1)\pi] = \cos[(\theta + k\pi) + \pi]$$
$$= \cos(\theta + k\pi)\cos \pi - \sin(\theta + k\pi)\sin \pi$$
$$= \cos(\theta + k\pi)\cos \pi$$
$$= [(-1)^k \cos \theta](-1) = (-1)^{k+1} \cos \theta, \quad \text{as required.}$$

This completes the second step of the proof. We conclude now by the Principle of Mathematical Induction that the formula $\cos(\theta + n\pi) = (-1)^n \cos \theta$ is valid for all natural numbers n.

20. With $n = 5$ and $a_n = 75$, the formula $a_n = a + (n - 1)d$ becomes $75 = a + 4d$. Similarly, wtih $n = 10$ and $a_n = 125$, the formula yields $125 = a + 9d$. We now have two equations

$$\begin{cases} a + 4d = \ \ 75 \\ a + 9d = 125 \end{cases}.$$

Subtracting the first from the second yields $5d = 50$, or $d = 10$. Then with $d = 10$, the first equation becomes $a + 40 = 75$, or $a = 35$. The first three terms of the sequence are therefore 35, 45, 55.